Death of a SALOON

PABLO YODER

CHRISTIAN LIGHT
PUBLICATIONS

DEATH OF A SALOON
Christian Light Publications
Harrisonburg, Virginia 22802
©2011 Christian Light Publications, Inc.
Printed in the United States of America

ISBN: 978-0-87813-695-7

Fourth Printing, 2022

Inside Art: Mark Yoder

Inside Photos: All photos supplied by
Pablo Yoder unless otherwise noted.

Cover Design: David W. Miller
Cover Graphics: ©iStockphoto.com; Thinkstock; Pablo Yoder

About the cover: Several of Teodolinda's children are buried in the graveyard shown on the cover. Although the miserable young woman is not Teodolinda, she would have looked very much like her. The hill on the back cover is Cerro Pelón.

DEDICATION

I dedicate this book to my Father
and His Son, Jesus, my brother.
I worship and adore them because
they saved the Valverdes from their sin,
and they also saved me!

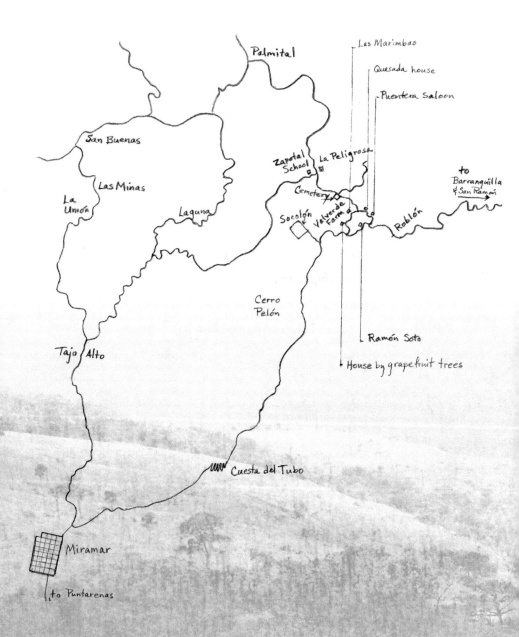

CONTENTS

Valverde Family Tree

All are listed from oldest to youngest.
The only grandchildren listed are those mentioned in the book.

Lico Valverde (LEE koh Vahl VEHR deh) August 8, 1906 - Nov. 21, 1986

Teodolinda Soto (Teh oh doh LEEN dah SOH toh) March 20, 1912
Married Lico July 16, 1932

Name (pronuncication)	Born/Died	Married	Children (in book only)
1. Luis (Loo EES)	Aug. 22, 1933	Manuela Hernández April 20, 1963	Lillian, Toño, Edwin, María
2. Ángel (AHN hehl)	Dec. 28, 1934/ Dec. 13, 2004	Never married	
3. Lidier (LEE dyehr)	April 27, 1936	Gregoria Monje, June 29, 1961	Lalo
4. Marina (Mah REE nah)	Sept. 18, 1937	Luis Elizondo, Feb. 11, 1956	Flor, Álvaro, Gloria, Lorena
5. Marcos (MAHR cohs)	Jan. 9, 1939/ June 1, 2004	Nena Quesada, March 5, 1960	Nelson, Uriel, Nuria, Ronald
6. Amable (Ah MAH bleh)	June 17, 1940/ Sept. 16, 1982	Juan Jiménez, Nov. 24,1973	
7. Gelo (HEH loh)	Oct. 8, 1942	Rafaela Gómez, Aug. 7, 1980	Liliana
8. Leyla (LEH ee lah)	March 17, 1944	Beto Gonzales, Nov. 21, 1964	

Name (pronuncication)	Born/Died	Married	Children (in book only)
9. Mireya (Mee REH yah)	July 27, 1945	Single	
10. Marino (Mah REE noh)	May 8, 1947	Nícida Vargas, March 14, 1972	
11. Belén (Beh LEHN)	May 28, 1948	Rut Quesada, March 26, 1980	
12. Sergio (SEHR heeoh)	Nov. 27, 1949/ Feb. 8, 1954		
13. Aurelio (a hoo REH leeoh)	Sept . 25, 1951	Carmen Barahona, March 10, 1974	
14. Victoria (Veek TOH reeah)	Nov. 2, 1953	Rigoberto Arrieta, Feb. 13, 1997	
15. Ulises (Oo LEE sehs)	Dec. 25, 1955	Ángela Piedra, Nov. 16, 1990	
16. Hugo (OO goh)	Aug. 18, 1958	Irene Barahona, April 26, 1981	

PUBLISHER'S NOTE

Many of us have grown up in reasonably good homes, churches, and schools, safely sheltered from much of the sordid, ungodly living around us. Not all of God's children have been so blessed.

Death of a Saloon is the true story of a family that lived a wretched life. They knew nothing better. The author tells it carefully, but honestly. Parts of the story are depressing to read, but for this family it was reality—day after day after hopeless, despairing day.

The wonderful message of the book is this—regardless of how dark one's soul or how far one has fallen, Jesus Christ offers redemption, deliverance, and a new life. The power of the Gospel to miraculously change lives will thrill and bless your heart. And if you're one still living in the dark and in despair, take heart. You can choose to follow Christ as the Valverdes did and find for yourself what they found: death to an old life and a new life in Christ.

INTRODUCTION

Teodolinda has loved her Bible from the day she met its Author. Just as happened with her new Master, she and the Bible just seemed to merge. And though she went to school for only a brief year and a half in her childhood and reads on a second-grade level, she pores over her Bible every chance she gets.

In February of 2008 I arrived at my brother Mark's house in Chachagua, Costa Rica, to start interviewing the Valverde family for this book. I was especially eager to talk with the main character, Teodolinda, now very old and nearing her eternal home. That evening Mark's oldest daughter Anita told me how much Teodolinda loved her Bible.

"Pablo," she said, "Teodolinda recently finished reading the Bible all the way through. Now she's starting all over again."

I knew Costa Ricans. Hadn't I been raised in this country? The old generation was rarely literate, and those who could read a little generally had trouble comprehending what they read. The doubting Thomas in me mused, *Right! This old woman is probably in her second childhood. She may spend hours poring over the book, but she probably doesn't understand a thing she reads. And even if she can read some, how could someone her age remember details?*

"Yeah, can you imagine her reading through Leviticus?" I said, chuckling. "She probably can't keep track of where she read last and thinks she finished the whole Bible in a fortnight."

Mark and Anita exchanged knowing smiles.

The next morning found us at Teodolinda's place for the first interview. The bed, covered with a colorful quilt that Teodolinda herself had recently sewn together, filled half of the tiny bedroom. The walls were a drab gray with nothing but a few mottos for decoration. Two chairs filled one corner of the room. On the straight-backed chair right beside her pillow was a large Bible, tattered and well-worn.

She does handle that Bible a lot, I thought. *It must give her something to do.*

On the Bible rested a pair of glasses that intrigued me almost as much as the old Bible itself. The rims were a very, very old style, and the lenses were the thickest I had ever seen. They made the bottom of a pop bottle seem thin.

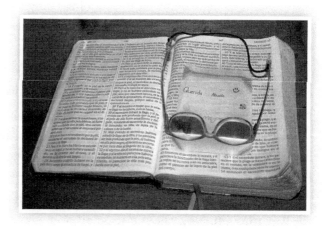

Teodolinda's Bible and glasses. Notice the bookmark—a card from her great-granddaughter.

In the other corner, right inside the door, I found Teodolinda in an old wheelchair. Her eager eyes peered at me through folds of skin, puffed to mere slits with age. Her thin arms, extremely wrinkled and deformed from oversized blood vessels, reached out to hug me in a Costa Rican greeting. I bent over almost reverently to greet the old matriarch I had come from Waslala, Nicaragua, to interview for her remarkable story.

Teodolinda wore a pink dress. Her prayer veil was pulled all the way to the front of her gray straggly hair. Though her body sagged with the posture of old age, her toothy smile was alive and cheerful. I knew I was standing in the presence of a saint.

After greeting Mark and me, she motioned for us to sit down. Mark took the empty chair beside the one with the Bible on it. Teodolinda stopped telling me to sit down, and I remained standing, just inside the bedroom door. "Mark," she said seriously, "I want to ask Gelo to make me a little table." Stretching out her long, bony hands, she continued, "I want a little table right here by my pillow, this long, this wide, this high." She measured out the dimensions with her hands. "I want to put my Bible there, and my glasses, so I can reach them easily from my bed."

Then I understood her predicament. The only chair left in the room was occupied by something far more important than the writer from Waslala—her precious Bible and glasses. Hadn't a visitor once sat on her glasses and broken them? She had cried in distress until someone fixed them. Now she was not offering me a chair, but was telling Mark how important the little table was. "And we need to make it higher. This high," she added, raising her hand high above the seat of the chair.

Her granddaughter Flor entered the room with a chair for me. I sat down beside the dear old lady. "Have you read your Bible today?" I asked.

"Oh, sure. I read my Bible every day. I used to just start reading anywhere, but some time ago I decided to read the whole Bible through. I enjoyed that so much, I'm doing it again. I just started over a few days ago."

I eyed the Bible incredulously, remembering the time I had raced through the Bible in a year. I had planned never to do it again, because I found myself always rushing to keep up with my prearranged reading outline and not getting much out of my frantic reading. Then I remembered struggling through Leviticus. There was no way this little woman had read that whole Bible.

"Where are you reading now?" I asked, winking at Mark.

But for some reason, his face was beaming. He had been her pastor for twenty years, and he knew her well. He picked up the book and cradled it reverently in his hands. Then he let it fall open where it would. The Bible flopped open to Genesis 18, where a homemade marker—a hand-drawn paper greeting from Megan, one of Teodolinda's many great-grandchildren—apparently marked the place she had been reading. I noted the title at the top of the page: "God promises Abraham a son."

What does this old lady know about Abraham? I wondered.

Pointing to the Bible in Mark's lap, she beamed, "Yeah, my head doesn't work too good anymore . . ."

Just like I thought . . .

"I get the names mixed up." She squinted her eyes in deep thought. "That lady, that, eh . . . Sarah. I forgot her name this morning . . ."

"After reading this morning," Flor interjected, "she was telling me the story. She called Sarah, Eve!" Flor chuckled.

"That's exactly what I did." Teodolinda smiled; then her face lit up and she began to tell us a wonderful story. "See, the man was standing there at the door of his house. They call it a tent, but it was really a house, of course. There was a big tree there that made shade for the house. Then Abraham saw three men coming in the lane . . ."

My eyes were glued to Teodolinda's face. I couldn't believe this! Mark watched Teodolinda with obvious delight, every now and then sneaking a glance at me.

Teodolinda launched into her story. "The first thing Abraham did was wash those men's feet. He just went right out there and washed each one of their feet! Then he turned around and told Sarah to make some bread. Oh, that fresh bread she made was good! Especially once you hear what she served it with."

I had been ready to throw her hints of the story to help her on, but I soon saw I didn't need to. She remembered it all. Better than I did, in fact.

"By the way, do you know what Sarah did? See, the men told Abraham that Sarah was going to have a man-child. Sarah was listening from inside the tent, and she began to laugh!"

Teodolinda's wrinkled face grew even more wrinkled as she broke out into the warmest, sweetest laugh. Just like old Sarah. Wasn't Sarah about a hundred years old too? I could almost see Sarah's face, full of wrinkles, laughing with all her heart, just like this dear sister.

"You'd better believe it! She hid back there in the tent and laughed. She knew she shouldn't, but she just couldn't help it!

"Then do you know what old Abraham did? He ran out into the field and caught a calf. Abraham turned that calf into a feast!"

By then it was almost too much. Tears welled up in my eyes as I realized what I was seeing. A sister, weeks from her ninety-sixth birthday, who did not live by bread alone, but by every word that proceeded out of the mouth of her God.

Mark closed the book reverently and laid it back on the chair. He picked up the old glasses from the bed where he had laid them and placed them back on the Bible. We knew she would need them again. Soon. Probably right after we left.

I stared at Teodolinda. I had heard snatches of her past. I knew why I was there. I was to write about the miracle God had done in this sweet little lady's life. My tears threatened to overflow. Was it possible that this same lady had once run a saloon so riotous and wicked that it was called La Peligrosa (The Dangerous One)? Could it be that this saintly lady had once sat on the floor of the saloon, so drunk she couldn't walk, shouting out drunken songs as she served her master, the devil?

My mind shouted, *No!*

But my heart whispered, *Yes.*

This was the same lady. And yet not. God had changed her. And Mark and I both knew how: "with the washing of water by the Word!"

Teodolinda wasn't finished yet. She gazed at her Bible wistfully. Then, looking deeply into my eyes, she almost whispered, "I have started to read the Bible all over again, but I don't know if I will finish it this time. I am just going to read until God decides it's time to take me home."

The knot in my throat threatened to choke me. In my heart I knew two things. I had found the introduction to this book. And the story the book was to tell was a wonderful, incredible, and very special miracle.

I

Her favorite tree was a gnarled, wind-whipped higuerón perched on the hillside right above their house. Teodolinda leaned against the rough trunk and gazed at the distant, cloud-covered mountain range. Somewhere up there was Zapotal—the strange new place her dad had been talking about lately. *Will we really move up there?* she wondered.

In the distance she heard the yigüirro* trilling his melancholy song. She knew that when Costa Rica's national bird sang, he was calling in the rains. Although it was only April, still a month before rainy season, the yigüirro was getting impatient. Just like her dad, who was impatient to move to Zapotal before the rains came.

Teodolinda turned and looked toward the lowlands. Just below her, half hidden behind the steep bank, their little house clung to the hillside like a hump on a camel's back. The house was built simply,

---

*clay-colored robin

with a grass-thatched roof, board walls, and a dirt floor. But it was home.

Beyond the house on the hillside lay the coastal plain, then beyond that the ocean, wrapped in the afternoon haze. San Ramón had been her home for years.

Teodolinda had just turned seventeen. She was dressed in simple Tico (Costa Rican) garb—a modest light blue cotton dress with an elastic waist. Her hair was done up in a simple bun. Her hands were almost as rough as the higuerón's bark from all the work in the house and on the farm. Most of Teodolinda's friends and neighbors thought she should have married already. But though she had plenty of suitors, Teodolinda was not ready to settle down and marry yet. She was not sure she was ready to move to Zapotal either.

As Teodolinda rested her tired, work-worn body against the tree trunk, her mind traveled back to her childhood. Sadness washed over her as she recalled her grandmother's death. She could still hear herself screaming, *"¡Yo quiero ir! ¡Yo quiero ir!"* (I want to go!) . . .

Her parents would not let her go along to the *vela.** She loved Grandma so much. She wanted to go along to the *vela* and to the burial so badly. But her mamilla, Angelina, did not think it would be good for her to see the dead. "Stay at home and be good," she snapped. "Take good care of the children."

Teodolinda stayed home, but she cried for a long time. Then she decided she would feel better if she worked. Besides, little Avelino was hungry. And she was feeling hungry herself. Though only five years old, she already knew how to work.

Teodolinda stirred the dying coals on the hearth, added a few pieces of firewood, and got the fire going again. Then she found the wooden block her father Ramón had made for her to stand on to work in the kitchen. She placed the block right next to the corn grinder that was fastened to the *molendero.*** Next she got a cup and ran to the big kettle full of cooked corn. She filled her cup, jumped up on her block, and started to crank the handle of the grinder. It was way too big for her, but she had done it before. She dropped only a few kernels of cooked corn into the grinder at a time. She knew that if she put in too many, the machine would choke, and she would not be strong enough to make the handle go around.

Grinding corn a few kernels at a time was a very slow process, but soon a little dab of corn dough formed in the pan under the grinder. As soon as there was enough to make one tortilla, Teodolinda took it and patted it out on the *molendero*. It did not turn out nearly as nice as her mama's did, so she got a cup and placed it upside down on the flattened

---

* all-night watch after a death
** long, wide board used as a work table

dough and pushed it down hard. It cut out a neat, round disk. A small tortilla fit for a king! Satisfied, she fried it on the clay skillet. Avelino ate the first tortilla, the baby the next one, and then Avelino ate the third one. Finally, sweaty and hot, Teodolinda got to eat the last two. Then she put the babies to bed and cried herself to sleep . . .

*   *   *

Teodolinda brushed aside the tears that had come with the memory. She was still leaning against the tree, staring out over the gulf. Now that her daydreaming spell was broken, Teodolinda was surprised that her mother had not missed her yet and called her in. She scrambled up into the branches of her favorite tree and, nestling down among its strong, rough limbs, allowed her mind to wander again.

Another day worked its way into Teodolinda's memory—the frightening day of the ambush . . .

Whenever her father had spare time, he worked for their neighbor Gabriel. Though Gabriel was not extremely rich, he was considerably wealthier than Ramón. Gabriel was always willing to help Ramón out when he was in a pinch, and Ramón always gave him a good day's work for his wage, so they became fast friends.

One day Gabriel asked Ramón to take his place on his weekly Saturday run into town to sell produce and buy groceries. Ramón took Teodolinda along, and they drove Gabriel's nice pair of spotted oxen and his fancy cart to San Ramón early in the morning, returning in the late afternoon. Ramón, as usual, stopped at the saloon and bought several drinks, so on the way home he was tipsy, though not drunk.

The sun was lying low in the west. As the oxcart bumped along slowly, Teodolinda was surprised to hear her father singing at the top of his voice. She hung on in the back of the cart, seven years old and so happy that she had gotten to go along to town. But now she was tired, and if not for the bumping of the cart, she would have fallen asleep.

About half a mile from Gabriel's farm gate, the road climbed a short hill to a lonely plateau. At the top of the hill the road curved and ran through a patch of high weeds before it plunged down the other side and on to Gabriel's farm. The oxen slowed way down as they plodded up the hill. It had grown dark, and Ramón had stopped singing. He had bowed his head low, thinking. Teodolinda was dozing.

As the oxen finally topped the hill, a bloodcurdling yell jolted them from their dreams. Three men burst out of the weed patch, yelling and brandishing their *cutachas.** The oxen stopped. Ramón only had time to jump off the front of the cart and extend his ox goad. He had forgotten his *cutacha.*

To Ramón's surprise, one of the frenzied men shouted, "Gabriel, get up and defend yourself! Today you are going to die!"

Ramón stood his ground and brandished his long ox goad, holding his attackers at bay. Everything was happening way too fast.

Teodolinda stood petrified in the back of the cart. The oxen cringed, but were too weary to bolt. All the while Ramón was swinging his goad, his mind was racing. *These must be the Jiménez boys,* he thought. *They are Gabriel's mortal enemies and have sworn to kill him. They think he is coming home from his Saturday run to San Ramón.*

Then it dawned on Ramón, *They think I'm Gabriel!* "I am Ramón Soto!" he screamed. "I am not Gabriel!"

The men were working their way closer in spite of Ramón's strong swing. Just as Ramón screamed, one of the swinging *cutachas* caught his thumb right where it grasped the hard goad pole and clipped it completely off.

Ramón's screams finally sank into the angry men's brains and they stopped in horror. They had the wrong man pinned against the front of the cart. And he was wounded. That was enough—they turned and fled.

Teodolinda was jumping up and down in the back of the cart, shrieking, "Papito, you are going to die! Papito, you are going to die!"

Ramón stared at his bleeding hand and shook his head grimly. He reached over with his other hand and grabbed the stub to stop the blood. "Be quiet!" he told Teodolinda. "I am not going to die. They only cut off my thumb. That was close, though! Hey, Teo, just be glad they

---

* thin machetes used as weapons, often carried at the waist in a sheath

didn't cut my head off. They thought I was Gabriel. Come, daughter, help me get this team going."

Teodolinda crawled onto the front of the cart with her father. He held his hand so it would not bleed, and she took the bloody goad and poked the oxen to make them go. They trudged down the hill as fast as a pair of oxen can go and soon arrived at Gabriel's gate, where Ramón left the ox cart and rushed home to clean up and tell Angelina. Crying softly, Teodolinda trotted along beside him. Meanwhile, Gabriel saddled up two horses, and in no time flat he and Ramón were riding hard toward the San Ramón hospital, where Ramón stayed for a week while his thumbless hand healed. Teodolinda was sick with worry during that long week . . .

*　　*　　*

Teodolinda's thoughts jerked back to the present as the yigüirro suddenly flew right into the upper branches of her tree. She held perfectly still, hoping the bird would not notice her. He cocked his head and looked at her for a full minute. Then, meowing softly like a cat, he flew off to find a safer tree in which to sing out the joy of his heart. Soon Teodolinda heard his soft song wafting up to her tree through the afternoon haze. Dreamily, she returned to her childhood reflections. This time, a happier memory surfaced . . .

She was eight years old. She was walking very slowly, barefoot, in soft plowed dirt. Even now she could almost smell the rich aroma of soil and sweat. She was dressed in a ragged, faded dress. Her hair hung loose, and her skinny legs were exposed because her dress was too short. Tied to her waist was an old battered tin can, which held the kernels of corn she was planting.

Plodding ahead of her was her father's team of snow-white oxen. They were Ramón's pride and joy. A perfect match. Good, strong oxen he had skimped and saved a whole year to buy. Now they plodded along, dragging the one-bottom plow. Their neighbor Pancho walked ahead of the team, his long goad resting on the middle of the yoke. Whenever the oxen slowed too much, Pancho jabbed the goad at their shoulders and hollered, "Gee! Gee!" The oxen would throw up their horns and speed up just enough to satisfy their guide.

Ramón walked behind the team, the plow handles securely grasped in his strong fists, his legs straddling the new furrow. Teodolinda's heart swelled with pride as she watched. Her dad was a hard worker. He raised the best corn in San Ramón.

Last in the train came little Teodolinda. She also straddled the furrow as she walked along slowly. Carefully she counted out three grains of corn from her tin can. Then she bent over and dropped the seeds into the rich, black soil. Next her deft feet swept a pile of dirt over the seeds. She knew the tiny plants would peep through four days later.

By noon Teodolinda was tired. She kept looking over toward the end of the field where they had started. Finally her watchfulness was rewarded when she saw six-year-old Avelino walking toward them with an *alforja** thrown over his shoulder. Teodolinda knew what that meant. She stopped her planting and ran to meet her brother.

Meeting Avelino under the shade of a tree, she found one of her father's old burlap sacks and spread it neatly on the grass. Then she took the *alforja* and emptied its contents onto the sack. The tortillas were wrapped in a towel. She laid them on one end of the sack, leaving them covered so they would not get cold. Then she carefully laid out the three little bowls of beans and scrambled eggs, leaving their lids on also. She placed the big gallon jug of lemonade on the sack too, with the three tin cups beside it. Then she called, "Papito, lunch is ready."

Ramón unhitched the plow and led the oxen to another shade tree. There they stood, their sides heaving, their skin wet with sweat. They would rest for an hour, just like the crew. Then they would be ready to plow until dusk.

Teodolinda took her food and sat close to the tree trunk to eat by herself. Little Avelino watched from a distance. After her meal, she stretched out in the grass to rest, as happy as she could be. She hoped it would not rain today as it often did during corn planting. If it rained,

---

* two small burlap bags sewn together like a miniature saddlebag

they would have to stop plowing and go home. She loved to help Papito work outside. It was so much more fun than working in the house. She loved her Papito and was his tomboy. He knew it and loved her for it.

*   *   *

"Teodolinda! Teodolinda!" Mamilla's voice woke her from her happy dream. Teodolinda knew she should hurry back to the house. Her mother would guess where she was. This was where she always escaped when she was tired. As the oldest daughter, she helped her mother run a house full of children—six more girls and five boys. But her mother would not come after her just yet . . . she could daydream a little longer.

She remembered the time army ants had invaded their house in the middle of the night. Her whole family had run from the house and slept in the field until morning. The ants had swept through, eating all the roaches and scorpions and bugs they could find. Two hours later they were gone, the house swept clean.

She remembered the many earthquakes. They lived close to Costa Rica's awful fault line. One night they had awakened, and the whole house was shaking—hard. The corn hanging by the husks from the rafters to dry rained down on them like a hailstorm. Papito had hollered, "Everybody get out! This is a hard earthquake!" Teodolinda had grabbed the baby and escaped to the yard. Mamilla was already there, kneeling in the dark, praying aloud to God. They had spent the rest of the night in a gully behind the house. Terrified, Teodolinda had vowed never to sleep in that house again. But she did.

It had rained steadily the following week, and everyone had been afraid of landslides. Teodolinda's mother had been sure the hillside would slide down and cover them forever. Every day Teodolinda had taken time to pray to Mamilla's saint. The tall plaster of Paris statue called Santo Salvador del Mundo (Saint, Saviour of the World) had been in her room for as long as Teodolinda could remember. In her fear, Teodolinda had spent many an hour standing in front of the statue, reciting prayers she had learned from Mamilla. But the fear seldom went away.

Then she remembered the first car that had driven into San Ramón. It was 1920, and Teodolinda was eight years old. She and Mamilla had been visiting her uncle, who lived in town. When they had stepped out onto the dirt street to leave, an awful green beast had roared past, a whole group of children and even several grown-ups running along behind, whooping and hollering. The strange rig had stopped at the end of the street, just beyond her uncle's house. The group of admirers had grown so large that the vehicle could not turn around to head back the way it had come without running over a dozen. So the driver had scolded the children, ordering them out of the way. Teodolinda had clung to her mother's skirts, ready to dash back into the house. After the rig had flown past again, full throttle, her uncle had shaken his head and muttered, "What is this world coming to? I never thought man would invent an iron horse. I wonder what they feed the thing. Pretty soon we won't need horses and oxen anymore. Watch and see!"

Teodolinda laughed now at the memory. She stretched and crawled out of her tree, slowly making her way down the steep hill to her house. She shook her head in amused embarrassment as she remembered the first airplane that had flown over San Ramón. She had been ten years old. Her mother had left for the day, leaving Teodolinda alone with the children. She had been sitting on the doorstep picking lice out of her little sister's hair when she heard the buzz. She stopped picking lice and looked toward the horizon. The buzz grew into a roar. Then she saw the machine flying over the horizon straight from San José, the capital. By then the noise was deafening. Not knowing what to think, she screamed and dashed into the house, grabbing several of the younger children on the way and commanding the rest to follow. Was it an earthquake? Was it the end of the world? Was the volcano erupting? She herded all the children onto the bed and covered them with a blanket made of burlap sacks sewn together. Then she crawled in with them, trembling from head to toe. The loud noise subsided, but she didn't dare leave the bed until Mamilla returned.

When Papito had come home from town that afternoon, he had explained. "A huge metal bird flew over town today. They call the thing an airplane. It tried to land in the plaza in front of the big Catholic church, but the plaza was so full of people cheering and whooping and yelling that it was impossible for it to land. They had to abort their plan and fly back to San José."

Teodolinda's reverie stopped as she arrived back at the house. Her mother's frown showed her disapproval of her hour of loitering.

"Where have you been?" Mamilla barked. "Daydreaming up in your tree again?"

Papito was sitting on the hammock stretched across the main room, wiping the sweat from his face. He had just returned from work. He held a cup of hot black coffee. He smiled at her, forgiving her for the time she had stolen for herself. That was why she loved her Papito. Yes, he drank *guaro* (liquor) heavily on weekends. Yes, he often got hopping mad. But he got over it soon, and he knew how to express love. Mamilla didn't. That was another reason she was Papito's tomboy.

Most of all, Papito was a dreamer. As Teodolinda started to roll cigars, a job they did for cash pay, he started to talk about Zapotal.

"Today I talked with Leandro again. He says sugarcane grows so well in Zapotal that you can produce rivers of cane juice. We could make an easy living up there by selling *dulce.** You could raise all kinds of vegetables. We could haul all these things down to Miramar to sell on market days. It never rains enough here, but up there it rains aplenty. I tell you," he almost stammered, pointing toward the distant mountain range, "that place has to be about as good as paradise! See, it's always cloudy up there. Here we are suffering from heat and dry weather, and there they have cool, wet weather year round. I think we should move as soon as possible."

Teodolinda and her mother wrapped dry tobacco leaves into cigars until their fingers ached. Tomorrow Papito would haul the freshly made cigars into town and bring up more leaves for them to wrap.

---

* brown sugar blocks made by cooking down cane juice and used instead of refined sugar

After the men had eaten, Teodolinda took her plate of vegetable soup and sat on the doorstep. She loved to sit there evenings. She could see what was happening in the house and still enjoy the outdoors she loved so much. Dozens of fireflies flitted around their tiny yard. They made Teodolinda's heart glad. They were so friendly and brought light. Inside, she was hearing what she so often heard—Mamilla complaining about their poverty again.

"You say we will be so much better off in Zapotal," Mamilla fussed. "How do you know? You've never been there. You believe everything Leandro tells you. We are poor. We always have been and always will be. We never have enough to buy extras here, and I am sure we won't there either. Here it doesn't rain enough; there it probably rains too much!"

"Listen, Angelina. Land here is so expensive anymore. We could sell our small acreage here and buy a huge farm up there. We could raise sugarcane and vegetables. Leandro says the corn grows even faster and nicer than the sugarcane. I am sure we could make an easy living up there. You just wait and see."

Teodolinda knew there was some truth in what both of her parents said. But since she had inherited her father's adventurous spirit, she figured she'd be ready to move long before her mother was. And Papito would finally win. He always did.

2

Clonk, clonk, clonk. The oxcart's wooden axle clonked every time the large wooden wheels turned. Though Teodolinda had been hearing the steady clonking for two days now, it still annoyed her. The clonking noise only emphasized the terrible slowness of the oxen and irritated everyone to exhaustion. Was it really going to take two long days to travel from San Ramón to Zapotal?

Teodolinda trudged along ahead of the ox team, the goad resting on her shoulder. Her ankles were swollen from walking for so long, and her bare feet were hot and sore. Her whole body felt tired enough to just lie down in the dry grass along the road and sleep forever.

Behind the team of white oxen lumbered the old battered cart. At one time the cart had sported lovely, colorful designs like most Costa Rican oxcarts. But the paint had faded, and the old cart's former grandeur was barely detectable now. Mamilla rode in the cart with the two smallest children, squeezed between their meager belongings. The rest of the children walked alongside.

An oxcart is the slowest means of transportation there is, with the possible exception of a snail. A child can easily outwalk an oxcart. Teodolinda knew that if they were riding horses, or even walking, they would already be in Zapotal. But they needed the oxen to haul their belongings.

They had left San Ramón early the day before. The first evening, weary and worn, they had stopped for the night at a farmhouse, where a kind lady had given them each a cup of hot coffee. They had arrived just at dusk. The poor family had had no accommodations for visitors, so they had all slept on the dirt floor on a piece of plastic.

They were taking the scenic route—a rough dry-season-only trail that ran along the top of the mountain range. The trail often dipped down off the backbone of the range, meandering along the side of the mountain where the route was easier, traveling along the same high sierra on which Zapotal was perched. On this second day, it seemed to go on forever.

"Gee! Gee!" Teodolinda yelled desperately as she goaded the oxen again. "We have to keep on going, or we'll never get there!" The oxen sped up briefly and then settled back to their slow *clonk, clonk, clonk*. The hot sun beat down mercilessly on their backs.

It had been hard for Teodolinda to leave all her securities in San Ramón, and her thoughts the last few days had dwelt on the negatives of this move. But as she saw the beauty of this clear morning, her heart was eager, and as she looked down at the hot Puntarenas shoreline, she was glad to be moving to higher ground. Her adventurous spirit kicked in, and she was Papito's girl again, raring to go.

They got to a high mountain town called Barranquilla at noon, where they stopped under a shade tree and ate the meager lunch Angelina had packed for the day—bean tamales and *agua dulce.**

"Now," Ramón admonished, "we need to be careful. The next several hours we will be traveling up a very steep mountain." Pointing toward the top of the mountain that towered over them, he added, "That's our last hill. We are going to climb that mountain all the way to the top. Up on top is Zapotal. Let's go."

---

* water mixed with sugarcane juice

This time Ramón led the oxen. Teodolinda took the children on out ahead. Every half hour the ox train stopped to rest. Each time they stopped, the air was cooler and the lowlands farther away. As they climbed higher and higher, the mist they had so often seen from a distance enveloped and cooled them.

The oxen were exhausted when they finally topped the mountain. The children walking ahead were also very tired. Ángel, Teodolinda's younger brother, was always cutting up. Avelino, the one next to Teodolinda in age, was better behaved. But now even Ángel threw himself into the grass to rest. Ramón and Teodolinda just stood at the edge of the mountain and stared. It was hard to believe they had actually climbed such a huge mountain. The coast seemed very far away now. The tiny peninsula the Puntarenas port was built on seemed as small as a child's finger protruding into the sea. The whole coastal plain seemed vast and strangely blue in the haze of the hot afternoon sun.

But up here on top of the mountain it was cool. They stood on the highest hill in Zapotal. To one side stood a great tropical roble tree. "This place is called El Roblón,"* Ramón told them, "because of this huge tree."

The highland winds had temporarily blown the mist away. The sun, over halfway between its zenith and the horizon, told them it was about four o'clock. It was time to move on.

Angelina appeared troubled as she looked beyond the clearing. All she could see was a massive jungle. Just beyond the mountain's edge, past the clearing, the land dropped into a valley. The whole area was a series of jungle-covered valleys and rolling hills.

The oxcart dropped into a gully and disappeared into the forest glades. Teodolinda and the children followed this time. Teodolinda's eyes opened wide as they entered the shadowy world of Zapotal. This was cloud forest. All the trees were wind-whipped and leaned one way. Everything was covered with moss.

---

* The Huge Oak

As soon as the trail disappeared into the jungle, it turned soggy. Even though it was the height of dry season, the thin oxcart wheels sank deep into the soft, damp soil. Teodolinda's bare feet also sank into the mud. The boys' eyes were big now, all mischief gone. The whole world was suddenly very different from anything they had ever seen before. The mists swept in again, turning the whole dense forest darker still.

The caravan slowly wound down the last hill, where they came to a small river with blue-green water. A log bridge spanned the river, but instead of crossing it, Ramón led the oxen downstream, off the main trail. "This is the Jabonal River,"* he announced, "and here is where our land starts. We just follow the river downstream a short ways, and we are home."

Ramón had made a quick trip to Zapotal several weeks before. He had bought a 150-*manzana*** place and had hired a young man from the neighboring farm to cut out a clearing. The place already had a makeshift house.

About five o'clock they wound around the last bend. The oxen were so tired they could hardly move at all. With one last "Gee!" Ramón encouraged them, and they burst out into the clearing they could now call home.

Ramón was delighted to see that the neighbor had kept his word. About an acre of land had been cleared, except for the largest trees that loomed over the clearing like giants from a strange land. The house was a small shelter built with pole walls and a thatched roof. Behind the shelter and down over a bank, a spring surrounded by a mass of green ferns gurgled from under a rock and bubbled on down the hill toward the Jabonal River.

The first thing Ramón did was to take the whole family down to the spring, where he encouraged his wife to enjoy one of Zapotal's greatest blessings: plenty of cold water. Hesitantly, she handed the baby to Ramón. Then she got onto her hands and knees and drank. The rest of

---

* Soapy River
** A *manzana* is 1.6 acres.

the children gathered around her like chicks around a hen and drank thirstily. Teodolinda bent down and drew a handful of water to her mouth. She gasped. The water was ice-cold.

After drinking, Angelina straightened and said matter-of-factly, "The water is lovely, but I hate these spooky woods. I am sure there are dangerous wild animals around here. Ramón, I am afraid. I don't know if I can live in a place like this."

Everybody pitched in and helped unload. Then Ramón took the oxen to a neighboring farm, since the newly cleared land had no grass at all. Darkness was sneaking into the jungle fast. Angelina shivered, both from cold and from a feeling of helplessness. Teodolinda also felt strange in this new fairyland, but she knew she would learn to love it. Papito was right. This was going to be a paradise. Suddenly a highland tinamou interrupted the evening silence with his resonant, throaty song. Avelino jumped and then giggled. Angelina shuddered. Teodolinda smiled. Ramón walked into the clearing and announced, "That bird is called a gongolona and makes wonderful eating. We will have plenty of meat to eat up here."

That night the family huddled together for warmth in the center of the house amidst their belongings. Their cooked food was all gone, and there was no dry firewood. So they drank cold spring water and went to bed hungry, wrapping themselves in the burlap coverlets they had hardly needed during the warm nights in San Ramón. Here they needed them not only to keep out the chill, but for security. It felt safer to be wrapped in burlap when you thought of the *león*.* Everyone slept fitfully.

The next morning the family awoke to the sound of the jilguero.** Its clear bell-like notes made the jungle come alive. The early sunlight filtered through the trees, catching the droplets of dew on the moss and making them shine like gold.

That day, and for many days to come, everybody was very busy. Ramón dedicated himself to fixing the house. The bigger boys helped. Angelina built an earthen cookstove. Everyone scouted around to find

---

* mountain lion
** black-faced solitaire

dry firewood, which was hard to come by. Ramón explained that they needed to find dead trees that were still standing. These were often dry enough to burn.

Then Ramón got Teodolinda and the smaller children started planting. "We have to plant so we have something to eat," he reminded everyone. He had wisely brought along a variety of seeds and plants. First he showed Teodolinda where to plant the bananas and the plantains. Next they planted yucca and other tubers native to the area. Last, Ramón planted pumpkins and chayotes (green prickly fruits that grow on vines). Leandro had told him these would grow well in the highlands. Later, after the house was finished and the first rains fell, they all pitched in to plant corn. Teodolinda thought it a delight to plant seeds in the rich black, wet Zapotal soil.

In the jungle, a mountaineer could find everything he needed to build a house. Palm leaves tied closely together with tough vines made excellent roofing. The walls were made of split guarumo logs, also tied with vines. The beds were made of palm saplings and covered with palm leaves. Once the house was done, everyone felt much more secure, and with a fire on the hearth, they were finally warm and dry.

The first hard rain hit the fourteenth of May. They had lived in Zapotal only one week. That afternoon the towering trees started swaying in the moaning wind. Big black clouds billowed over the eastern horizon. It was only one o'clock, but the jungle grew dark and cold. The many birds all sought shelter, and the rain started to fall. Even the few chickens Angelina had brought along looked for their roosts. Soon the rain was pouring in torrents. It flooded the jungle floor and rushed into the house. Ramón had stored some logs up under the steep thatched roof, and now everybody scrambled to move their belongings up onto the logs. Fortunately, the roof didn't leak.

Ramón went out into the cold rain and dug a ditch around the house to divert the torrents of water that gushed through the jungle. Finally some of the children crawled up under the roof to stay dry. It rained all afternoon.

By the time it stopped raining, it was dark, and Angelina lit the *canfinera*.* They had a little dry firewood stashed up under the roof. Slopping through mud, Angelina started a fire on the earthen cook-stove. She warmed the beans she had cooked that morning and served them with cold tortillas. Soon everyone was huddled around the fire to warm up. Outside, the crickets squeaked out their cheery song. Other night noises sounded strange and scary to their ears. It was not even six o'clock, but it was totally dark.

Early the next morning Teodolinda ran down the trail to the spring to get water for coffee, mud squishing between her bare toes. Again the whole jungle sparkled as the sun peeped through the huge trees and filled the clearing with light. As she bent over at the spring to fill her clay pot, a sudden movement in the tree above caught her attention. She straightened and gazed at a lovely sight. Right above her sat a resplendent quetzal, perched on a branch facing her, his bright red breast contrasting with his emerald-green body and white under-tail. His long silky tail dangled beneath him like an emerald pendant.

A wild coffee tree loaded with orange and black berries hung out over the spring. The quetzal suddenly sallied out and plucked a berry with his beak. Then he flipped around and landed on the same branch. Teodolinda's smile grew. That green tail undulating through the air was a sight to behold. *No wonder the Indians called you the snake bird,* she thought. *Your tail follows you just like a lovely green snake. You sure are pretty!*

Teodolinda slipped and slid as she tackled the trail back up to the house. The air still felt chilly, though the sunlight was flooding the clearing and beginning to warm it. As she drew near the house, the familiar, acrid smell of smoke made it feel like home. This was Zapotal. She suddenly felt very glad they had moved. She hurried along the last stretch of the trail, thinking of the delicious hot coffee she would soon enjoy and how well her plants would grow after that rain.

---

* small kerosene lamp

3

About a month after moving to Zapotal, Teodolinda went with her father to plant beans on borrowed land in Tajo Alto, a town a few miles down the northern slope of the mountain. The altitude in Zapotal was too high for beans. On the way they had to cross a river, jumping from stone to stone. As Teodolinda nimbly jumped from the last stone to the bank, she noticed two men by the shore waiting to cross—an old man and a younger one she assumed to be his son.

The young man did the talking. "Where are you from?" he asked.

"We are from San Ramón and have recently moved to Zapotal," Ramón answered. "We live just beyond Leandro's place. And where are you from?"

"We are from Tajo Alto. We are looking into buying land up in Zapotal. That's where we are headed now."

"Well, it's good to meet you. My name is Ramón Soto, and I am at your service."

"My name is Manuel Valverde, but everyone just calls me Lico. My dad here is half deaf. His name is Rafael."

Teodolinda stood off to the side analyzing the new people. They were going to be neighbors. That sounded exciting! There were so few neighbors on that highland plateau. *But,* Teodolinda groaned inwardly, *those men sure are ugly!*

Lico's thoughts ran an entirely different course. He had heard about the new family that had moved up to Zapotal. He had heard they were hard workers and good Catholics. Now that he met them face to face, he liked what he saw—a tough, wiry girl who jumped from stone to stone as nimbly as a deer, unmarried, and in her upper teens. Then and there he made a decision: *Someday I will propose to that girl!*

Soon after the Sotos moved to Zapotal, another man started buying cheap land on the plateau. He had supposedly made a killing on beans close to the old gold mine near Miramar and was now investing his money in land. He bought two hundred *manzanas* right next to Ramón's land. He rode up to Zapotal on his mule, dressed in cowboy boots and a big felt hat, always stopping in at Ramón's place to catch up on the Zapotal news and enjoy a cup of fresh coffee. Soon he and Ramón were fast friends. But to everyone's surprise, Don Tilo Barrantes never moved up to Zapotal. He had never planned to.

Don Tilo hired Ramón to cut a clearing in his jungle and paid him well. Then he got Leandro to build him a house. Several months later Don Tilo moved in a lady named Conchita who had four children. The rumors were that she was his mistress, though he had a wife and family in Miramar. Conchita was a hard worker and could do more than most hired men. Don Tilo would leave money with her to pay the workers and only rode up once a month to check on things. Soon Conchita had planted a nice sugarcane field and enough grass for several cows. Conchita milked them, and her little boys were quickly learning to work. Don Tilo was the first farmer to put in a sugarcane mill. Now everybody in Zapotal knew where to get *dulce*.

The first several months were rough on the Soto farm. Their plants were growing nicely, but the food they had brought along ran out long before the harvest was ready. First they ran out of beans. The beans they had planted at Tajo Alto were not ready yet. So the family was down to eating tortillas and whatever else they could come up with in the jungle. They became experts at whacking down the palmitos and cutting out the crisp, healthy hearts of palms that tasted like something between celery and cabbage. They ate them raw or fried them with eggs, or they were especially good when fried with meat.

Ramón learned to hunt pacas. The rodents were about twice the size of rabbits, and their meat was delicious. Thousands of pacas ran wild in the jungle. Ramón would run them into their dens with Duke, their old hound dog, and then dig them out and butcher them. Pacas were the Soto family's main source of meat those first years, though they also dug out armadillos and trapped tinamous.

But the occasional meat was not enough to feed their large family, and Angelina's fears soon became reality. Zapotal was not a paradise after all. Two things came, one right after the other. The rain hit them first—hard. Then the hunger followed.

Once rainy season really settled in on that high plateau, Teodolinda's family learned a saying heard among the mountain dwellers: "If you want to see the sun in Zapotal, tack a picture of it on your wall." Though an exaggeration, after two weeks of *temporal** they could understand its origin. Not only was the sun hidden, but cold drizzle and miserable fog enveloped the whole mountaintop. Often the wind whistled up the deep canyons surrounding the plateau and grabbed the drizzle and mists, driving them right into every shelter in Zapotal. The cold dampness penetrated their bodies to the bone. Some claimed it even reached the soul.

Ramón and his sons would leave for work after draining their cups of hot coffee—if there was dry firewood available to make the coffee. They would work all day, soaked to the skin, their boots sloshing, full of water. It was such a relief to come home to a dry set of clothes and a dry house, but after four days there were no more dry clothes. Teodolinda washed the clothes thoroughly, but they would not dry. So the men had to wear damp clothes.

For the women, the *temporal* was even worse. Not only did it coop them up in the house all day long, but it was cold and miserable. The

---

* rain squall

men at least kept warm with manual labor, even if they were wet. The women tried to keep a fire burning in the hearth, but eventually that became impossible for lack of dry wood.

The children also had their share of troubles, especially when the first colds hit. If it was hard to keep the clothes clean, it was impossible to keep the children clean. So the mothers in Zapotal, including Angelina, just gave up and let their runny-nosed children run like savages.

Then one morning Angelina told Ramón, "We only have enough corn for tomorrow. The coffee is all gone too. I don't know what to do."

The next day Teodolinda decided to go work with the men. It would be better than sitting in the shack. They were cleaning the plot of land that Teodolinda had planted with the children when they had first moved. Ramón gave her a machete, and they started to clear the weeds out from among the plants. In spite of the chilling drizzle, the garden looked beautiful. Everything was growing like wild—including the weeds. After cutting the weeds off right at ground level between the pumpkin vines, they paused to admire the patch. The vines were just starting to bloom, and Ramón wondered if the flowers would fall off with all the rain. The chayotes were planted among the brush piles alongside the cleared area. The lush green vines crawled over the brush, and it was easy to see that soon there would be chayotes galore. The banana and plantain stalks were already chest high. The sugarcane was growing well too. But best of all was the corn field. Never had Ramón seen such corn. It was about to tassel, and the stalks were much taller than Ramón himself. Soon there would be food enough.

As Teodolinda knelt in the dirt, whacking at the weeds among the pumpkin plants, she remembered Leandro telling her father that the people of Zapotal ate pumpkin shoots and chayote shoots. He had called them *quelites*.

Just before noon, Teodolinda started picking the tips off some of the thousands of pumpkin and chayote vines. She took a batch of them home to show her mother. Angelina was not excited, but allowed Teodolinda to use several of her precious eggs. Teodolinda cooked the *quelites* slightly; then she fried them with the eggs. Her father and brothers were so surprised when their meal had some variety. Tortillas and *quelites!* And they were delicious!

The next day Ramón walked to Miramar to look for food. He left before daylight, taking Avelino and Ángel with him. It was still drizzling.

Just before lunch, the rain finally stopped. The sun peeped out, and the jungle surrounding their home looked like a paradise again. The birds were happy to see the sun after two weeks, and their songs filled the jungle. Teodolinda and two of her smaller sisters ran to the spring to see the quetzals. They were not disappointed. A pair was out feeding. The female did not have the long tail, but her colors were just as bright and her movements just as graceful as her mate's. The girls stood in awe and watched them for a full fifteen minutes. Then in a flash they were gone, the male's tail flowing behind him like a kite's.

At dusk old Duke began to bay toward the trail. A minute later, Ramón and the boys came in, drenched in sweat and dead tired. As soon as they reached the house, they threw down their burlap sacks and opened them. They had borrowed fifty pounds of beans and fifty pounds of corn from a friend. This friend had also given them plantains—green ones to cook to take the place of tortillas and ripe ones to fry. They had also bought some coffee. Teodolinda and her mother got to work right away. Angelina made the coffee while Teodolinda fried ripe plantains. Teodolinda had cooked a lot of *quelites* for lunch that day, so they served the cooked greens as well. The whole family was happy. Their provisions should hold them over until their corn and beans were ready to harvest.

The wind was up again that evening. After the delicious meal, they all huddled around the fire and Ramón told stories about their journey. Teodolinda was all ears, just like the rest. The most interesting tale was Ramón's description of La Cuesta del Tubo (Trench Hill).

"Once we got to the edge of the Zapotal plateau, all of a sudden the world just dropped out from under us," he said. "We took this trail down, down, and down some more, all the time winding between huge, deep canyons. At one point we thought we'd walked the longest, steepest hill we'd ever seen. Then we reached the real hill. On a peak covered with woods, the mountain seemed to drop straight down. To the right, a thin, muddy trail switched back and forth all the way down the mountain. We counted eight switchbacks. Once we got to the bottom and looked back up, we were shocked to see how steep the mountain really was.

"There are a lot of rocks on this mountain range," Ramón continued. "At some places the trail passes between huge rocks so close together that a horse could barely get through, though it was no problem for us on foot. The whole trail is muddy and slippery, with troughs from horses' hooves always stepping in the same place. Some of them are so deep that the horses sink in up to their bellies.

"We also walked along the high mountain's backbone, where the world drops off on either side of you. It's only about six feet from one side to the other." Ramón spread his arms as he spoke, their span showing the width of the path. "Then the wind catches you, and you feel like you'll be blown all the way down to the gulf!"

*   *   *

Two years passed. Though no one in the family still called the wild, high country a paradise, they were getting used to its harsh climate. The bean crops down in Tajo Alto had done well. The second year the bean prices had been very good, and Ramón had earned enough money to buy a cow. Now they had their own milk.

One Sunday morning a young man walked into their clearing. Teodolinda recognized the young Valverde they had met on the way to Tajo Alto two years before. He was dressed poorly and looked frightened. His eyes darted from side to side as he neared the house. Teodolinda did not think he was quite as ugly as he had seemed the first time she had seen him.

Ramón went out and met him under the big potato tree in front of the house. Teodolinda peeped through the small window in the kitchen. The two men shook hands and seemed to be talking earnestly for a while; then the young man left without looking back.

Soon after he left, Teodolinda took the jug to fetch water from the spring. Her father met her in the yard. Without much ado, he announced, "That fellow who was talking with me is Lico Valverde. Do you remember when we met him?"

Placing her jug on her knee, Teodolinda answered, "Sure I do. What did he want?"

"He wants to court you. He asked for permission to start coming to see you. I told him the decision is yours."

"Papito, what shall I say? I barely know the man."

"I know. And I had hoped you wouldn't leave home so soon. We would really miss you. But then again, he is a hard worker and a devoted Catholic. Maybe you should consider it."

The next Sunday Lico stopped in again, even more nervous than before. Ramón invited him closer to the house, and they sat down on several old blocks of wood that served as seats. Teodolinda listened to their discussion from the safety of the kitchen and peeped through the cracks. She heard her father give Lico her positive answer. She heard them discuss the future. Ramón agreed that Lico could come see her every other week, but he made it clear that he did not want things to go too fast. "We would like to have our daughter for a year yet," he said firmly.

Teodolinda was relieved to hear that it would be at least a year before they could get married. When the two men started talking about mundane things, she turned and started a batch of coffee and set a pot of roasting ears on the stove. Soon she shyly walked out to the men with two steaming cups of coffee.

"*Buenas*,"* she said.

"*Buenas*," Lico answered.

For a brief moment their eyes met. That was all. Then she brought out a plate of corn and set it on a stump.

---

* hello

"Gracias," Lico said softly as she returned to the kitchen.

Lico continued his courtship, though he never really courted Teodolinda. He courted her father. He was such a shy young man, and Ramón loved to talk. Every other week he came, right on time. He wore his best clothes, which were not very good. But he always had his hair combed, and he looked better to Teodolinda every time.

Lico never did get enough nerve to talk to Teodolinda, but he talked for hours with Ramón in the yard. Teodolinda always served something. They always exchanged a greeting, and their eyes always met, sometimes for longer than others. Slowly Teodolinda came to love this man who wanted her for his wife.

Lico somehow managed to convince Ramón that a full year was not necessary. So Lico and Teodolinda decided to marry in dry season, seven months after starting their courtship.

In Tico culture, the groom provides for the wedding costs. But Ramón was determined to have enough food to throw a party for his favorite daughter. So Angelina fattened a pig, and Ramón made sure he had plenty of corn and beans.

Lico was making his share of preparations too. He was working to make enough money to buy a new wedding dress for Teodolinda. Before the wedding date, he borrowed a good white shirt, and he bought a white wedding dress for his bride. He also bought several bottles of liquor for the occasion.

According to their Catholic tradition, every man who married needed a *padrino* (godfather), and every girl needed a *madrina* (godmother). During one of his last visits, Lico discussed this with Ramón. They agreed that Don Tilo, the man who had bought the farm next to Ramón's, would be a good *padrino*. He was a friend to both families and a devout Catholic. His wife could be Teodolinda's *madrina*.

The wedding was scheduled for Sunday, July 16, 1932. Ramón took Teodolinda down to Miramar the Friday before. It was her first time down the famous La Cuesta del Tubo, but it would not be her last. He scheduled the wedding with the priest and then left Teodolinda at

Tilo's place and headed home with provisions to help prepare for the wedding feast. Lico hiked to Miramar on Saturday and stayed with his friends.

The morning of the wedding, the weather was perfect. The town of Miramar was perched partway up the Zapotal mountain, so it was not nearly as hot as the Puntarenas gulf, but neither was the weather as harsh and wet as it was in the Zapotal highlands. To Teodolinda it seemed wonderful to come to a warm world that had a dry, clean place to put your feet. Tilo owned a nice house, so Teodolinda lived in better accommodations those two days than she had ever lived in before. That bright, clear morning, Teodolinda was excited and actually felt ready to get married.

When Teodolinda, Tilo, and his wife got to the big Catholic church in front of the plaza, Lico was already there. He was dressed in a long-sleeved white shirt with his old black pants hitched high, his simple leather belt tightly hugging his middle. Teodolinda noticed that he was barefoot. That was nothing new for Lico Valverde. He did not even own a pair of shoes.

Teodolinda felt awkward in her long white wedding dress. Her father had bought her a pair of black shoes, the first she had ever owned. She had felt like a princess as she slipped them on, but now her wide, calloused feet were aching from being so tightly locked into leather. She was thankful for the sheer white veil that hung over her face and helped hide her emotions.

They met in front of the church and discussed their simple plan. Don Tilo would walk Teodolinda in; then his wife would lead Lico in. The priest would tell them what to do after that. Then Tilo noticed that Lico was not wearing shoes.

"Lico, you can't get married barefoot!" he exclaimed. "You need a pair of black shoes. Is it too late to go buy you a pair?"

"It doesn't matter," Lico answered. "I never wore shoes in my life. Why would I want to wear them now?"

"Yeah, but your wedding day is an exception," Tilo argued. "If I knew the priest would wait, I would go buy you a pair."

"I wouldn't want you to do that," Lico said. "There is no disgrace in marrying barefoot. I'm sure I don't mind."

"I know you don't, but I will not go in there in shoes if you, the bridegroom, are barefoot. Here," Tilo suggested, leaning against the wall of the church and jerking off his shoes. "Wear mine."

Lico was mortified. "I could never do that!" he exclaimed. "I would never wear someone else's shoes! Plus, what would you wear?"

"I'll go barefoot. See, you are the bridegroom and have to have the best. Get those shoes on fast. I think the priest is coming."

Sure enough, the priest was approaching from inside the front door. He motioned them in. Lico shook his head at Tilo and walked toward the church house door.

Don Tilo grabbed the shoes and pitched them into a corner. "If the bridegroom goes in there barefoot, then I will too." And he did.

Don Tilo led Teodolinda to the front of the huge cathedral. Next came Tilo's wife with Lico on her arm. Several friends were there to watch, but it was not the custom to invite people to the ceremony. Everyone would come later to the party at the bride's home.

Tilo and his wife placed the nervous couple right in the center of the aisle in front of the altar. The priest stood in front of them and began intoning long religious words about marriage. While the priest talked, Teodolinda peeked through her veil. The vastness of the huge church brought back memories of her childhood and the church in San Ramón. The grandeur, the brilliant colors, and the seriousness of the priest's tones made it seem as if God were just around the corner. A shiver went up Teodolinda's spine. She glanced over at Lico, her husband to be. His eyes were closed and he seemed to be in deep meditation. *He must be a very religious person,* she concluded.

The next thing she knew, the priest was taking them by their right hands and bringing them together. It felt funny to be holding Lico's hand. She had never even touched his hand before. Now she suddenly realized that this hand would be hers from now on. Lico would be her guide and her master. Tears welled in her eyes. Though she felt sure this was the right thing to do, it still made her nervous. There were so many unknowns ahead, and no one had given her any instructions on how to be a wife and mother.

Then the priest gave them each a small white disk. It looked like a cookie, except it was paper thin. He was talking about things she did not understand. He placed the cookie on her tongue, and when she closed her mouth, it melted and tasted faintly of fresh flour. He said this was the body of Christ, but she wondered how that was possible.

Then she was walking out of the church on Lico's arm. He walked with a confident stride, and she could feel that he had a strong arm. She needed that as she thought of the life that lay ahead. That night they stayed at Don Tilo's house, and the next day they climbed the mountain and walked home, just the two of them.

They arrived at Teodolinda's house about mid-afternoon. Preparations were in full swing. Lico's brothers and sisters were there helping. Old Rafael, Lico's father, sat out in the yard on a stump. He was deaf and walked with a prominent limp. No one paid him any attention.

Though Teodolinda's mother barely acknowledged her arrival, her father gave her a hug. Teodolinda burst into tears and ran down to the spring to compose her emotions and wash her face. Then she ran back to the house to help finish the tamales.

Lots of Zapotal neighbors came for the fiesta that night. Everybody ate tamales and drank black coffee sweetened with cane juice. Then Lico brought out his bottles of *guaro*. He gave the first swig to his father-in-law. Ramón wasn't surprised and accepted the drink. Teodolinda was shocked. That was not what she had planned for her wedding feast. She was especially angry when she saw that Avelino, eighteen years old, and Ángel, just sixteen, were drinking too.

Some of the folks complained that no one in Zapotal had musical instruments. "If we did," Don Tilo announced, "we would have a grand dance."

Just before midnight Ángel started to get loud and boisterous. He threatened to fight with several of the visiting boys. The last straw was when he made bold threats about fighting with Don Tilo. Tilo rode off in a huff on his big mule. Ramón was embarrassed and hauled his son outside and scolded him thoroughly. The crowd dispersed. The party was over. But the marriage had just begun.

4

Lico built a lean-to room against one side of Ramón's house, and Teodolinda kept right on cooking for the whole family as usual. More and more of the workload fell on her capable shoulders. Not only did she do more than her share of the housework, but she found ways to earn extra cash. She raised chickens. She kept several hogs. She planted vegetables to sell and made good money on a load of cabbages they hauled down to sell at Miramar when the price was high. Lico was proud of his efficient young wife.

Lico and Ramón were great friends. Lico also did more than his share of the work, and Ramón began to prosper. Soon after the wedding, Lico helped Ramón and his sons plant three *manzanas* of beans in Tajo Alto. The beans did well, so Ramón was able to buy two more cows and a bull. There was plenty of pasture on the farm now, and they were always cutting down more jungle and planting more grass and more vegetables.

News spread quickly when Ignacio Monje moved into Zapotal. Everyone called him Old Nacho. He was a *rezador.** Up until now,

---

* a man who leads rosaries

there had been no Catholic activity in Zapotal unless the head of the home recited the rosary in the evenings before the family went to bed. Now they had a real *rezador*, and they could begin to have public rosaries.

Teodolinda felt she was a sinner, and the thought haunted her. She decided to plan a *rosario*. The *rezador* would need to be paid and the people fed, so she started to save money. Lico agreed and contacted Old Nacho. They chose a Sunday evening for the *rosario*. The Saturday before Lico traveled to Miramar to buy the things they needed—as well as several bottles of *guaro*. To Teodolinda's disgust, he came home very late, filthy and stone drunk. He had blown all the precious money she had saved. He had bought her the groceries she had ordered, but had wasted all that was left on *guaro*.

Old Nacho showed up at Ramón's place early Sunday evening. Teodolinda was busy preparing the food for the *rosario*. She looked up when she heard a noise at the kitchen door. There stood Lico in the doorway, a mischievous look on his face. "Nacho says he needs a shot for his throat so he can lead the prayers."

Teodolinda was thoroughly disgusted. How could a Christian leader want to drink *guaro*? Shrugging her disgust aside, she found one of the bottles on the shelf above the stove. "That's just the way men are, I guess," she muttered. Not only Nacho got a drink. Lico got two, and even her father got one.

At dusk the people started coming. Teodolinda was surprised to see so many. Where had they all come from? Zapotal must be growing fast.

One wall in Ramón's living room was special. It was built out of upright sticks, just like the rest of the house, but on this wall they hung their religious symbols. Lico had hung a string of rosary beads there. Angelina had brought an *estampa** from San Ramón and hung it there. And that afternoon she had gotten out her plaster of Paris statue of El Santo Salvador del Mundo and placed it on the shelf Lico had built for such things. Teodolinda's little sister had cut a bunch of wildflowers

---

* picture of a saint

and hung them around the *estampa* and the statue. Now they lit several candles, dripped the hot wax onto the shelf, and stuck the candles in the wax. The decorated wall looked lovely.

Old Nacho carefully pulled a plastic bag out of his *alforja* and tenderly unwrapped a tiny plaster of Paris image of Jesus. He gently placed it on the shelf and announced, "Now we begin."

Everyone packed into the living room. Teodolinda left her duties in the kitchen and joined the crowd. They all stood together facing the decorated wall. Even the children stood reverently, heads bowed. Then Nacho began chanting.

"Dios te salve María, madre de gracia, el Señor es contigo. Bendita eres entre todas las mujeres, bendito sea el fruto de tu vientre, Jesús . . ." (May God save you, Mary, mother of grace; the Lord is with you. Blessed are you among women, and blessed is the fruit of your womb, Jesus . . .)

The people chanted in response, *"O santa madre de Dios . . ."* (O holy mother of God . . .)

As Old Nacho chanted each phrase of his memorized prayer, he slipped another bead along the rosary's string. Bead after bead slipped through his fingers as he chanted the same words again and again and again, until the whole section of pink beads had passed through his fingers. Then he took up another chant that corresponded with another section of beads.

While Nacho was praying, Teodolinda peeked. Some people had their eyes closed reverently and seemed sincere. Lico was one of them. But most of them, and especially the children, had their eyes open, and she could see that they were not even thinking about God. Then she looked at Nacho himself. He did not look saintly at all in the light of the *canfinera*. His eyes were closed, but he flicked the beads along the string too rapidly. His prayers were fast and mechanical. She got the feeling that he was hurrying because as soon as the prayers were over he would get another shot of *guaro*. In her heart Teodolinda knew that he was a sin-sick sinner just like all the rest of them.

Teodolinda was afraid of God. He seemed so austere and distant. That was how she'd always felt when she was little and her mother had taken her to mass in San Ramón. That was why they cried out to Mary in the rosaries. The priests taught that Mary was the only one who would really listen. Jesus was just like God, since He was His Son. He always seemed angry and generally didn't have time for people. So they went to Mary with their pleas. Then Mary would go to Jesus and ask Him to go discuss the plea with the Father. Mary would beg Jesus, just as she had at the wedding in Cana. Supposedly Jesus had not really wanted to turn the water into wine that day, but since His mother asked Him, He did. Nowadays, if Jesus did not cooperate, Mary reminded Him that she had nursed Him and raised Him. Then Jesus supposedly always gave in. Teodolinda wondered if Mary could convince Jesus to forgive their sins. She seriously doubted it. And her heart felt empty.

The praying lasted forty minutes. When Old Nacho ended the service, the crowd dispersed. But they didn't leave. They knew what was coming. Teodolinda ran back to the kitchen with her mother. A noise at the door caught her attention. By now it was dark, but she could see Lico's face in the shadows from the light of her *canfinera*.

Here we go again, she thought.

"Nacho needs another shot."

Teodolinda just gave Lico the whole bottle. By the time the ladies had served the corn flour pudding and black coffee, the men were already tipsy. Out in the dark Teodolinda could hear her father talking loudly and the others laughing at his jokes. Lico, she knew, would be quiet. That was one good thing about her husband. He was bashful and hardly ever raised his voice. Even when he was drunk, he was low-key and quiet. Teodolinda knew he wouldn't make any trouble. But she was worried about her brother Ángel. He was rowdy even when he wasn't drunk, and as soon as he touched liquor, he went wild.

But something deeper was amiss. "Drinking doesn't go with praying," Teodolinda whispered to her mother. "I just know this is wrong. But what can I do? I am just a young woman."

"Everybody mixes drinking and prayers," Angelina retorted. "Even a good leader like Old Nacho. There's nothing wrong with a little fun after a *rosario*."

Teodolinda shook her head. She wasn't satisfied. *It must be an evil that God overlooks,* she finally concluded.

Suddenly everyone hurried to the front of the house. Teodolinda ran to the door and looked out. She saw two young men flailing at each other with their fists. Though she could not see who they were, she guessed rightly that one was Ángel. Folks shouted and cheered, egging them on.

The fight did not last long. Old Nacho's son Julito took the beating. Ángel crowed out his victory. Teodolinda was embarrassed. Why couldn't her brother stay out of trouble? And on this, of all nights?

*   *   *

Don Tilo bought two more farms in Zapotal. Soon he had placed a woman on each farm to manage it. Eventually these women began having children, and rumors began circulating about Tilo and his mistresses. One thing was sure—his farms did well. His women took good care of things, and they cost him less money than hired men.

Soon after the *rosario,* Lico's brother Pedro came and talked to him for a long time. Teodolinda did not like the looks of this brother-in-law. He looked rough, and though Lico was a loner, Pedro was a hermit. He would hardly talk with anybody.

After Pedro left, Lico approached her. "Look, you know Mama died and Dad lives alone with Pedro and his wife. Well, Pedro says Dad is getting worse and they can't take care of him anymore. They want to move to their new place, and the family is asking us to move in and take care of him. What do you say?"

"You know I'd rather not," Teodolinda answered. "That old man has always given me the creeps, and I hate that dark river bottom where he lives. But if you think we should, I am willing to give it a try."

A week later, Lico and Teodolinda moved in with old Rafael. By now he was so lame he could not even leave the house without help. He was so deaf they had to shout to make him hear. Not only that, but he shouted whenever he tried to talk, since he could not hear himself. He had a terrible cough and was slowly wasting away.

Life was not too bad for Teodolinda when Lico was home. He helped his father and served his every whim. But when Lico left for the fields, Teodolinda felt as if she would lose her mind. She had to take care of the old man, plus do the housework. When Rafael was not lying in bed moaning and groaning, he was sitting on his old chair. Every now and then he would holler, "I want a drink of water," or "Where's my son Lico?" or "I'm hungry," or "Take me to the bathroom." Then Teodolinda would have to drop whatever she was doing and take care of him.

Rafael's house stood in a small clearing in one of the Jabonal River bottoms. Across the river and on the ridge behind the house the jungle was thick and tangled. The black howler monkeys often made the valley vibrate with their howls.

The house itself was just a stick shack with so many large cracks in the walls that they gave little protection from the cold and the dark, creepy night. Lico and Teodolinda often heard the *león* screaming on the ridge. Teodolinda would lie awake trembling, unable to sleep. Lico snored away as if he was perfectly at home, which of course he was.

Soon after their move, Teodolinda discovered she was expecting. She survived the difficult days at the river bottom until the baby was born. A local midwife came and helped with the delivery. Little Luis Rómulo Valverde was born April 22, 1933, while old Rafael hollered and groaned out on the porch with no one to see after him.

Soon after the baby came, Teodolinda approached her husband. "Valverde," as she called him, "I can't take it here anymore. I'm sorry. I know I will lose my mind. I can't sleep nights. I am afraid. During the day I have to take care of Rafael, and he is so hard to please. I think he hates me, and he gives me the creeps. If you love me, get me out of here."

Lico loved little Luis and his mama, so for their sake he asked Pedro to take Rafael to his home. Lico explained that they couldn't care for him any longer because Teodolinda's mother was going to have a baby, and Teodolinda needed to be there to help.

By the time they moved back to Ramón's place, Angelina was expecting her twelfth child. She knew Teodolinda could handle the role of midwife since she had assisted with her last birth. Besides, Angelina was a midwife herself and had taught Teodolinda. Baby Luis was forty days old, and Angelina was due in less than a month.

Zapotal was having another *temporal*. The yard around the house was one big muddy mess. Ramón brought his cows into the yard every morning to milk them. While he milked, the other cows, their calves, and the bull milled around and made the mud worse. Angelina did not complain because she was glad for the milk.

This morning was rainy. It had been raining steadily for a week. Teodolinda let her mother sleep in and got up early to make the coffee. Lico drank his coffee and left for work at the crack of dawn. Ramón got up soon after Lico left, wrapped plastic around his shoulders, and went to get the cows. A few minutes later, Angelina got up and drank a cup of coffee.

Teodolinda had started grinding the corn for tortillas when she heard the ruckus. Her father was shouting angrily, and then their ugly gray Brahman bull crashed onto their lean-to porch, whirled around, and stood with his head lowered, facing the yard. Teodolinda slammed the door that led from the kitchen to the yard and then peered through one of the many cracks in the wall. The bull stood trembling like a leaf in the wind, his crazed eyes spitting fear and anger. Fear gripped Teodolinda's heart. This bull was dangerous.

She ran to the front door and met her father, who was panting and almost as angry as the bull. "The cattle were in the sugarcane patch. I had a hard time getting them out. I beat the old bull until he moved. Where is he now?" he bellowed.

"Papito, be careful! He's on the porch, and he's very angry. I think he's dangerous!"

"Dangerous? That stupid animal couldn't hurt a flea. I'm the one who's angry, and I'm dangerous too! Just wait until I get my hands on him!"

With that Ramón disappeared around the house brandishing his stick. Teodolinda and her mother returned to the kitchen and watched through the cracks. Ramón and the bull stood face-to-face, sizing each other up. Which was the angrier? Which was the stronger?

"Come on out, you beast!" Ramón yelled, stick in hand.

The bull charged. Ramón swung his stick to hit him, but slipped on the muddy surface and lost his balance. He never hit the bull, but the bull hit him—and knocked him flat.

Teodolinda opened the kitchen door and was horrified to see the bull bending over her father, who was wriggling in the mud like a

salamander. The bull picked him up with his horns and flung him out ahead. Teodolinda screamed when she saw her father go down again. *"¡El toro está matando a mi papá!"* (The bull is killing my father!)

Then Angelina took action. Forgetting that her baby was almost due, she grabbed the homemade broom and raced into the yard, whacking the bull from behind with the broomstick.

The bull did not even notice. Ramón was slipping around in the mud trying to get up, but the bull was too quick. *Wham!* Ramón went flying again, the bull pursuing. Angelina followed, whacking as hard as she could.

The bull kept knocking Ramón down and pushing him ahead for about fifty yards. Every time Ramón tried to get up, the bull knocked him down. Teodolinda screamed again. "O Holy Trinity, help us!" she cried.

Then she remembered their dog. Duke had helped Ramón chase the cattle out of the cane field. Now he lay by the door panting. Teodolinda called him, and he raced around the house and launched himself straight at the angry bull's nose. The bull stopped. Then the dog bit again, this time in the bull's ribs. The bull swung around in a frenzy. Ramón got up and raced into the house. He was muddy from head to toe, and his pants were torn wide open, but he seemed to be all right. As he passed the two women, he grinned and asked, "Why were you so frightened? I told you that bull couldn't hurt a flea!"

Ramón marched into the bedroom and grabbed his new twenty-two rifle. He marched back out, snarling, "I am going to shoot that bull!"

Teodolinda and Angelina calmed him down and convinced him not to shoot the bull. Angelina's pains started right away. Ramón milked the cow and left for work. Teodolinda gathered the things she would need for the delivery and followed her mother into the bedroom. Little Rigo was born that night. Teodolinda was twenty-one years old.

5

Teodolinda stood up to her knees in water. The big flat rock she leaned over was just the right height. As usual, Lico's pants were very dirty. Teodolinda had wet them by plopping them into the river. Now she took the round bar of blue-gray soap and rubbed it on the dirtiest spots—the inside of the waist, the knees, and the hem. She turned the pockets inside out and soaped them too. Then she began scrubbing the pants by sections. Her strong hands grabbed the legs by the hems and scrubbed them against the upper leg. The rubbing movement brought the suds out fast.

As Teodolinda scrubbed, she stared out over the rippling waters of the Jabonal River, blue-green in the sunlight. The green moss-covered branches of the jungle hung over her, protecting her from the hot sun. It was only nine o'clock.

Twelve years had passed since she and her family had moved from San Ramón to Zapotal. She could not remember one sick day in her life. After little Luis was born, she and Lico had built a small house of their own about a hundred and fifty feet downriver from her father's house. They had lived in that little house for eight years now. Ángel had been born a year after Luis. Two years later came Lidier. A year after Lidier, Teodolinda was delighted to have her first little girl, whom she called Marina. Three years after Marina, she had delivered Marcos. A year after that, her second daughter, Amable, was born.

On this bright morning, Luis and Ángel, the two oldest boys, were out working with Lico, and the rest of the children were over at Grandma's house. They had even toted baby Amable along. Angelina often helped take care of Teodolinda's babies so she could get her work done. Now, as Teodolinda leaned over the rock and scrubbed the dirty clothes, she was expecting her seventh child.

During these eight years in their own house, Teodolinda had always been healthy and strong. Even now she was able to do all of her work by herself, especially if Angelina occasionally helped with the babies.

Next, Teodolinda scrubbed Amable's diapers, which consisted mostly of old rags. The cool water swirled around her legs, and her strong arms were beginning to ache. *After two hours of scrubbing clothes, your back sure hurts,* Teodolinda mused. *And it looks like a storm is coming. Rainy season is on the way. It is the middle of May, after all. I'd better hurry if I don't want to get soaked.*

The house was perched high on the riverbank. Teodolinda nimbly traipsed up the steps Lico had dug up the long steep hill. She got to the house just in time. Lightning flashed and thunder shook the cabin. Soon the rain began to fall in torrents. Lico was out working, so Teodolinda began to prepare the noon meal.

Toward evening, Teodolinda slipped out to fetch some water for their early morning coffee. She ran across the grassless yard she always kept swept clean, and carefully made her way down the steep trail to the river, her toes digging into the red clay. The rain had turned the dust into slick mud. She was glad Lico had dug out the steps down the steep bank to the river. She was also glad she did not have to use river water. Since the rain, it was a swirling brown torrent, rushing its way to the ocean, dragging sticks and logs along in its mad dash.

Lico had found a tiny spring up the riverbank among a tangle of vines and bushes. He had taken a bamboo pole and sliced it in half, chipping out the section dividers to make a perfect canal. He had set one end at the base of the trickle and sealed the leaks with mud and then propped the other end on forked sticks stuck into the ground. The bamboo pipeline came out just at the edge of the jungle, where Teodolinda now filled her aluminum kettle and her five-gallon plastic bucket.

Minutes later she was picking her way precariously up the slick bank again, one hand balancing the full bucket on her shoulder while the other hand grasped the heavy kettle. She was just about at the top. The last step was a flat rock, half buried in the dirt. She did not realize that the rain had soaked the dirt and loosened the rock. As she placed her foot on the rock and shifted her weight, doubled by the baby and the containers full of water, the rock dislodged and flipped out from under her so fast that she hardly knew what had happened. She fell forward, her face landing right in the muddy hole where the rock had been. But she didn't stop there. She slid down the steep embankment to the river, feet first.

Teodolinda lay beside the rushing torrent and regained her composure. Thankfully, she had not rolled into the river, and she had not been knocked unconscious. Though the fall had knocked the breath out of her, none of her bones seemed to be broken. But the pain made her very afraid for her baby. Slowly she got to her feet. The bucket and the kettle lay beside her, abandoned. She limped up the steps again and hobbled over to her mother's place, where she told the whole family the story.

"Hey, you'd better be glad you're alive!" her brother Paco interjected, laughing at his sister's clumsiness.

"It's not funny," Angelina retorted. "She might lose her baby."

"I think something is wrong, Mamilla," Teodolinda said weakly.

Angelina, herself sick with a fever, walked her daughter home and put her to bed. She brewed a tea from a wild plant to stop the bleeding. Late that night after everyone was in bed, Angelina went back home.

The next morning Teodolinda felt better. She was sore all over, but she felt good enough to get up and make the early coffee. Since it was Sunday, Lico decided not to go to work. Teodolinda was glad, because she was still worried about the baby. She did not feel any movement. After breakfast, Teodolinda was getting another batch of dirty wash ready to take down to the river when sharp pains gripped her abdomen.

The public trail ran right past their house, and people traveling from Zapotal to Miramar often stopped by to chat. Just then she heard a man shout from the yard. It was Eladio, their overly talkative neighbor. She was thankful that Lico was at home to entertain him. Lico stuck his head out the window and listened, commenting occasionally.

Teodolinda knew she should get her mother, but she did not have the strength, and her mother had not been feeling well the night before. Instead, she sent the children and the baby over to Grandma. All she wanted to do was rest. Grabbing a handful of diapers, she went to bed. Her pains hit hard, but she did not cry out. Lico was still leaning out the living room window, talking with Eladio.

An hour later Teodolinda crept past Lico unnoticed. In one hand she carried a machete. In her other hand she carried a tiny infant wrapped in a diaper. She slipped out the back door and weakly walked toward the jungle's edge. Tears blinded her eyes until she could hardly see the trail.

Teodolinda looked back. Eladio still sat on his horse, talking animatedly and waving his arms. The sun shone brightly, and everything looked exceptionally green after the hard rain the day before. She ducked under the first branches and stepped into a shady glade. A squirrel chattered as it scampered up a tree into the green canopy. Teodolinda stumbled to the center of the clearing and knelt on the damp layer of dead leaves. Tenderly she laid the bundle on the ground beside her. Then she took her machete and began to dig. Her tears mixed with the soft dirt that piled up as the hole deepened.

Once the hole was a foot deep, she laid the tiny dead baby in its shallow grave. When she was ready to cover it, she felt as if she should pray. But all she knew were the memorized prayers her mother had taught her or the chants she had learned at the rosaries. She shook her head and quickly buried the baby. She found several small rocks among the leaves and placed them on the fresh dirt in the form of a cross.

Before she got up, she mumbled one *Padre Nuestro** and crossed herself. Then, sobbing, she got up and went back to bed.

Eladio left a few minutes later.

"Valverde," Teodolinda called out weakly from the bedroom.

Lico came into the bedroom with questioning eyes. "What's going on?"

---

* Lord's Prayer

"Go call Mamilla. I am bleeding badly again. I lost the baby," she said, a fresh flood of tears coursing down her cheeks.

Angelina's tea and care stopped the hemorrhaging. By the next morning Teodolinda, though weak, was up before dawn making the coffee and grinding corn for tortillas.

Less than a year later, in 1942, Teodolinda was rewarded with a tiny baby boy. He seemed special from birth, so they chose a very special name for him—Domingo Evangelista (Sunday Evangelist). Was there something prophetic about the name? Time would tell. Meanwhile, everybody just called the baby Gelo.

Two years later Leyla was born, then Mireya. After a while came another boy called Marino, then Belén. The family was growing by leaps and bounds.

6

"Radishes, pumpkins, chayotes, and cabbage! Come buy fresh vegetables! Fresh vegetables from Zapotal!" Luis called. He sat on a block of wood at the market in Miramar, his clear young voice ringing through the marketplace. The white skin he had inherited from his mother looked unnatural on the distinctly Indian features he had inherited from his father. His clothes were tattered and his hair unkempt. Luis was not the most skilled fellow on the block, but he could sell vegetables.

That morning, as soon as Lico had dumped the vegetables into the long wooden box in front of his son, he had gone to hang out with his friends at the food stands. Little Luis, only ten years old, had sorted the vegetables into piles. Then he had started shouting.

Other vegetable stands were scattered around the market square, but a lot of people recognized the quality of the fresh Zapotal crops and came to buy from Luis. As soon as Luis had sold some vegetables, Lico came and asked for the *pesetas.** That made Luis angry. He knew his father was using the money to drink with his buddies. But Luis

---

* twenty-five-cent pieces

kept on hollering and earned more *pesetas*. Before long his dad came and took them too.

Lico and Luis had left home at four o'clock that morning, walking while their horse carried the vegetables they had packed in sacks and carefully arranged on a padded wooden frame on his back. The trip to Miramar had taken four hours.

By noon the sun was hot, and the vegetables were not selling well anymore. Lico came back for money for the fifth time, and Luis could see that he was drunk. "Papito," he fussed, "remember what Mamita said. You should buy groceries before you drink."

"Yes," Lico hiccupped. "I . . . I . . . will do that next. How much money do you have?"

"I don't have any for drink. You need to buy groceries."

Meekly, Lico obeyed and bought the groceries. He was too drunk to remember some of the things Teodolinda needed and bought some things she didn't need. Then he and Luis went to a friend's house for the night.

The next morning, after some more drinking, they tied the small amount of groceries on the horse's back and headed for Zapotal. Luis rode while Lico stumbled along behind.

It was afternoon when Lico and Luis finally reached home. Teodolinda was waiting, her sharp tongue honed and ready. After Luis dismounted, she checked the groceries. As always, some things were missing. "Luis, is this all he bought?" she snapped.

Luis nodded.

"Does he have any money left?"

"Not a cent." Luis shrugged.

Lico had taken refuge in the cane patch. Teodolinda found him there, emptying his last bottle. "Lico!" she lashed out. "Why can't you learn? You had enough money to buy extra things, and now you didn't even bring all the groceries I need. Think of all the money you blow on liquor. If you wouldn't drink, we could buy all kinds of extra things. As it is, we will never get ahead. We will be poor forever!"

Teodolinda stalked off. As usual, Lico didn't say a word.

*   *   *

Every year rainy season came and stayed for too long. Then dry season slipped in at last, converting Zapotal into a paradise for a couple of months. Then the rains would come again, soaking the high plateau and bringing in the next wet year. Sometimes it seemed as if every year competed with the last to see which could bring more rain.

Don Lico and Teodolinda progressed in spite of Lico's drinking problem and the many mouths to feed. Teodolinda spent a lot of time out of doors helping raise the vegetables. Every year they planted beans in Tajo Alto. They saved enough money to buy a larger, one-hundred-*manzana* farm. They built a new, larger house beside a small creek. Right in front of the house was a row of grapefruit trees. Very close to the house, by the creek bank, was a lovely spring. Crystal-clear water trickled right out of a rock on the bank. Lico chipped a little bowl out of the rock for his family to get their drinking water. The public trail passed just beyond the row of grapefruit trees.

Lico also bought a small horse. They called him Jabón, meaning "soap," because he was the color of the blue-gray soap they bought at the market to wash clothes. He was a fiery little horse Lico used for riding and hauling cargo.

The cow herd grew, slowly but steadily. Teodolinda and the girls took care of the cattle. She kept the heifer calves and sold the males at weaning age for cash. Now she milked five or six cows. If there was more milk than they needed, they made a squeaky white cheese. Teodolinda worked harder to keep the farm under control while Lico spent more and more of his money on drink, especially when he went to Miramar to sell vegetables.

Marina, the oldest girl, turned out to be a good worker. Increasingly, as Teodolinda helped manage things out of doors, Marina was forced to take the load in the house, which increased as Teodolinda gave birth to her twelfth child and eighth son. They named him Sergio. From the start he was a healthy, lively baby.

Luis, the oldest, was growing up. Teodolinda pitied him because his carefree, lazy personality meant he was always in trouble with Lico. Lico considered it an unpardonable sin to be lazy. Ángel and Lidier, the next two boys, were good workers, so Lico looked to them more and more for help on the farm. As Teodolinda watched Luis's pain, she pitied him and took his side, and Luis became Mama's boy.

Every year Lico set a goal of cutting down two *manzanas* of jungle. He didn't always get it done, but this year he again was determined. Close to their house was a fertile hillside which he decided to clear next. His daily routine consisted of getting up early, drinking coffee, and then heading for the jungle with his sons and their machetes and axes. The smaller children carried lunch to the men around ten. Then the men worked until late afternoon and came home for the large evening meal. Feeding a bunch of hardworking, fast-growing boys was no simple task.

In the jungle, the first job was to slash out the underbrush. That was fairly easily done with machetes. But the next job was tough. They had to cut down all the trees with their axes. Many of the trees were small, but some were so big it took a measure of engineering and a lot of brute strength to make them fall.

Today they faced a huge potato tree, named for its fruits, which were shaped like potatoes. The tree measured fifteen feet in diameter. But the biggest problem in cutting down these huge trees was their buttresses, some of which protruded six feet from the trunk. To get around them, the men built a scaffold out of poles and vines to work from.

Chip by chip, the axes bit their way into the tree's flesh. Ángel worked on one side and Lidier on the other. Lico, Luis, and even young Marcos cut down smaller trees from a safe distance.

After hours of hard work, the potato tree was about to fall. The boys grew tense, glancing upward anxiously after each swing of the ax. Finally the tree started leaning, and they had only a few seconds to jump off the scaffolding and run the opposite direction while the tree swept down toward the ground, bringing smaller trees down with it. In the awful second when the huge weight of the tree crashed onto solid ground, the earth shook, and bark and branches flew.

"Boys," Lico told Luis and Marcos after hearing the crash, "I am going to make sure Ángel and Lidier are okay. You stay here and work."

Lico checked on his boys and then surveyed the monster tree, thinking of the big job awaiting them. It would take a long time to chop up the mass of vines and branches. He planned to burn the brush in dry

season so the black dirt would be cleared and ready to plant before the first rains in May.

An hour later Lico returned to check on Luis and Marcos, but they were nowhere to be seen. Lico saw at a glance that they had hardly done a thing since he had left. He searched angrily for the boys but could not find them. Later they showed up and sheepishly admitted they had gone swimming.

"Swimming!" Lico growled. "And here the rest of us are working like mules! Is that fair? Luis, you're the oldest boy in this family, and you go swimming right in the middle of the day?"

Luis mumbled a few words that made Lico even angrier.

"I tell you the truth, young man, I am disappointed in you! You have never been worth your beans. You should be ashamed that your younger brothers can do more than you. I can't even put you up on the platform to cut down a big tree. You'd lie down in the cut and fall asleep! Then the tree would fall and smash you flat. And it would serve you right!"

Luis stood still, his face white and hard as stone. A little jerk at the edge of his mouth was the only sign of his deep emotions. He didn't answer, but stalked home to seek comfort in his mother's more encouraging words.

That night Luis sat outside for a long time and watched the moon rise. The nighthawks sang their mournful songs, but they could not assuage the pain and anger that raged in his heart. *Someday I will show my dad that I am a man too! He only has good words for Ángel and Lidier. I am sixteen now. I will grow a bit more and whip them all.*

Then he dropped his head to his chest and cried.

One morning Lico had a strange request for the boys. "Lidier and Gelo, I want you to ride to Uncle Tino's place in Barranquilla and ask him if he would loan me his *Sagradas Escrituras* (Sacred Scriptures). It's a big book, and you will need to be extremely careful when you bring it. Take this sack and this big plastic bag. Wrap the book in the plastic bag first; then put it into the sack and tie it very securely to the saddle."

The boys rode double on Jabón, dismounting to greet their uncle in his yard and explain their mission.

"Yes, I'll loan Lico the *Sagradas Escrituras*," Uncle Tino agreed. "He's my brother, and it's a good book. But listen, you need to promise to take good care of it. I want you to bring it back in one month."

The boys arrived home just before lunch. Lidier had carried the Bible all the way from Barranquilla because he was afraid that if he tied it on the saddle it would work itself loose. Now he handed the bundle to his father, who brought it into the house and laid it in on his bed. "We will look at it this evening," he announced.

Later that evening, after supper, Lico asked Lidier to bring the Bible. Lidier hurried into the bedroom and brought the bundle to the small table where Lico was sitting. Teodolinda placed the *canfinera* in the center and stuck several candles to the rough boards for more light. The children crowded around as their father unwrapped the huge Bible. It was an elaborate Catholic Bible with colorful paintings sprinkled throughout the text. "Stay back," Lico growled. "We need to be respectful when we look at this book. This book is sacred. Some people call it God's Word."

Reverently, Lico opened the book. The candles flickered in the dark room and played tricks with the shadows on Lico's face, which showed many wrinkles despite his being just over forty years old.

Luis took a special interest in the Bible. Each painting depicted a story, but no one knew what the stories were about. There was a huge man towering over a little one. The big man carried a giant *cutacha* and wore sandals. It sure seemed strange that a man would wear sandals! The little man carried only a leather pouch at the end of two thongs. Luis wondered what had happened to the poor boy. He was sure the big man had killed him.

They also saw a picture of two women crying. A richly dressed man on a golden chair had a baby by one leg and a *cutacha* in his other hand. It looked as if he were going to slice the baby in half. Luis shuddered. *That must be a horrible story,* he thought. Then they found a painting of Mary with baby Jesus in the manger. Luis knew that story. He had often seen nativity scenes in Catholic homes.

"Look, it's Mary and the baby God," Lico whispered; then he crossed himself. The whole family crowded around in awe, certain it was an actual photo. Now they had seen Mary and her Son, Jesus!

"How beautiful!" Teodolinda exclaimed, looking over Lico's shoulder.

Don Lico started to read aloud to his family. He read slowly, like a second-grader. For an hour his voice droned on and on. Soon the children were yawning and heading for their beds. But Luis sat and listened intently. Finally only three were left—Lico, Luis, and Teodolinda.

For a month the Bible was the center of attention. Most of the family tired of looking at the pictures and hearing Lico read, but Luis never did. When the month ended, Luis rode Jabón to Barranquilla to take the Bible back.

For a while, things were different for the Valverde family. Lico started to call the family together to pray the rosary every evening. He would take his bead chain and try to pray just like Old Nacho did. But the only prayer he knew was the Lord's Prayer. So he would chant that as many times as there were beads on the string. He even slowed down his drinking during the month they had the Bible, but he didn't stop. It would take more than a month with a Bible to make Don Lico stop drinking.

*   *   *

Little Sergio was an exceptionally lively little boy. He learned to talk sooner than some of the other children had. He was witty and won the whole family's hearts. Soon after the Bible episode, when he was four years old, little Sergio got sick. That was normal. The children often got sick with colds and fevers due to the harsh, damp climate. But little Sergio grew steadily worse, and the cold developed into pneumonia.

Teodolinda was fast becoming the Zapotal doctor. Not only did they call on her to deliver babies, but whenever there were broken bones or bad sprains, everybody asked for Teodolinda. She had a natural knack for rubbing sore places and getting bones back into place. She also learned all she could about local herbs, and many people came to her for home remedies. Now Teodolinda tried everything she knew on her son.

In the beginning stages of the sickness, she mixed lard with baking soda and rubbed it on his chest every night. But it didn't seem to help. One evening Sergio seemed worse. He looked frail, his eyes were sunken, and he could hardly catch his breath when he coughed. So Teodolinda heated lard and mixed crushed garlic in it and plastered his chest. She placed a thick rag across his chest and laid him beside her in bed. His coughing subsided, and they all went to sleep.

At about ten o'clock Sergio called out for her. Teodolinda had a match ready and lit the *canfinera*. Little Sergio crawled across the bed to her. She felt his forehead. It was terribly hot. Then he whispered,

"Mamita, me voy donde Tatica Dios." (Mama, I'm going to my Daddy God.)

Fear struck Teodolinda's heart as her little boy's eyes widened. She tried to wake Lico. "Valverde, little Sergio is dying! His fever is terribly high!"

Lico just rolled over in bed and mumbled, "He's not dying. He's just got the fever." Then he snored on.

Little Sergio whimpered again, gasping for every breath. Teodolinda knew the time had come. She sat up in bed beside the *canfinera* and held her little son. By its light she watched his face. She whispered, "Sergio, do you want to go to Tatica Dios?"

"Yes, Mamita," he nodded, "I want to go . . ."

Teodolinda held him close. Suddenly he opened his eyes even wider, as though he was seeing something. Then he whispered again, "Mamita, I am going to Tatica Dios."

Teodolinda held him tightly. Again his eyes opened wide, and she knew he was seeing something. By the look on his face, whatever he saw was wonderful! She wept, and her salty tears fell on his face as he died. She held him for half an hour before she woke anyone else.

Finally she woke Lico and the older children. Soon the house was bustling with activity. Luis slipped out into the dark night to let the closest neighbors know. They came by twos and threes. One brought a bag of coffee. Another brought some *dulce*. Many brought candles.

Teodolinda dressed Sergio in his best clothes and laid him in the middle of the living room on a bench covered with a blanket. She covered him with a sheet. Marina helped her light candles at the head and foot of the makeshift bed, attaching the long, thin candles to the wooden bench with drops of their own melted wax.

Teodolinda's parents were the first to come. There was very little show of emotion. Angelina brought along her plaster of Paris Santo Salvador del Mundo, and Ramón brought his rosary beads. They placed these items on the shelf on the special wall Teodolinda had set up in her home. Some folks even brought flowers they had picked by lantern light along the way.

Next Teodolinda went to the kitchen to help her girls make a big batch of coffee. It was about midnight when she first caught on that someone had brought along a bottle and was passing it around. Lico was grinning as he did when he got tipsy. *Oh, no!* she groaned. *This can't happen at little Sergio's vela!*

Then one of their new Zapotal neighbors came in carrying a guitar. They were going to party and dance! She marched to the door and stood leaning against the doorjamb. All the men were out in the yard, ready to party. Some were laughing and joking. Others were already drunk. Her brother Ángel was entertaining Lico with jokes.

Teodolinda took a deep breath and spoke in a commanding voice. Though she was only a short little wisp of a woman, everybody respected her. "Listen, if you want to party, go somewhere else. Can't you respect a mother's grief? You can all be here and enjoy the evening, but I will not have wild music and dancing. Finish that bottle you've started, but no more, please! I'll have plenty of coffee for you to drink."

The men were embarrassed to be corrected by a woman, but they knew she was right. That night there was no wild music, no dancing, and the drinking never got bad. But there was a lot of black coffee served. Later Old Nacho led them through the *rosario.* They even sang some songs Nacho chose, the guitar accompanying them.

The next morning several neighbors helped Lico nail together a makeshift box for a coffin. Teodolinda and the girls served food to the family and to the neighbors who had stayed all night. Many had left in the wee hours of the morning. By ten o'clock a long procession was walking toward the Zapotal graveyard. It was a mournful scene, but there were no hysterics or wild emotions, just soft weeping.

Teodolinda walked alone. Her husband walked out ahead with the men who took turns carrying the coffin. Her children were mixed in with the crowd. Teodolinda's heart felt as heavy as a stone. She had no tears left at the moment. As she walked, she remembered little Sergio's last words. A strange peace filled her soul. *At least this son of mine will never experience the hard life we live here in Zapotal. He will never drink the wine of our poverty. He will never come under the terrible grip of the guaro that is becoming more and more available. And I know he went to Heaven. I saw the look on his face! This son of mine is probably the fortunate one. In this I will rejoice . . .*

*   *   *

The hot Costa Rican dog days of dry season were at their peak, but Zapotal never suffered much. Though it was April, there was always enough fog and rain to keep Zapotal cool and green.

One evening Lico said to Teodolinda and the boys, "I really wish I didn't have to go plant beans at Tajo Alto this year. As soon as it rains, I'd like to get the vegetables planted. I know we need both beans and vegetables. We need the beans as our staple all year round and the vegetables to sell for cash. But I can't be both places at once, and you boys aren't quite old enough to take full responsibility for either."

Then Teodolinda had an idea. She knew she probably shouldn't, but she enjoyed outdoor work much more than housework. And now she had big girls. "I will go to Tajo Alto," she announced. "If you give me Luis and Ángel, we will plant the beans. You can have Lidier and Marcos. They are younger, but they can help you plant vegetables. Luis and Ángel can do most of the work in Tajo Alto, and I can cook for them."

Lico agreed, and as soon as the rains started, Teodolinda and her boys marched off to Tajo Alto. Jabón carried two hundred-pound bags of bean seed and the few simple utensils they would need for cooking.

A friend of Lico's, Otilio Chávez, had enough land to spare. He loaned them two *manzanas*. It was good land, well rested after letting the weeds take over for several years. Now Teodolinda and her two boys moved in with Otilio's family and got to work.

The first day, the boys made wide trails four or five yards apart through the high weeds. Teodolinda cooked for them at Otilio's place and hauled the food out to the field so they would not lose any time.

Ángel planted the beans the second day. He was nineteen now, and the best worker Lico had.

Planting the beans looked easy, but it was not. Luis carried the beans to Ángel, who made a pouch out of a burlap bag, tied it around his waist, and dumped several pounds of beans into it. Then he walked the trails, flinging the beans into the high weeds on either side of the trail. It was hard enough to throw beans into high weeds, but to throw them so they fell through the weeds and onto the ground evenly was harder yet. So as Ángel walked, he sprinkled the beans into the weeds on either side of him with precision and care. Lico had taught him well.

After watching, Teodolinda said, "Ángel, I can do that. Let me try."

Sure enough, Teodolinda could do it, and together they threw the two hundred pounds of beans into the weeds in one day until the big hillside was covered with small black beans. But the main job was still waiting.

Starting at the lowest end of the hillside, the two boys now began the hard work. With razor-sharp machetes, they systematically cut down the brush, hacking the weeds off right against the ground. Every machete swath had to leave the black dirt bare. Using a hooked stick called a *garabato*, they hooked the weeds after each cut and swept them behind themselves. Soon the precious bean seeds were covered with a thick mat of weeds. At the end of the day, they went over the whole piece they had cut and chopped the big weeds into smaller pieces.

By noon the third day, Luis wanted to stop. "Come on, Ángel, look how much we have done. We've done great. Let's quit early today. Then we can run into town tonight."

"Humph!" Ángel snorted. "And what would we tell Mamita? You know she's coming with lunch soon. If she doesn't find us here, she'll have our hides for sure! We will work until four o'clock."

Two weeks later the work was done. The bean seeds were all covered with a thick mat of chopped weeds. Teodolinda and the boys hurried back to their Zapotal home.

The weed covering served as mulch, and the seeds sprouted quickly with the afternoon rains. At first the new bean sprouts working their way through the mat of weeds were spindly, but firmly rooted in the soft dirt and warmed by the morning sun, they turned lush and green, promising a good crop two months later.

*   *   *

During the two weeks Teodolinda was gone, Lico planted vegetables. Marina, who had just turned sixteen, cooked the meals, washed the clothes, and took care of the children. Twelve-year-old Amable helped. Nine-year-old Leyla tried, but she was often more trouble than help.

While Teodolinda was away planting beans, ten-year-old Gelo got sick. Gelo had taken care of the calves ever since he was six years old. After the cows were milked in the morning, the calves were turned out to pasture with their mamas. Gelo would round up the calves in the afternoon, carrying a short rope to hit them with when they were ornery. If one was too wild, he would use the little rope as a lasso and pull it to a stop. Then he would haul the calf in and tie him up for the night, sometimes battling for an hour before the job was done. Often Gelo would take one of his brothers or sisters along, but as often as not, he went alone.

When Gelo came in one day with the calves, he tied them up and ran in, crying, "Marina, my head hurts! I feel sick. I wish Mamita were here."

Marina sent Gelo to bed hot with fever. Soon he fell asleep, and Marina forgot about him as she worked. By evening he was worse, and he cried and cried for his mama. Before going to bed, Lico went in and stared at him. Gelo was lying on the simple board bed on a mat made of banana leaves and bark. He looked frail beneath a burlap blanket. Lico pitied him but did not know what to do, so he went to bed and slept.

Marina was up with Gelo most of that night. His fever would not go down, and his headache tortured him. Gelo was not a boy to complain quickly or cry easily, so Marina knew he was very sick. Placing cool, wet rags on his head gave him enough relief that he could rest off and on.

Gelo's fever never left him during the week that followed, and it was often so high that he would hallucinate. During the night he would cry out for his mother again and again. His horrible nightmares made the nights a terror for him and his family. At first the whole family tried to help and Marina stayed awake, but after five days the family was so exhausted that they slept right through his cries. During the day Lico spent more time outdoors just to get away from Gelo's groaning.

Two days before Teodolinda returned from Tajo Alto, a neighbor lady came to help. She recommended some herbs to take the fever down. By then, Gelo, who had been the liveliest of all the children, had wasted away to a skeleton. He could not walk, and Marina had to carry him to the outhouse and back. Marina just could not get all the other work done, and the whole family suffered.

When Teodolinda returned, she was shocked. Try as she might, she could not nurse Gelo back to his former health. He fought the fever for another week.

Finally the fever broke, and Gelo started eating again. Teodolinda set him out in the living room on a bench while she did her work. His now skinny arms were twisting out of shape so badly that he could not even feed himself. His legs were also slowly twisting out of shape, especially his right leg, which twisted around and pulled up toward his back. At the time nobody knew what had crippled little Gelo. Years later they learned it was polio.

One night Teodolinda was still up after everyone else was asleep. She heard a tiny whimper from the bed where Gelo slept with his brothers. She tiptoed over with the *canfinera* and asked, "What's wrong, son?"

"Mamita," Gelo sobbed, "I'm not sick anymore, but my legs don't work. Will I ever be able to play like the other boys?"

Teodolinda thought for a while before answering. "Son, I can't be sure, but I think Tatica Dios will make you well, and someday you will be able to play and run like everybody else. Go to sleep now, my boy."

Gelo stopped crying, but it was a long time before he drifted off into a slumber deep enough for him to forget his troubles.

8

Soon after Gelo got better, Teodolinda had another baby. To Gelo's delight, it was a boy. Again the family gave him an interesting name: Aurelio.

Little Aurelio became Gelo's favorite pastime. One morning when Gelo was bored he crawled outside and sat on his rock in the shade, where he often sat and whittled with his crooked hands. Teodolinda brought Aurelio out and placed him in Gelo's arms. Gelo held him for a long time and watched him make funny faces and coo. That started a relationship that deepened as they both grew. Little Aurelio became Gelo's shadow.

One day when Gelo was almost eleven years old, he got impatient. "Mamita, I'm better now. I can't rot here in this house forever. I want to go outside and do things like other children. You told me that someday I could. What do you say now?"

"I don't know, son. I know you aren't sick anymore, but how can you get around with that leg twisted so badly it almost touches your back? And your straight leg still has no feeling."

"My hands are useful again," Gelo countered. "They're a little out of shape, but they work as well as anybody else's."

"I know what. Let's make you a pair of crutches. I'm sure you are tough enough to walk with them."

"What are crutches, Mamita?"

"Wait and see. I'll go make a pair right now."

Teodolinda grabbed a machete and disappeared outside. Gelo did not have to wait long. Soon his mother was back with two guayaba branches. She had chosen two sticks with wide forks. Now she measured them against Gelo and whacked off the ends. Then she explained to Gelo how to whittle the forks so his armpits would fit in better.

Gelo spent hours working on his new crutches. First he peeled all the bark off the sticks; then he whittled away at the forks until he knew they would fit. Next he asked Mamita for some rags, which he folded into the forks and tied tightly. Then he tried them. He was out on his rock in the yard again, all alone. He stood carefully on his straight leg and fitted the crutches under his arms. Then, ever so carefully, he hobbled across the yard, unsteadily at first, then with greater confidence as he learned to manage his new tools.

All the men were still out working. His mother and the children had gone to the river to wash. No one was there to see what he had accomplished. Gelo was so excited! He hobbled over to the house and hid the crutches behind the door. Then he crawled into the bedroom where baby Aurelio lay in his mama's bed. He put his arm around his little brother and whispered, "Aurelio, I will never crawl again! I can walk now! I can run and be normal like other children!"

Aurelio could not understand, but he cooed his approval and giggled at Gelo's excitement. Gelo lay on the bed for a long time, daydreaming about what all he would do now. He had been bedfast for almost a year, but his bedridden days were over.

That evening he asked his father to take him to his rock. In one swoop, Lico lifted the frail little boy into his arms and laughed. "Wow, you weigh less than a feather. Remember to always carry stones in your pockets so the Zapotal winds don't carry you away!"

As Lico carried him over the threshold, Gelo said, "Papito, bring me the sticks from behind the door."

Lico pulled the door forward. Sure enough, there were two guayaba sticks. He grabbed them with his free hand, figuring Gelo wanted to whittle. He set the little boy gently on his stone and handed him the sticks. Then Lico straightened and looked toward the western horizon. The sun was just setting, and it set the whole sky on fire. The jungle-crested mountain looked like a giant's head with a blazing background.

He turned from the dazzling scene as he heard Gelo shout joyfully, "Papito, watch!"

Teodolinda stood at the kitchen door watching the two. She did not catch on to what was happening until she saw Gelo take off. In a series of clumsy hobbles, little Gelo crossed the yard with his crutches. Once he reached the other side, he swung around and rushed back like a young man racing for home base after hitting a home run. His face was beaming. Lico cheered and grabbed him up into his arms, the crutches falling to the side. Teodolinda did not move, but tears sprang to her eyes.

Hearing Lico's shouts, the rest of the family rushed out to see what was going on. "Look!" Lico almost shouted. "Watch Gelo! He can walk!"

He put Gelo down and handed him his crutches. Gelo took off again. This time he was faster and his hobble smoother. On the home-stretch everybody cheered. Gelo was actually running!

* * *

One evening after supper the Valverdes were sitting around talking. The smaller children had already gone to bed. It was raining again, as usual. The wind whistled and whined at the shuttered windows as if trying its best to get in to chill them to the bone. Though supper was over, Teodolinda still had a piping hot fire going just for warmth.

"Some new neighbors moved into Zapotal today," Lico announced. "I was talking to Leandro about starting a school up here, and he told me a family had moved to a farm close to one of Don Tilo's. From what I've heard, they are quite a group. The main guy is called Vicente, and he is a *rezador* and a guitarist. He's going to give Old Nacho a lot of competition. They say he's really good at the prayers, but he's best when he leads out in a dance. He is super good with his guitar, and his two brothers are almost as good as he is. One plays the accordion, and the other plays guitar."

That gave Teodolinda an idea. "Let's plan another *rosario*, Valverde," she suggested.

"Yes, let's," Luis echoed. "It's time we got something fun going around here. I get bored sitting around evenings like this."

The young people were more than ready for a good time, so they decided to plan a *rosario* for the next Sunday night if it suited Vicente Jiménez. And to avoid problems with Old Nacho, they would get Nacho to do the *rosario* and ask Vicente to lead out in a dance afterward.

The next Sunday seemed long in coming for the Valverdes. They didn't know it, but most of the highland people were feeling the same way. When it became known that the Valverdes were planning a *rosario* and a dance, the community, many of whom had moved from more populated areas with more social activities, was excited.

Lico sold a calf for cash and rode to Miramar to buy provisions. This time they were not only going to serve coffee, but food. And lots of *guaro*. Teodolinda did not even try to convince Lico to drop the liquor. She knew it was no use. She still had not figured out how liquor and prayers mixed, but even her mother thought it was okay, so she suppressed her conscience and entered into the preparations with zest.

Lico went to Miramar the day before the *rosario*. Teodolinda wanted him home early so she could get on with the cooking and other preparations, but Lico did not come home until way late. As usual, he was drunk. Teodolinda held her tongue this time. He would hear from her, but she would choose the right moment—after the *rosario*.

Teodolinda was again surprised to see how many people came. Zapotal was growing. As before, Old Nacho was there early and needed his swig. Lico was already tipsy, and the bottle was passed around freely. Not nearly everyone came into the living room for the prayer time. That bothered Teodolinda. She thought the prayer should be the focus. But most had not come for the prayer. They had come for the dance.

Halfway through the prayer the Jiménez family arrived. To Teodolinda's surprise, they stayed outside, laughing and visiting with the unfaithful. It seemed they had no interest in the prayers. Or maybe they just didn't want to compete with Old Nacho.

After the prayers, the women stayed inside while the men gathered in the yard to laugh and talk and drink. Soon Teodolinda's three oldest girls were serving food. As they stepped out into the dark to serve the men, the fun began—though not for the girls. Marina was the center of attention, since she was sixteen. But the half-drunken men even flirted with Amable, who was only twelve.

Then Pepe, one of Leandro's boys, reached out and grabbed Marina by the arm when she walked past. She tried to jerk away, but Pepe hung on. The next thing he knew, somebody had kicked him from the back and sent him sprawling. The men roared with laughter. Marina ran inside and refused to go out again all evening. Pepe prowled around the yard trying to find out who had kicked him. He guessed it was one of the Valverde boys, but he could not figure out which one.

About then Teodolinda announced that the meal was over and that people could come in for the music. Vicente stepped into the house for the first time. Teodolinda looked him over. He was dressed better than most. He wore a cowboy hat and cowboy boots, which was totally unheard of in Zapotal. Only Tilo Barrantes wore a cowboy hat. But now they had a man among them who dressed nicely, wore expensive boots, and carried a big guitar.

Old Nacho asked Teodolinda for a sheet. Innocently, she brought him one. With Lico's help, Nacho approached the special wall where the saints hung. Very carefully they draped the sheet over all the *estampas* and Santo Salvador del Mundo, which Angelina had brought along for the occasion. Teodolinda was shocked when Nacho winked at Lico and explained, "We can't let them see what comes next."

Then Vicente Jiménez took the floor. He and his two brothers stood in a corner. "Come on in, ladies and gentlemen," he invited with a flourish. "This will be Zapotal's first real dance!"

The people gathered around eagerly, especially Lico's sons. His girls stayed in the kitchen and watched through the door. Lico was self-conscious and hung in the background. Teodolinda stood right in front and watched it all. She wanted to see what was going to happen in her home.

"How many of you know how to dance the *Panadera?*" Vicente began.

A few people raised their hands.

"Well, if you didn't know the *Panadera* before, you will learn it tonight. My brothers and I will start the song, and then I will choose one lady to start the dance. I will choose her by putting my hat on her head. After that, the song will tell you what to do. Are you ready?"

The brothers started playing, and Vicente dropped the hat onto his sister's head. She stepped out into the open space in front of the three singers. Then Vicente and his brothers began singing. *"Baila, baila la panadera . . ."* (The baker lady dances, dances). And dance the lady did.

The living room floor was packed. The most interested people stood in front, shoving and pushing to get a better look. Luis was in the middle of the circle, right in front. The song changed its tune and told the girl to choose a companion. To everyone's surprise, she danced to the edge of the crowd and plopped the hat on Luis's head. Luis was shocked. Everyone roared and laughed. The Valverdes were bashful, and no one could imagine Luis dancing.

But Luis had no choice. He had never danced before, and he had not expected to begin that night. But he had been watching with interest. To everybody's surprise, he danced. Though clumsy at first, he soon loosened up and began showing off. His antics thrilled the crowd, and they clapped and howled until finally Vicente had to call them down. Luis eventually passed the hat to a young, popular girl named Manuela. The *Panadera* kept going for a whole hour, exchanging hats and matching couples. But no one danced as long as Luis or was as funny.

More music and dancing followed, and the bottle passed from one man to another. The ones who were drunk stayed outside. Eventually more men were outside than inside. Teodolinda's brother Ángel called Pepe aside and whispered into his ear, "It was Luis who kicked you before the *rosario.*"

That was all it took to start a fight. Luis was still inside. His little brother Marino came up to him and whispered innocently, "They want you outside."

As soon as Luis stepped out among the men, Pepe came at him, his fists swinging. But Pepe's drunkenness left him at a disadvantage, and as soon as Luis got over his surprise, he fought back. Soon Pepe was on the floor crying for mercy.

That night after everyone left, two people had a hard time going to sleep. Teodolinda knew what had happened was bad. And yet she had enjoyed some of it. Her parents were too Catholic to allow dances in their house. They had not stayed after the prayers that night, and she knew why.

Teodolinda did not like seeing her husband drunk. Neither did she like the fighting. She despised the way Luis had gloated about beating Pepe. But most of her fun-starved family had enjoyed the evening. Only Marina was not impressed.

Luis could not sleep because he was savoring the highlights of the evening. Finally he was a hero, or at least he felt like one. He had done two things that made people notice him—dance and fight. He knew people were surprised that he could perform. But one question still haunted him: *Is my dad proud of me?*

*   *   *

Time marched on. Marina got tired of the hard work in her home. Teodolinda was often working outside or off planting or harvesting beans in Tajo Alto. By now there were fifteen children at home if Marina counted herself. Soon after little Aurelio had been born, Teodolinda had had another girl named Victoria. Ulises had followed not long after.

A young man named Luis Elizondo started coming around. He asked to marry Marina, and Lico accepted the terms. Soon they married, and Marina's new husband took her far away to Guanacaste.

Amable was fifteen, Leyla was twelve, and Mireya eleven. This new crop of girls would soon be able to shoulder more of the workload. But for now, Teodolinda had to get back into the harness of housework. She did not relish the thought, but as usual, she did what had to be done.

9

As the big fancy bus careened around yet another corner, the crippled boy asked yet another question. "Señora, how long will it take until we get to Cartago?"

He had already asked many times, but Doña Chepa answered kindly, "I don't really know, Gelo, but it won't be long. Do you see how the trees are all gnarled and covered with moss? That means we have left the Central Plateau and are driving into the Cartago mountains."

Gelo laid his face against the window again and stared. Sure enough, through the fog he could see the shapes of trees as they zipped by. They looked much like the trees in Zapotal. As they bowed in the wind, Gelo could almost feel the frigid blasts that whipped the tops of Costa Rica's highlands.

Gelo and his godmother Doña Chepa, a family friend, had left Zapotal two days before. The first night they had stayed at Miramar. Then the next day they had traveled by bus to Orotina and stayed at a friend's place for the night. One of Doña Chepa's nephews had pitied Gelo with his crude guayaba crutches and made him a new pair. Gelo was delighted and tried them out right away. They fit him perfectly. Gelo had wanted to throw the stick crutches away, but Doña Chepa had asked to take them along.

Now, the next day, the bus flung around yet another curve, and Gelo started asking questions again. "Tell me about the *virgencita* (little virgin) again," Gelo said, puckering his forehead in one of his inquisitive looks.

Doña Chepa launched into the familiar story. "Years ago, a poor man was working on a coffee plantation. As he was cleaning around the coffee plants, he came upon a big black rock. There, resting on the rock, he found the *virgencita* made of black stone. He took her home to his poor hut because she looked so beautiful. He suspected right away that she was divine, so they prayed to her that evening during their rosary. But she never answered their prayers. The next morning she was gone. The man rushed to the big black rock, and there she was again. He picked her up and ran back to the house. 'At her favorite spot,' the man told his wife. 'The *virgencita* is not happy that we have her here in the house. She wants to be back on her own rock. We will leave her there and pray to her from here.'

"The old man took the *virgencita* back to her rock, and all the illness in his home was cured miraculously. It was the calendar day of La Virgen de los Ángeles (the Virgin of the Angels). From that day on, the virgin has healed people who come to worship her. That's why I am bringing you today, on the day all Costa Rica celebrates her day. I hope your legs will be healed. I have been praying to the *virgencita* for weeks."

Again Gelo looked out the window. The longing in his heart was growing. Could he possibly be healed? Today? Would he be able to throw his crutches away and run like other children? He sure hoped so!

As he stared out the window, he noticed groups of people walking in the rain. They hunched over as the rain and wind slashed at them and tore at their clothes. Some wore raincoats. Some had wrapped themselves in pieces of plastic. But most just got wet.

"Where are all those people walking?" Gelo asked.

"They have made a promise to the virgin. Maybe she healed someone in their family, so they promised to make this trip on her day. These devotees come from all over Costa Rica. Some of them have walked for three days to get here and are tired and sore. They have to walk to fulfill their promise, but then they can ride the bus home."

Finally the bus stopped. Doña Chepa and Gelo crawled out and stopped to stare. Out ahead of them masses of people all made their way toward a huge cathedral. Old men and women, adults of all ages, youth boys and girls, even children like Gelo had all come to see the virgin. The dozens of people were divided into two groups. To one side the people walked slowly across the huge, paved courtyard. In the other group the devotees were on their knees, slowly hobbling toward the virgin's fancy house.

"Well, let's go, Gelo. I don't have the strength to cross the courtyard on my knees, so we will walk. Come."

Gelo and Doña Chepa joined the crowd walking ever so slowly toward the cathedral. Gelo watched the people who were walking on their knees. In spite of the slow drizzle, they were sweating. The raindrops mixed with the sweat as it rolled off the foreheads of the penitent pilgrims. One little old lady struck his heart with pity. She was so tired she was down on her hands and knees, crawling. Her knees were tattered, and sweat and blood mingled with the raindrops.

Just before arriving at the cathedral, Doña Chepa announced, "We will go see the *virgencita* first; then we will go into the church to pray."

Still following the throng, they turned off to the side and approached a shrine. Once inside, they took winding steps down into what seemed like a dungeon. As they wound down the steps, Gelo asked his godmother, "Why do they keep her down here?"

"They tried to keep the *virgencita* up in the cathedral, but it never worked. Every day they would bring her to the huge house they'd built for her. Every night she would disappear back to her rock. The rock was down in this gully, and now they've built this shrine over it. In just a minute we will see her rock."

Minutes later they came to a small dark room. To one side was the big black volcanic rock. The *virgencita* was perched on top. A metal fence separated the devotees from the rock. The people could not reach the virgin, but they could touch the rock. They took turns walking past, crossing themselves and reaching out to caress the rock as they passed. All were silent or talked in whispers.

Right beside the rock a tiny crystal-clear stream gushed by. "The water of that stream is blessed," Doña Chepa whispered to Gelo. Sure enough, each pilgrim had a small bottle ready and stopped to quickly fill it before the next person pushed him on. Doña Chepa chanted like everyone else as she walked in front of the rock, crossing herself repeatedly. Gelo hobbled along on his crutches in reverence. He reached out and touched the black rock as they passed. When they got to the stream, Doña Chepa quickly bent over and filled two bottles with the holy water. Before she was done, the people behind her were hissing, "Hurry!"

Once they got to the cathedral, Doña Chepa gave Gelo the water bottles and her purse. "I am going to the altar to pray," she whispered. "I will pray for you all the way. Follow me."

Doña Chepa walked very slowly, praying all the way. The fancy cathedral was huge and very quiet. As Gelo followed his godmother, the grandeur, the colors, the paintings, the statues, and the chandeliers filled him with awe and wonder. Doña Chepa was going to the altar to pray for him! Would he be healed?

Once they got to the front of the church, Doña Chepa spent a long time on her knees praying to all the saints hanging there. Gelo stared at the huge statue of Jesus on the cross. He wondered if Doña Chepa was praying to Jesus too. Gelo wandered around the front of the cathedral looking at all the saints and paintings. Suddenly, out of the blue, a nun was standing in front of him in a modest white dress with a big veil on her head. At first Gelo was frightened. He was sure he would be scolded for trespassing. But as Gelo gazed into her eyes, he saw that they were kind, and that she wore a smile. His fears were immediately erased. He had found a new friend!

"And what's your name?" the kind lady asked. "Where are you from?"

Soon Gelo was following her around the cathedral as she showed him everything. Then he sat on one of the steps by the altar, and she asked him about his sickness and the reason they were there. Doña Chepa soon joined them, and the nun asked, "Gelo, would you like to give the *virgencita* your old crutches?"

"Why would she want them?" Gelo asked innocently. "Can't she walk either?"

"No, it's not that. It's just that when she heals someone, she likes it if the one healed gives her a gift. The crutches would be special because they would remind her that she healed you and that you don't need them anymore."

"Do you really think I will be healed today?" Gelo asked the nun anxiously.

"I can't promise," she replied thoughtfully, "but if I were the *virgencita*, I sure would!"

"She can have my old crutches," Gelo whispered as he handed them to the nun, his warm feeling for her filling his voice and eyes.

Back in Zapotal, his godmother gave him one bottle of holy water and kept the other for herself. She instructed Gelo to rub it on his bad legs every evening before going to bed. Gelo did it faithfully for two weeks until the bottle was empty. It was obvious that the *virgencita* was not going to heal him. Maybe she couldn't. Maybe she didn't care. Maybe none of those religious stories were true after all.

Gelo tried to push the incident out of his mind. At least he had new crutches that made walking much easier for him. But his doubts and disappointment were not forgotten.

10

One evening after a hard day's work, Lico stretched his hammock in the yard between two trees to rest. He felt trapped in poverty. The family was growing, and the children were dressed in rags. There was never any money left Saturdays to buy clothes.

Suddenly their new spotted hound dog jumped up and ran toward the trail, barking. A squat, white-skinned man opened the gate and rode in on a strawberry roan mare. He was dressed neatly and looked as if he had some class. Lico felt like hiding, but he sat up in his hammock.

The man smiled as he rode up and greeted Lico with a very friendly, "*Buenas.* How are you doing?"

"*Buenas,*" Lico answered. "Dismount, if you aren't in a hurry."

The stranger dismounted and tied his horse to one of the grapefruit trees. Then he walked over to the hammock and shook Lico's hand. The older boys gathered around to watch and listen. Little Aurelio brought the man a block of wood to sit on. Teodolinda was all ears from the kitchen. What could such a grand fellow want in Zapotal?

"My name is Andrés Rodríguez, and I have moved over close to La Palmera, about an hour's ride from here. I have heard about your family, Don Lico. They say you are hard workers, right?"

"Yes, that's true," Lico acknowledged, thinking, *This Andrés is a smooth talker.*

Andrés kept the conversation rolling. Lico was a good listener. After talking for a long time, Andrés finally got to the point. "You know, Don Lico, we are living in hard times. There is never enough money to catch up."

Lico nodded.

"I know of a way to make a good living," Andrés said casually, carefully choosing each word. "It takes quite a bit of work, but one of your boys could easily handle it."

Gelo was whittling on a stump nearby. His ears perked up. *Would it be something I could do?* he wondered. *I'm thirteen now, and even if I'm lame, my head and hands work well . . .*

"This business I offer you would be on shares. Fifty-fifty. You do the work, and I provide the raw materials. We should both be able to make a good living."

No Valverde spoke, but the air itself screamed the question, *What business?*

Lowering his voice, Andrés shared his secret. "Let's put in a *fábrica.* * Making guaro *contrabando*** is a good business. Of course, there is the problem with the *resguardo*,*** but we live so far back in that they will never find out. They don't give a hoot what we do back here."

Lico imagined the *resguardo* climbing La Cuesta del Tubo, and he grinned. Andrés was right.

"Think about it, Don Lico. There is no whiskey available anywhere in Zapotal. Everybody has to go all the way to Tajo Alto or Miramar for a drink. If we could provide it here, we would make a killing. You could set up the still down in that jungle." Andrés pointed down over

---

*   still
**   moonshine
*** contraband police

the hill where the jungle canopy shone blue-green in the afternoon sun. "Nobody would find it. I will provide the equipment and bring the *dulce* every week. All you need to do is make the stuff. Every week I'll stop by and take my half. The rest you'll sell for your own income. And I tell you, Don Lico, that stuff really sells!"

"I will let you know," was Lico's quiet answer. Andrés promised to stop by the next week. Then he mounted, spurred his high-stepping mare, swung around gracefully, and rode down the trail toward the creek.

As soon as Andrés left, Teodolinda joined the group at the hammock. Everybody talked at once. Gelo quickly got his bid in. "Dad, don't you think that's something I could do?" His eyes shone eagerly.

Luis was all for the still. Lidier and Ángel were in favor of it. Teodolinda was the only one who balked. "Remember what he said about the *resguardo*," she warned. "I remember how the *resguardo* used to try to confiscate the still Old Pancho had in San Ramón. The government owns the liquor business, and the contraband stuff doesn't pay taxes like the legal whiskey does. *Guaro* can be made so cheaply that there is no way the legal stuff can compete. And folks like the contraband stuff better, so the police would have good reason to try to shut us down."

"But look, Teodolinda," Lico countered. "Can you imagine the *resguardo* coming all the way up here? Can't you just about see them petering out on La Cuesta del Tubo?"

Luis laughed. "Aw, Mamita, you worry too much! If the *resguardo* would come, we would run them right back off the mountain. Look at all of us!" He motioned toward the hammock and all the boys standing around.

Lico clinched the subject with his quiet answer. "We need the cash. I am sick and tired of always being out of money." What Lico didn't say was that he had another reason for wanting the still. He was thirsty. Recently he was always longing for a drink, and Miramar was so far away.

Teodolinda acknowledged their need for cash. And though she expected the *guaro* would bring them trouble, she finally nodded in agreement. And with that nod, the *fábrica* was as good as set up down in the damp green jungle.

*   *   *

One week later Andrés was back. They met out on the porch, and Lico gave his answer. Andrés was pleased and started explaining carefully what they needed to do.

"You need to make a wooden box six feet long, two feet wide, and two feet deep. You also need to get fruit together to make the *fermento*.* You collect a bucket full of any kind of fruit or cooked corn and let it rot for several days. Pineapples are the best, but they are hard to come by. Once you have a good base of *fermento,* it's easy to make the *chicha*** that is used to make the *guaro.*"

"That doesn't sound hard at all," Gelo said. "Dad, you make the box, and I'll get the *fermento* going right away."

Teodolinda was listening from the kitchen. Her doubts rose again when she heard Andrés' closing statement. "One thing, Don Lico. It's best not to tell anybody about our business. Not that it's dangerous; it's just that it's not necessary to let everybody know what's going on. When they ask you where you got the *guaro,* tell them you bought it in Tajo Alto to resell here. Don't let anyone know you have a *fábrica.*"

After Andrés left, Lico got his hammer and his saw and found some old boards and set to work making a box. Gelo asked his mother for a bucket and hobbled out to the banana grove. In less than two hours, Lico had the completed box hidden in his bedroom. Before he was half done, Gelo had a bucket full of bananas and pineapples, some already overripe. The pineapples were delicious to eat, but very tart—so tart that eating more than several slices actually cracked the tongue. He finished filling the bucket with naranjilla, a fruit the locals used to make juice. Andrés had said to drop a piece of *dulce* in the bucket

---

* fermented base
** cider

too, so Gelo begged a piece off his mother and buried it deep in the fruit. Then he covered the bucket with a cloth and hid it in his dad's bedroom.

The next day Lico was as excited about something he had found in the jungle as he was about the still. Lico and his sons spent a lot of time in the jungle hunting. The afternoon before, he and Lidier had been hunting for the great curassow, a large turkey-like bird that made a delicious meal. They had decided to hunt on the topmost border of their farm, right at the edge of the mountain range. Now he was telling the boys what they had found.

"We got to the edge of the farm where I had never been before. Right at the top of the mountain, just before it drops off toward the Miramar foothills, we found a little valley of about two *manzanas*. The jungle is particularly lush there, not just a stand of small, wind-whipped trees. Since it's protected from the winds, everything grows twice as big as other places.

"In the upper corner of the plot we found the biggest roble tree I have ever seen. In the middle of the tiny valley a huge rotten potato tree had fallen. The area where the tree had fallen was all smashed down. With plenty of sunlight, the new undergrowth is so lush and green that I just know that plot would grow wonderful vegetables. I have never in my life seen such large wild chayote vines!"

"We plan to cut the jungle down and plant the area with corn and vegetables," Lidier said, just about as excited as his father. "I'm sure we can flood the market in Miramar!"

Teodolinda listened to the new plan. She liked this plan better than the plan to make *guaro*. She knew her men could grow a lot more food than they did. There just had not been much initiative to plant for the Miramar market. Maybe Gelo could run the still, and the others could really get something done up in that wonder valley.

*   *   *

Everybody was surprised when, Saturday morning at five o'clock, the dog started barking madly toward the front gate. Teodolinda was up stirring the fire to get the coffee going. Lico jumped out of bed and grabbed his twenty-two. He ran to the front door and opened it a crack and peeped out. Then he heard the customary Costa Rican greeting from the yard.

"*¡Upe!*"

"Don Andrés! What's up?"

"Good morning, everybody! Get out of bed; it's time to get to work!" Andrés shouted.

The boys piled out of bed and came to the door to look. The trees to the east were still dark silhouettes against an inky black sky. But through the twisted, moss-covered branches they could see glimpses of pink. Morning was near.

Andrés parked his loaded mule right in front of the door and began unloading a cutoff metal barrel, a copper cylinder, a long copper pipe, several buckets, and a whole *alforja* full of *dulce*. Lico hauled it all into the living room. Andrés tied his mule behind the house and entered also.

"What in the world do you mean by coming at such an unearthly hour?" Lico asked him.

"You didn't think I was bringing you a bag of Christmas candy, did you? What I was hauling wasn't exactly a legal package. You'll learn, Don Lico, that things like this are best done in the dark." Andrés threw his head back and laughed.

The coffee was soon ready, and they drank it in a hurry. "Let's head down to the jungle before anybody comes around," Andrés suggested. "Lady," he grinned at Teodolinda, "if anyone asks for Lico, tell them he left for Miramar early this morning." He turned back to Lico. "Bring a shovel, a bamboo pole, and some rope. Bring the box and the bucket of *fermento*."

Fortunately, there were enough boys and men to haul everything. They looked like a trail of leaf-cutter ants, each with his load, as they wormed their way through the brush and down into the jungle, following the little creek until they reached a larger creek. Gelo came last, hobbling on his crutches. Nothing stopped him anymore, not even the thickest jungle. He always fought his way through and refused to let anyone help him.

In a tight green glade right before a curve in the creek, Andrés stopped. "This is perfect. It's far enough away that no one will detect the smoke from the fire. I'm sure no one will find it here. Here is a nice, flat place to set up the *fábrica*. Let's get to work."

"Gelo, you watch closely," Lico said. "This is going to be your job."

They set up the long box on the flattest spot. "Now bring the *fermento*," Andrés said.

Andrés dumped the bucket full of slop into the box. He picked up a handful and smelled it. "Perfect!" he exclaimed, looking at Gelo. "It couldn't be better. Now watch."

Andrés spread the goop across the box bottom and then chipped a block of *dulce* into small pieces with his sharp *cutacha*. After cutting up eight blocks, he spread it out over the goop. Then he ordered six buckets of water and dumped them on top of the fermented pile. "By tomorrow morning this will be wonderful *chicha*," Andrés chuckled. "Some people like the *chicha* just as much as the *guaro*."

Next Andrés took a shovel and dug a trench that he lined with creek stones. Then he set the barrel on top of the natural cooking stove. "Here is where we will start the fire tomorrow," he said, pointing to the gap under the barrel. "Then you will see what happens. Let's hide the rest of the stuff in the weeds and call it a day. We will have our fun tomorrow. Gelo, tomorrow at noon I will come again. I want you to put a little bit of water in this barrel and get a fire going under it before I get here. Then you will receive the rest of your lesson. If Andrés Rodríguez teaches you how to make *guaro contrabando*, you will make the best moonshine this side of Miramar! Do you hear?"

By noon the next day, Gelo had a fire going and plenty of firewood for later. All the Valverde men and boys were waiting. Lico seemed as excited as anybody. The thought of a shot to quench his thirst made him most willing to do his part. Andrés arrived exactly at noon. The Valverdes were surprised to see him come in a back way. That, he explained, was only a precaution.

Andrés uncovered the wooden box. The fermented juice was all brown, covered with foam, and the surface was bubbling. He took a sieve and dipped the foam and crud from the liquid. Then he asked for a cup. He downed a cup full of *chicha*, smacked his lips, and bragged, "This stuff is potent!" Then they all drank the sweet, tangy cider.

Andrés hauled several buckets of *chicha* and dumped them into the cutoff barrel, sealing it with a heavy lid. "Give it the fire now, Gelo! Soon we'll have the real stuff!"

Andrés ran a copper pipe through a hole in the lid and into a trough of cold running water. The trough was a bamboo pole cut in half lengthwise, and propped on forked stakes. From behind the barrel, he ran the other half of the bamboo pole, also perched on forked sticks, into the creek. The creek water splashing down the bamboo trough over the copper pipe kept it nice and cool. The water eventually spilled back down into the creek.

Gelo, hobbling around on his crutches, watched the whole process like a cat. When Andrés was done and announced that now they just had to wait, Gelo declared, "I can easily do all of that!"

Everybody cheered.

"Once the *chicha* boils," Andrés explained, "the vapor has no place to go except out through that copper pipe. This vapor is potent stuff. Next it steams out through the copper pipe, where the cold water makes the steam condense into liquid again. Soon it will start dribbling out the spout. That stuff is the best liquor there is. The first cupful we call the *cabezón*. That's the best shot of all. You collect the stuff until you can taste that it's losing its power. Then you add more *chicha* to the barrel until all the *chicha* is used up. This batch will make four gallons. Two for me and two for you."

"How do you know when it starts boiling?" Gelo asked.

"The barrel begins to hum," Andrés explained. "Just wait and you will hear."

Gelo kept the fire crackling hot. The thin stream of smoke snaked up into the treetops and was whisked away by the Zapotal wind. The men sat in a circle on the rocks by the creek and chatted. Andrés did most of the talking. Every now and then one of the boys threw in a question to keep the man going.

About a half hour later the barrel began to hum. Andrés jumped up, cup in hand. Putting his index finger on the little spout to test the pressure, he gazed up into the treetops and waited. "Here it comes!" he announced. Then he bent over and smelled the spout, rolled his eyes, and said, "Boys, come smell this. This is the real thing!"

The Valverdes crowded around and took turns. The smell was sweet and spicy.

Just at the right moment, Andrés held his cup to the spout. The clear, condensed steam dripped into his cup. Andrés waited until it was almost full and then yelled, "Bring a jug!" He placed the jug under the spout, tipped his head back, and drained the cup. When he was done, he belched as if that were part of the ritual and then laughed. "That's life, my boys! The next time you will have the *cabezón*. Today it's mine because this whole thing was my idea."

Lico was frowning now. "I want a swig," he growled. Still laughing, Andrés held the cup to the spout again. For Lico. Then for Luis. Then for himself again. And on down the line. Even little Aurelio got a shot. It did not taste nearly as good as it had smelled, but the more they drank, the less they cared. Two hours later, when the sun was dropping behind the horizon, Andrés got up to leave. He took his two full gallons of liquor. The Valverdes had only a jug and a half left.

That night the Valverdes did not get to bed until after midnight. Teodolinda prepared a big meal of paca meat, and they partied long into the night. All the men and boys from Aurelio up were stone drunk. Even Gelo stumbled and fell on his way to bed.

That night Teodolinda cried before going to bed. She suddenly saw what was going to happen to her family. It was the curse of God, she was sure. She started planning her next *rosario*. If they drank hard and long, they would have to pray hard and long. Maybe God would forgive them.

11

The afternoon sun hung low on the horizon. A three-wattled bellbird rang its unique good evening bells. The swallows crisscrossed the pink-gray sky at terrific speeds, catching their evening snack of insects. Lico was resting inside the house on his hammock after a normal day of hard work.

The peaceful scene was interrupted by a rider galloping in the lane at breakneck speed. The rider, staggeringly drunk, jumped off his panting horse and began shouting and brandishing his sharp *cutacha*. "Lico, you scoundrel! Show me your face!"

Gelo hobbled into the living room and hissed, "Dad, it's Uncle Ángel. He is terribly angry and very drunk."

Several of the other boys gathered around the hammock, wondering what Lico would do. Lico just lay there. He knew perfectly well what the problem was. A week before, Ángel had come and asked him to cosign for him at the Miramar Bank. Lico had not promised, but he had sounded positive. But several days later he had talked to one of Ángel's brothers, who had warned Lico, "Hey, save your money and don't sign for my brother. He's a crook. He did exactly the same thing to me and didn't pay. To save my name, I had to go and pay his debt. To this day I haven't seen a cent." After hearing that, Lico had backed out of the deal and sent word to Ángel that it was all off.

"Lico, come out here and be a man! I hear you're going around saying I'm a snake in the weeds. You call me a thief. Come call me a thief to my face, if you dare!"

Lico got up and calmed his excited boys. "I don't think he'll do anything. He's all noise. Just stay out of his way and be careful."

To everyone's surprise, Ángel stumbled across the yard and into the house, cursing and swearing and brandishing his *cutacha*. Everyone ran out the back door except Lico, who was unarmed. Teodolinda, who was expecting another baby in about a month, tried to reason with him from the kitchen door. "Ángel, calm down! You can't do this! This is private property—"

"Private property! What do I care? If this man of yours called me a thief and a liar, I'm going to have his hide!"

Lico stepped aside as Ángel slashed at him with the *cutacha*. Ángel was just sober enough to be dangerous. Backing out the rear door, Lico looked for something to disarm Ángel, but Ángel didn't give him time. He ripped through the back door and dived at Lico again. Again Lico dodged. Teodolinda ran back into the kitchen and burst out crying, certain her brother would kill her husband.

As Ángel prepared for his next attack, Lico was as pale as a sheet, still glancing around for something to defend himself with. Ángel lunged toward Lico. Suddenly Lidier grabbed a pole and jumped between his father and the angry man. Ángel stopped in his tracks. The fight was over, and he knew it.

As Lico explained the situation, Ángel calmed down. Lico finished by offering him some fresh *guaro*. After several drinks, Ángel left, and Lico took several himself for his nerves. Then Lico went to look for Teodolinda. He found her in the bedroom, still crying.

"Teodolinda, he's gone," he reassured her. But Teodolinda was still distraught. "Hey, take a shot of this," he offered, lifting his bottle.

Teodolinda shook her head. But minutes later a neighbor ran to the door asking for Teodolinda to come help his wife, who was in labor. She knew she had to go, but she felt weak and deliveries were stressful. So she accepted two sips from Lico's bottle. *What have I done?* she thought. But she did feel strength for the stressful task ahead.

From then on, Teodolinda took a drink before each delivery.

*   *   *

After the horrible scare with Ángel, Teodolinda's health deteriorated. She had always been a healthy woman, but now she felt drained all the time. She talked to her mother about it, and her mother told her frankly that she should go to Puntarenas to have her next baby.

That night Teodolinda could not sleep. She tossed on their hard board bed for an hour until she finally woke her husband. "Valverde, do you think I should have my baby here in Zapotal?"

"I don't know," Lico said grumpily. "Do what you want."

"I just don't know what to say. Mother thinks I should go to the Puntarenas hospital for this baby. I am almost forty-six years old . . ."

"Don't go by what she says. How do you feel? You have always had fairly easy births. How do you feel about it this time?"

"Well, I do feel different. Maybe it's just in my head because of what everyone else is saying. But I admit that I feel a lot older, especially since that awful scare with Ángel. Valverde, I have had fifteen children and two miscarriages. I should be all worn out. I don't really feel that bad; but yes, I do feel tired all the time."

Lico suddenly felt a special touch of tenderness for this woman, the uncomplaining mother of all his children. Sure, she complained about his drinking, but not about the work she'd had to do for all these years. He realized he had married an exceptional woman.

"Maybe we'd better go to Puntarenas," Lico whispered. "I could sell that calf that's just at weaning age. I could take you out. When would we have to go?"

"Right away. I'm only two weeks from my date."

"How will we travel?"

"We'll have to walk. There's no way I could ride horseback that far, and the oxcart would shake me and the baby to pieces."

"Yes, we'll have to leave early in the morning and travel slowly. I'll do that for the baby's sake. It will be our last one. Number sixteen, if we count little Sergio. This baby will be a very special baby, I'm sure. I hope it will be a boy."

"Humph! I think it should be a girl. You already have nine boys, and I only have five girls, and one already flew the coop. That's not fair! What would you want with another boy?" Teodolinda giggled.

* * *

Day should have been breaking. The sun was near the horizon, but the thick fog and swirling mists hid any traces of its light.

Lico and Teodolinda walked up a hill. The trail was sloppy and muddy, so they walked slowly, barefooted. Both were wrapped in sheets of plastic, but the howling wind and slashing rain made it impossible to stay dry. Lico held Teodolinda's hand in the most slippery places. With their free hands they held tightly to the plastic sheets.

The horse Jabón followed slowly behind them, his head bowed low against the wind and rain. On his back he carried a medium-sized load, also wrapped tightly in plastic. The horse's rope was tied to Lico's waist. When Lico or Teodolinda slipped on the trail, Jabón paused until they were ready to move on.

When they topped the hill, Teodolinda stopped. She pulled Lico to her and shouted over the storm, "Do you know what I'm thinking?"

"No!" Lico shouted back. "Why are we stopping here, of all places?"

"Sergio would be nine years old if he hadn't died," Teodolinda said, looking past her husband.

"What does that have to do with walking down this miserable trail at this unearthly hour?"

"He is buried over there." She pointed. Sure enough, through the mist they could just barely make out the ghostly graveyard across the valley.

Suddenly Lico tugged her hand. "Teodolinda, let's go. If we don't, you will start crying . . ."

But it was too late. Teodolinda was already crying, the tears streaming down her cheeks and mingling with the raindrops. "Valverde, you are right," she shouted over the rain and wind. "It's going to be a boy! And he will replace my little Sergio."

The couple walked on. The sun never appeared, but it did get lighter as they walked mile after slow mile. They could see the trail easily by the time they stopped to catch their breath at the top of one of the highest Zapotal peaks. The wind was slowing, and Teodolinda was not as cold. The walking kept her warm.

As the couple topped Cerro Pelón, the wind carried the last of the clouds away and the rains stopped. Teodolinda suggested they stop to rest. They walked off the trail and through the grass to the edge of the mountaintop and sat down at one of Zapotal's awesome overlooks.

Cerro Pelón had never had trees, at least not that anyone could remember. It was a hilltop of maybe ten *manzanas,* rounded and covered with grass and black volcanic rocks. On this wet morning, the sun was turning the mountaintop into a garden of grasses, boulders, and blue sky. But Teodolinda and Lico did not look at the mountaintop. They looked at the distant world beyond.

Far below the mountain range they could see the Puntarenas gulf. Zapotal seemed another world on some higher plain. Way down at the bottom was Costa Rica—the real, modern Costa Rica where people had cars and lived in cities. Up here lived the mountain people. Teodolinda was ready to get off the mountain for a while. She wanted to have this little boy down there in a clean, dry hospital.

Teodolinda rose clumsily and walked over to Jabón and untied a little bundle. Then she sat in the grass with her husband again. They were soaked and muddy, their clothes patched and re-patched, but Teodolinda was not ashamed to be associated with the mountain folk. They were happy. They made their own living and did not need the other world below. Not usually. This was an exception. She and Lico did not need civilization. But the little baby did!

Though the *gallo pinto** and eggs were cold and served in cheap plastic containers, it was still food fit for kings. As they ate, Teodolinda

---

* refried rice and beans

mused, *Even if someday I become some grand lady, I would still want my gallo pinto until the day I die. There's just nothing better on a chilly morning. Gallo pinto and steaming coffee . . .*

This morning their coffee was only lukewarm, but it was sweet, and the drink would give them the energy they needed for the many miles ahead.

The baby moved and Teodolinda smiled. *He's impatient, but I have to rest.* She lay on the plastic in the grass and fell into a deep sleep while the kind sun soaked the chills from her bones.

Teodolinda did not know how long she slept, but when she awoke, Lico was gone. Jabón was chomping the lush mountain grass. Teodolinda got up. She felt awfully cramped and sore, but she knew they had to move on. She tied her plastic and the leftover food onto Jabón's pack and led him back to the trail. Knowing that her husband would show up somewhere, she led the horse down off the mountaintop and toward the gulf. She guessed it was about ten o'clock.

Lico soon caught up with her. He had wandered off to wash and had brought her a bottle of fresh mountain water. Teodolinda smiled at him as she drank. That was one thing they had that the people down by the gulf did not. They had the best water in the world.

The rest of the day they hiked down, down, down. The vegetation on this side of the continental divide was totally different. The deep-green moss on the trees was gone. The trees were scrawny and their bark was gray and rough. The soil was not nearly as fertile, and all the area was covered with rocks, some as big as their house in Zapotal. Even the birds were different.

At noon they rested their weary bodies in the shade of a huge rock. They did not talk now. They just rested and drank cool water from Lico's jug. Beside the rock grew a tall naked Indian tree, so-called because of its red bark. High in the branches Teodolinda saw a huge white wasp nest. She hoped the wasps did not mind the wind that shook their branch. She could not imagine running from angry wasps in her present condition.

Finally they pushed themselves to move on. As they walked down the next series of steeper hills, Teodolinda announced, "I think walking downhill is worse than climbing up. My legs can hardly make it anymore. If I'm not careful I'll just roll off the mountain."

When they came to La Cuesta del Tubo, Lico looked at Teodolinda and grinned. Teodolinda gasped. It had been a long time since she had traveled down this path. Would she ever get used to it? They walked out onto the mountain point that jutted out over the plains below. At the tip, where the mountain just dropped off into space, Lico showed her where a man's horse had once tumbled over the edge. The cliff was so steep and high that the owners never even tried to rescue the saddle. The horse, they knew, was smashed to pulp.

They veered off to the side and took the trail that wound down among the trees and rocks and disappeared into the nothingness below. Teodolinda grimly followed her husband, holding tightly to his hand. The horse chose his footing gingerly as he followed them. It was the height of rainy season, and poor Jabón floundered up to his belly in

mud while Lico and Teodolinda stepped on the firm sections between each trough.

The sun was setting when they reached Miramar. Teodolinda's feet were swollen and she was nearly sick. Lico immediately went out and got drunk. Teodolinda was disgusted. But then, he had been so kind to bring her out. Lico left for Zapotal the next morning on his little Jabón, leaving Teodolinda with their friends. He did not see her again for nearly a month.

Teodolinda stayed in Miramar for several days; then she traveled by bus to Puntarenas. A week later little Hugo was born in a clean hospital. He was the first and only Valverde to be born in such luxury.

12

Little Victor Hugo Valverde Soto, the last baby born to Lico and Teodolinda, entered the world on August 18, 1958. Mother and child stayed in the hospital overnight and then traveled by bus to Miramar, where they stayed with her friends for over two weeks, resting and enjoying the more civilized lifestyle.

Her son Ángel came to take her back to Zapotal. He brought little Jabón and a big bay mare Teodolinda had bought recently. The day after Ángel arrived, they started for Zapotal early in the morning. Teodolinda had packed a lunch to eat on the way. She was not sure how to carry the baby, but the friendly lady they had stayed with had an idea. "I will loan you a sheet. Lay the baby on your chest and wrap the sheet over your shoulder and across your chest. That way you will have him in a papoose, safe and warm." She strapped Teodolinda and her baby together. The baby was cozy and safe.

The two horses and their riders left the city and started up the first hills toward the highlands. To their left they could see the old abandoned mine down in the valley by the river. Far ahead they saw the top of the mountain range, shrouded in fog, as usual, though the morning was bright and clear on the plains. The horses and riders were eager to leave the valley's heat for Zapotal's cool climate, but they knew it would be hours before they arrived.

Teodolinda was eager to get home and see her children, especially four-year-old Victoria and little Ulises, who was not quite three. Aurelio was almost seven and could take care of himself. She wondered how Gelo was faring. Since he could get around on his crutches, there seemed no end to his antics. Amable, now eighteen, could easily handle the cooking, she knew. There was probably nothing to worry about, but good mamas worry anyway.

But the main cloud that hung over Teodolinda that bright morning was her dread of La Cuesta del Tubo. If walking down was horrible, how would it be to ride up with a tiny baby at her breast?

They stopped to rest twice as they climbed the foothills. The second stop was at a lonely farmhouse perched on a steep hill half a mile before La Cuesta del Tubo. The owner had built a shack there and a large corral where he worked with his cattle. Teodolinda asked for water and rested in the shade of the big bougainvillea that hung out over the bank of the trail. The owner was an unsociable old hermit. After giving them water he disappeared into the house and wasn't seen again.

At the foot of La Cuesta del Tubo, they stopped to let the horses catch their breath.

"Are we ready?" Teodolinda asked.

"Yes," Ángel answered. "As soon as the horses are rested, we climb."

Ángel should have remembered that saddle cinches loosen after an hour or two of riding. He should have checked the bay's cinch before climbing that awful hill. But he didn't.

As they climbed, Teodolinda's hands, freed by the sheet that held her baby, were busy hanging on to the bay's long mane. Little Hugo slept soundly.

The big bay climbed wonderfully, taking slow, careful steps. When the trail narrowed and led right past the abyss, Teodolinda refused to look down into the tree-choked chasm. She just prayed the rosary and hung on. Where the trail passed between two gigantic rocks, she had to watch to keep her legs from being crushed.

Finally they were sloshing out of the eighth switchback near the top. Bathed in sweat, the weary bay took the troughs bravely, carefully sinking her hooves into each mud-filled trough with a splash and then making sucking sounds as she pulled them out again. She was almost as eager to top the hill as Teodolinda. She took the last step a little too eagerly, lurching and swinging to the side as she jumped onto the plateau.

The next thing Teodolinda knew, the saddle had slipped under the horse's belly and she was lying flat on the ground on her side. Baby Hugo was howling. Looking up, all she saw was the horse's mud-splattered underside. Any instant the horse might go wild and hammer her and the baby with her hooves. Teodolinda knew she should do something, but she was too exhausted to move. Thankfully, the mare was also. So all three just stayed put, gulping deep breaths.

Ángel happened to look back. Horrified, he jumped off Jabón and was at the bay's head in a second, holding the rein. Then in a very quiet, controlled voice he commanded, "Mamita, just crawl out from under the horse. I don't think she will move. She is too tired."

As Teodolinda crawled out from under her horse and got to her feet, she suddenly discovered that not only was little Hugo crying, she was bawling too. "Ángel," she sobbed, "what can we do with this baby? He's probably hurt and dying . . ."

"Did you fall on him?"

"I don't think so. Maybe he's just frightened. Here, help me loosen this sheet. I want to check him."

Teodolinda was used to setting bones in Zapotal, so it was not hard for her to determine that no bones were broken. But what about internal injuries? She had no way of knowing, and he was still crying mightily. By the time Ángel tightened the horses' cinches, Hugo was calm. Just as Teodolinda was ready to strap him back onto her chest, Ángel surprised her by suggesting, "Mamita, strap him onto me. I won't fall from my horse. I'll take good care of that little baby."

Tenderly, Teodolinda strapped the baby to Ángel's chest. Then they both mounted, and within an hour and a half they rode into their homestead. Everyone was so glad to see them, but poor Teodolinda was worn out. Amable helped her get into bed; then she took the baby and bathed him.

Later, little Ulises came to the bed where Teodolinda was nursing the baby. "Mamita," he asked, "is that going to be my little brother?"

"Yes, Ulises. He already is your brother. He's just very tiny yet. See how tiny his little hands are?"

Ulises leaned over and stared at the tiny hands. "Mamita, was I ever little like that?"

"Of course. I still remember when you were born. You actually looked very much like Hugo does. Like peas in a pod."

"I can't wait until he gets big and can play with me. I'm glad he is a boy and not a girl."

"I'm glad too, Ulises. For your sake and for your father's sake. He wanted a boy too."

*   *   *

One Saturday Don Lico was leaving the market in Miramar once again. He and Luis had gone out the day before and sold their vegetables. As usual, Lico had gotten drunk, and it was the next afternoon before he was finally ready to leave. Now they were on their way at last, Luis riding Jabón and Lico leading Teodolinda's bay mare with the groceries tied on her back.

As they passed the last store in Miramar, a bar open to the street, Lico noticed that the place was full of people drinking and talking politics. It was a group of Mariachis, the political group that favored Calderón for president. Lico favored candidate Otilio Ulate. To Luis's horror, Lico yelled, "Long live Otilio Ulate!"

The slogan infuriated the already riotous group. Lico picked up his pace, suddenly aware that he had dropped a match onto a pile of dynamite.

One of the angry men threw a beer bottle at Lico, but the bottle fell harmlessly at Lico's feet. Lico grabbed it and flung it back into the middle of the drinking men.

That was the last straw. Five men left the bar, running after Lico. Just up the street from the bar lived the Ponchets, who were great friends of the Valverdes. Not only that, they were also in favor of Otilio Ulate and despised the Mariachis. Young Sergio Ponchet had seen what happened and sprinted to Lico's defense.

Since Sergio was sober, he got to Lico before the others. Just as the first drunk reached for Lico, Sergio grabbed the man by his shirt and threw him backward. The drunk fell in a heap. When the others saw their buddy groaning in the dirt, they turned and fled back to the safety of the saloon.

Lico thanked Sergio, and he and Luis walked on. But Lico was still angry and threatened to return to Miramar. Luis tried to persuade him not to, but to no avail.

"Luis, you are going home through La Cuesta del Tubo anyway. I am going to Tajo Alto to check on my beans. So you go on home, and I will go to Tajo Alto in the morning." With that, Lico turned on his heel and returned to Miramar.

Darkness was falling as Luis reached La Cuesta del Tubo. By now Luis was so afraid he was shaking. Not only was he afraid to travel the desolate trails after dark, he was also afraid his father would tangle with the Mariachis again and get hurt or killed.

But Lico knew better. After returning to Miramar and drinking some more, he stayed with friends and traveled to Tajo Alto the next day, just as he had said.

Luis prayed all the prayers he could think of as he climbed the steep switchbacks on Jabón. By the time he reached Cerro Pelón, he had stopped trembling, but he still prayed. His prayers were not sincere cries of anguish to a God who cares, but rather cries of fright with a faint hope that maybe the prayers he had memorized as a child would work like some magic spell for his protection. As soon as he neared home, the fear left, and when he rode up to the house he was laughing.

Later Luis told the tale to his family, and the children laughed and shouted, "Long live Otilio Ulate!" But Teodolinda had a hard time going to sleep that night. Would her husband come home safely the next day, or would she have to go search for him? Would she find him dead in some ditch? Such things happened all the time to people who drank and caroused. As she went to bed, she prayed several *Padre Nuestros* before finally falling into a fitful sleep.

13

Ever since his childhood, Luis had wanted to be a good Catholic. When he was four years old, his parents had made a pact for him with La Virgen del *Carmen.** He was to carry her *escapulario*** for the rest of his life. The symbol was big and cumbersome. As a young boy he had worn it proudly and faithfully. But as time went on, he had begun to be ashamed of the funny thing hanging from his neck and had stuffed it into his shirt. Later it had gone into his pocket. Eventually he had dropped it altogether. The pact had also included giving ten cents to the virgin as an offering every week for the rest of his life, but, because of their poverty, he had not been able to keep up with that part of the pact.

Because of this, Luis was by far the most religious member of the family. But that did not make him the best behaved. Actually, it seemed to work the other way.

Luis was fifteen when he got drunk for the first time. Before that, he always said he did not want to be a drunkard like his dad. Besides, the stuff tasted horrible and burned his throat like fire. But when his buddies finally convinced him to drink, he did not know when to stop.

---

* the Virgin of Carmen
** scapular, a religious symbol hung around the neck

He grew wild and finally fell into a drunken stupor and lay unmoving for hours.

As a teenager, Luis started going to Miramar for all the holy days. He would confess his sins to the priest. He would take Mass and participate in the religious processions. He came to have a great faith in La Virgen del Carmen. He bought a book about her and an *estampa* that they hung with the rest of their religious symbols on their special wall. Whenever they held a *rosario*, Luis prayed especially to her.

Once when Luis became ill, he promised La Virgen del Carmen that if she healed him, he would wear her habit for a month. He did get well, so he had a set of clothes made in her color, a dull brown.

Grandpa Ramón had moved back to his hometown of San Ramón, and it happened that the town celebrated its patron saint during the month Luis wore La Virgen del Carmen's habit. Luis went to participate.

He traveled down La Cuesta del Tubo on Jabón. Both were in a lively mood. Never had Jabón plunged down the mountain so fast or with such agility. Luis hung onto the back of the saddle with one hand and clung to the leather strap on the front of the saddle with the other as Jabón took the switchbacks as fast as he could. Luis was dressed in the virgin's habit, the same drab brown he had worn for two weeks already. The *escapulario* hung loose on his neck and swung back and forth with the horse's stride. Luis wore a white canvas Tico hat. Held firmly in his mouth was a lit cigar. He had started smoking lately because he felt it made him more of a man. Most of the older men in Zapotal, including Lico, smoked cigars.

Tied onto the saddle was some precious cargo. Luis grinned as he thought of the gallon jug of Gelo's *contrabando*. That was especially for Grandpa. Then he patted the saddlebags, remembering the bottle he had brought along for himself.

After the worship celebration for Saint Ramón, a dance was held at a neighbor's. Ramón and Angelina went home early, Ramón carrying his half-empty jug. Ramón guzzled *guaro* like any other old timer, but he, and especially Angelina, did not appreciate the dancing.

Luis had long since emptied his bottle and now drank what others shared. Finally he was so drunk that a local schoolteacher dragged him into the kitchen.

When Luis woke up the next morning, his face lay in the ashes at the base of the cookstove. Slowly he sat up and looked himself over. He blushed at the faint memory of the pretty schoolteacher tugging at him. Getting to his feet, he wiped the ashes from his face and tried to shake the dirt and ashes from his brown habit. Beside the stove lay a smelly puddle where he had thrown up during the long, miserable night. He felt ashamed. He, supposedly a religious young man, looked worse than a beggar. He had a splitting headache, and his hands shook like leaves in the wind.

Luis trudged over to his grandfather's place. Ramón was still sleeping off his hangover. Angelina was up and gave Luis a shot of *guaro* to assuage the pain of his hangover. He asked for water, but after several glasses his thirst was only slightly slacked.

Riding back to Zapotal that evening, Luis knew he had to change something. He was not much of a man. And he was especially interested in impressing Ofelia Monje. That was part of the reason he had gotten so serious about religion. Ofelia was the Old Nacho's daughter. They were known as the most religious family in Zapotal. Now Lidier was seriously courting Gregoria, Ofelia's sister. If Lidier could win Gregoria, why couldn't he win Ofelia? It did not matter to him that Ofelia was a lot younger than he was.

The next day Luis sent Ofelia a letter. He was too embarrassed to go propose personally. Ofelia's answer was positive, though she wanted to wait to get married until she was nineteen, which was four years away. Luis was encouraged.

When Lico found out Luis had sent Ofelia a letter, he was furious. "Luis," he shouted, "what do you think you are doing? What makes you think you have a chance with that popular girl? Are you crazy? All you do is run around to all the religious activities, and if you think that will impress a girl or a father-in-law, you are wrong!"

"Lidier is courting Gregoria," Luis whimpered.

"Yes, but that's a different story." Lico drove the knife deep into his firstborn's heart. "You are far from being a Lidier. Lidier knows how to work. You are a lazy bum. Old Nacho knows this, and Ofelia isn't blind. A husband has to be able to make a living, not just sit around drinking and praying to a hundred saints!"

Luis had won a guitar in a raffle and was trying to learn to play. He wanted to be able to play at the *rosarios* and the dances. He especially wanted to learn to play the *Panadera*. But now he sold his guitar and bought a nine-foot handsaw. He got his brother Ángel to help him, and they started sawing lumber.

Zapotal had plenty of good timber, but no way of cutting the timber into boards. They used metal wedges and sledges to hew out rough pieces that they honed down to size and shaped with their axes and machetes, but it took a long time and did not make nice lumber. Now, with the new saw, Luis and Ángel would be able to produce nice, straight boards.

First they dug a slice out of a bank. Then they made a frame and rolled their logs off the bank onto the frame. Luis stood under the frame and took hold of the saw from below. Ángel stood up on the frame and grabbed the saw from the top. Slowly but surely, they pulled the saw back and forth, cutting the board to whatever size they chose.

Cutting boards was very hard work. One hour of sawing, and the men were drenched in sweat. It took all their strength to pull the saw through the wood, especially if it was hard wood. But Luis was determined to prove to his father that he was a man. Though Ángel always worked the top, taking the responsibility of guiding the saw on the snapped line, Luis did his share of the hard work.

When the family saw the boys' success at cutting boards, everyone got excited about building a new board house. They would make the house bigger and put in a board floor. But most important of all, they would haul in tin from Miramar for the roof. More and more tin roofs were going up in Zapotal, and the Valverdes did not want to be the last to have one. Luis and Ángel set to work and cut boards galore, excited to help with the project.

Not long afterwards, Luis and Ofelia took a trip to Puntarenas as a dating couple with some other youth. While they were there, Luis offered to elope with her and take her to Guanacaste where Marina lived, but Ofelia flatly refused. This made Luis angry, and when they stopped by Miramar on the way home, he went out and got drunk.

That afternoon when they were ready to set out for Zapotal, Ofelia refused to go over La Cuesta del Tubo with him, insisting that she would go the Tajo Alto way. She wanted to attend a *rosario* that night in Tajo Alto where her father would officiate and then return to Zapotal with him. Realizing she had lost interest in him, the brokenhearted Luis bought another bottle of *guaro* and decided to cross La Cuesta del Tubo alone.

By the time Luis got to La Cuesta del Tubo, it was dark. The moon was bright, almost full, but the moonlight did nothing to calm Luis's fears. Trembling from head to toe, he started to climb the switchbacks as fast as his horse could carry him. Luis hung on for dear life and every so often stopped to take another draft from his bottle, all the while frantically praying the prayers he had learned at the rosaries. The demon called fear was unleashed by the drink, and it clutched at his heart like an octopus.

Luis reached a place where banks flanked the trail on either side. Suddenly he noticed a large black animal pacing slowly ahead of him.

Luis just about swallowed his heart in fright. The animal had a big, long tail. The horse stopped abruptly. Luis had no power left to make him stop or go. Not a squeak escaped his mouth.

The animal leaped up onto the bank and continued to lead the way. Luis jumped in fright, but his horse followed cautiously. The next thing Luis knew, the animal had leaped over a fence and disappeared into the night. Luis spurred his horse and raced home, more afraid than he had ever been in his life.

Once he was sure things were over between him and Ofelia, Luis left the board cutting to his brothers and drowned himself in drink. Weekends he would saddle his horse and ride through the community after dark, carousing and making a pest of himself. It got so bad that Nacho tried to convince Ofelia to take him again. But by the time Ofelia was ready to give in, Luis had left for Guanacaste to stay with Marina for a while.

In Guanacaste it was not easy to buy liquor, so Luis made his own brew of rubbing alcohol and condensed milk. This cheap but powerful concoction did what Luis wanted—it helped him forget Zapotal and Ofelia.

Several months later, Luis returned to Zapotal. As soon as he arrived, they told him the news: Ofelia had married a widower. Luis was devastated.

Luis's life became a turmoil of questions for which he had no answers. Was he a man or wasn't he? Did people respect him or scorn him? Was his father impressed with him? Luis was a quiet, pensive, bashful man, but under the influence of liquor he was a cutup who would do anything for attention.

Life in Zapotal made men strong and weak. Strong to survive in such a harsh climate in such primitive conditions. But weak spiritually, since they knew no Saviour for their sins and lived loose lives according to their flesh. Luis's search for meaning was far from over. And the answers he craved would not be found in a bottle.

14

L idier Valverde, dressed in a new set of clothes and riding little Jabón, was leading a procession of four. His white long-sleeved shirt did not match the rough surroundings. His black pants were already covered with dust, and sweat dampened his shirt.

Right behind this gallant *campesino** rode his fifteen-year-old bride on her mother-in-law's big bay mare. She wore a full white wedding dress with a veil draped over her face and a white crown on her head. She looked just as lovely to Lidier after the long ride as she had that morning at the Catholic church when the priest had married them. The bride was fair-skinned and had a head full of thick hair as black as a raven's feathers.

Not only was Gregoria pretty, she was popular. Wasn't she Old Nacho's daughter? Lidier, Lico Valverde's third son, had won the charming girl's heart. He had courted her respectfully and carefully. Because Lidier was Lico's best worker and manager, Nacho had happily agreed to the friendship. Now, several months later, they were married.

Behind Lidier and Gregoria rode Leyla and Beto on their own steeds. Leyla was Lidier's younger sister, and Beto was her fiancé. The pair had served as witnesses for the ceremony.

---

* peasant

Now the procession made its way up La Cuesta del Tubo. No one talked. They just hung on and concentrated on managing the terrific climb.

Lidier's mind wandered. They had ridden down to Miramar the day before and slept at a friend's house. In the morning they had gone to the big Catholic church to be married. First they confessed their sins to the priest. Lidier grinned, remembering how he had lied to the priest. *Why should I confess my sins to another sinner as bad as myself?* he had grumbled to himself.

Just before marrying them, the priest had prayed and given them each a piece thin waffer. "Listen, son," he told Lidier, "you may not drink any liquor today. This Host literally became Jesus' flesh after I prayed, and it gives you eternal life. You have to wait to drink until tomorrow."

Now, as he rode up La Cuesta del Tubo, Lidier knew he would miss his drinks that evening at the fiesta. But at least he had gotten what he wanted. Nacho's pretty daughter was his wife!

Waiting on top of Cerro Pelón was a much larger procession. All of Lidier's friends and relations who could find a horse had come to the *tope.** In Costa Rica's tradition, in the back-in country, when a couple got married, they rode home on horseback after the marriage ceremony in town. All their friends and relatives gathered all the horses they could to come meet the couple and their witnesses. When they met, they set off firecrackers and shouted to greet the couple. Then they all rode back together to the home of one of the families for the fiesta.

In Zapotal, the *tope* was always held at Cerro Pelón, where a group of at least twenty now awaited the couple's arrival. They had all stopped their horses at the mountain's edge and were gazing down on the gulf. Far below them lay La Cuesta del Tubo.

"We don't have any fireworks," Ángel Soto growled.

"We can have a *tope* without fireworks," Lico answered. "We'll see the married couple; that's the most important part anyway."

---

* encounter

"And we have plenty of *guaro*," Luis added, "thanks to Gelo. That's what will make the party, not the fireworks."

"I still think we should have fireworks," Ángel insisted. "Maybe I can come up with a solution."

Gelo had borrowed a mule for the *tope*. Now he hung on to the saddle strap and grinned. He was glad he had learned to ride. He had to have help to mount his horse, but once mounted, he tied his crutches to the saddle, balanced himself well, and rode like the wind.

When the four horses and their riders topped Cerro Pelón on the trail from Miramar, everyone galloped toward them, shouting, "Congratulations! Congratulations!"

Ángel Soto, Teodolinda's hotheaded brother, rode a fast buckskin. Lico rode a horse he had borrowed from Leandro. Now they rode hard, racing. Both men had already had some *guaro,* and both were angry.

"We're in for trouble," Gelo remarked to his brothers.

"There will be a fight tonight at the fiesta, for sure," Luis agreed.

Ángel won the race. He jerked his horse to a stop. The four from Miramar had already pulled up their horses, waiting on the Zapotal procession. Just as the rest of the horses crashed into the growing circle,

the riders shouting and cheering, Ángel pulled out his six-shooter and shot all six bullets into the air. His horse reared.

After a moment of shocked silence, Lidier shouted, "Ángel, what are you doing?"

Lico was angry. "Ángel, you're crazy! This is a marriage *tope*, not a shootout!"

Ángel, hurt and angered by their reprimands, rode off ahead. He did not join the crowd until later when the fiesta really took off at Lico's home. But the rest of the group did not allow Ángel's antics to kill their fun. Shouting and laughing, they escorted the newlyweds home.

At home everything was ready. Teodolinda's mother had come to help. They had butchered a turkey and several chickens and were cooking up a feast. Several ladies from Nacho's family were helping too. The girls had ground corn for tortillas. Teodolinda was in charge of the big kettle of stew. The younger children hauled water and brought extra firewood.

Gelo had made a big batch of *guaro*. Lico and Ángel had already made a big dent in one of the gallon jugs that morning, but two more jugs were hidden in the high grass behind the house. This fiesta would have plenty of food and liquor. And there was talk of another dance. Teodolinda had tried her best to discourage it, but her plea had been drowned out by the men's loud planning.

Lidier kept his word to the priest. He did not drink on the day of his wedding, though he made up for it the next day. But no one else had any scruples about drinking that night. The Valverdes' wedding party was the wildest Zapotal had ever known.

The Jiménez brothers came just as it got dark and took over the corner of the living room for the dance.

The first time the Jiménez brothers had played the *Panadera*, Luis had passed the hat to a popular girl named Manuela. At that time he had been interested in Ofelia, so he had not really meant anything by it. And Manuela had had a boyfriend herself. But now her boyfriend had ditched her, and Manuela was brokenhearted, just like Luis was. Recently, at another *rosario*, Luis had had the opportunity to talk with this slim, friendly girl. They had shared stories and found they shared a kindred spirit. Weren't they both hurting from lost love? Weren't they both ready to show their old flames that it didn't matter?

This was their chance.

Vicente started the dance with the *Panadera* again. He passed the hat to one of Old Nacho's girls. After dancing a while, she remembered the fun Luis had provided the first time and plopped the hat on his head. Luis did not let the crowd down. For a full ten minutes Vicente made up foolish verses, and Luis cut up to match each one.

When the song asked Luis to find a companion, he tossed the hat onto Manuela's head and danced with her as he had a few years before.

By the time Luis returned to the crowd, Vicente had noticed the friendship developing between them. Thinking that Manuela could take the jokes like Luis did, he threw in a few teasing verses. But the jokes were too much for Manuela. She stopped dancing, jerked the hat off her head, and threw it straight at Vicente. Then she marched out into the night. In a fit of rage, Luis jumped into the inner circle and kicked Vicente's guitar right out of his arms, smashing the instrument against the wall. Then Luis followed Manuela out into the darkness.

Vicente borrowed his brother's guitar and tried to get someone else to pick up where Manuela had left off, but the dance was dampened for the rest of the evening. More and more people were gathering out in the yard, where things were getting wilder.

The women watched from the kitchen door. Gelo and Marcos even came in and tried to get the girls to drink. Amable finally took a sip. Teodolinda complained, but she did not make them stop. Her own stand against liquor was weakening.

It was the middle of dry season, and the full moon lit up the whole yard. By now the men were working on the third gallon jug of liquor. Lico and Ángel Soto were still angry.

When Lico stepped into the moonlight to serve more liquor, Ángel grabbed for the jug. "Give it to me!" he demanded.

As Lico jerked the jug back, it flew from his hand and rolled across the yard, spewing the vicious brew across the dirt patio. As the jug rolled one way, Lico and Ángel rolled the other, pounding at each other as they went. The onlookers hooted and laughed. Both were too drunk to hurt each other.

But two people were not laughing. Teodolinda stood in the doorway, watching in disgust. Why did her husband have to act like a drunkard? And little Aurelio lay in bed, trembling. He had crawled into bed about the time the dance had ended, but he could not sleep. Earlier he had seen his father acting funny in the yard. It frightened him to see his dad loud and boisterous when he was usually quiet and reserved. It also scared him when his sisters took their first drinks. Aurelio was a quiet, thoughtful little fellow who liked solitude and peace. The atmosphere of the evening unsettled his young heart. But what really shook him was the fighting. Only a thin wall separated him from the noisy brawl. The blows seemed to be striking at his very heart.

Finally Lidier and Luis pulled Ángel off their dad. Lidier was laughing like everyone else, but a streak of anger and hatred burned deep in his heart. As he hauled Ángel's body up off the prostrate Lico, he jabbed him hard in the stomach with his fist. Ángel doubled over and cried out in pain.

The crowd dispersed. As the boys hauled Lico off to bed, he was still mumbling about Ángel and what he would do to him if he had a chance.

Later everything was quiet. Everyone was asleep—everyone but Aurelio. He was wide awake and shaking all over. He buried his face in his homemade pillow and wept. Slowly his emotions calmed as he gave vent to his sadness and fear, but still he wondered: Would he ever be like that?

Aurelio had always followed easygoing Gelo like a shadow, but his sensitive nature just wouldn't allow him to enjoy the wild Zapotal life. So he suffered alone as sin battered his family, his tender heart sustaining scars that would take a lifetime to heal.

15

The overgrown trail led through a mile of wild, wonderful virgin cloud forest. For nine months out of the year it was very muddy. Its users did not try to make it broad and comfortable. They had to crawl over logs, duck under fallen trees, wade the creek, and walk around large rocks. The hike led through an enchanting land of green moss, exotic orchids, quetzals, and jaguars. But to the Valverdes, it was just a trail.

In the middle of the jungle, just as the trail topped the mountain range, was a big gap. A hole. A two-*manzana* wound on the mountain's green back. It was actually a little valley that, instead of trees, vines, heliconias, and ferns, grew row after row of vegetables.

Tico farmers used big, wide shovels to make seedbeds. They made long, six-inch-high, two-foot-wide beds instead of furrows so the rainwater would run off the rows. These rows covered every inch of the acreage in the *socolón.**

One corner of the field boasted a beautiful stand of corn. A large cucumber patch was covered with the greenest vines and the finest harvest of cucumbers anywhere. Then there were the radish beds, onions, peppers, cabbages, and pumpkins.

---

* natural clearing in the jungle, often overgrown with high weeds

In the center of the valley where the huge potato tree had fallen years ago was the *chayotera*. The old potato tree stump and the huge mound of dirt that had been uprooted with the tree were now totally covered. All around the dead stump the Valverdes had made a bamboo bower, which was now overgrown with chayote vines. Already the vines had hundreds of little prickly pear-shaped chayotes on them.

It was the middle of July. As soon as the rains had hit in May, the men had started to clean the place up. Then they had dug the seedbeds and planted the precious seeds in the soft black dirt. Now, two months later, the rich soil had produced the lushest, greenest vegetable patch in Zapotal. The morning sun shone down on the garden, still wet from the rain the night before, and the whole garden sparkled and shouted praise to its wonderful Creator.

Surely Lico had discovered a gold mine when he had found the *socolón*. Lico was a hard worker who liked to do things right. And he could grow vegetables. There was probably only one thing he put more effort into than growing vegetables, and that was drinking. That was where the problem came in. The *socolón* and the drink did not go together well at all.

After starting the still, the Valverde men spent a lot of time making and drinking *guaro*. The wonderful project up in the clearing suffered.

On a typical Sunday, all the Valverde men spent the day at home selling liquor and drinking. Even Lidier, who was married now, sometimes showed up. Often the partying would draw other people and result in fights, especially on Saturday and Sunday nights. It became well-known that plenty of drink and wild fun could be had at the Valverdes' place.

On Mondays the Valverdes and many of their neighbors had horrible hangovers, so the men stayed home and slept them off. Of course they had to have a drink or two to help ease the hangover, and they sold *guaro* to their neighbors for that reason too. Often Mondays ended up like Sundays, and they had to sleep off their hangovers on Tuesday.

There was always one Valverde up and going on Monday. Regardless of how much he drank Sunday night, on Monday Gelo was out collecting the *fermento*. If he did not get the *fermento* going Monday, there would be no *guaro* come Saturday. And he did not trust anyone else to do it. Anymore, he used cooked corn, with a little fruit for flavor. Using corn was easier than searching for so much fruit. And he never forgot to put a nice chunk of *dulce* into the bucket to speed things up.

Usually Lico was able to get his sons back to work on the *socolón* by Tuesday morning. There was always too much to do, cleaning, weeding, planting, and replanting. A truck patch that size took a lot of work, especially to keep it in top-notch condition. And that was Lico's style.

Wednesday was a full day of work again. Thursday Lico and the boys picked the produce and got the vegetables ready for market. That was a full day's job, and Lico often took several of the girls along to help with the packaging. The tender green pumpkins and chayotes had to be packed in dry banana leaves. The radishes were tied in little bundles with thin, tough jungle vines to sell for a peso apiece. The tender, young onions were also tied in bundles. The roasting ears and cabbages were thrown into sacks. Then all the vegetables were hauled out through the jungle on their backs to a hiding place close to the trail.

Four o'clock Friday morning always found Lico and one the boys loading up the two horses in the light of their *churu-cas*. The lamps were made by nailing a tin can on a stick, cutting a gaping hole in the side, and putting a candle in it. If they walked slowly, the candle did not go out.

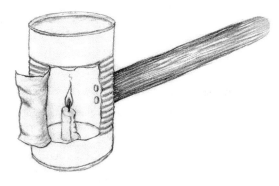

When everything was ready, Lico and his son would hike to Miramar. Friday was market day, and it always got too late to come home the same day. Before the still, Lico invariably stayed up late Friday night drinking and often spent half of Saturday drinking too. But now he would hurry home early Saturday morning and be back in time to get the *cabezón*. His own liquor was better than any in Miramar, and it was free!

The boys worked the vegetable patch until Saturday. Usually the liquor they had made the week before was all sold or drunk by Thursday. So Thursday and Friday ended up being the only good workdays. As long as there was *contrabando* around, the boys could hardly let it go. By Friday evening, Gelo would have a gallon or two of *chicha* ready. Though not nearly as strong as the *guaro*, it still helped slake their ever-growing thirst.

By Saturday everyone was thirsty again, and not just the Valverdes. A lot of their neighbors knew about what time Gelo's brew would be ready. They came from all over. On Saturday mornings the Valverde men did not work at all. Instead they went down to watch Gelo give the *guaro* its finishing touches. Then they would fight for the *cabezón*. If Lico made it back from Miramar, which was about half the time, he usually got it. If he was not back, the boys gathered around to see who could get to it first.

"It's coming! It's coming!" Gelo would shout. "Get the cup ready!" And they would all race and push each other to get their cups under the spout at the right moment. Often the *cabezón* was wasted in the mad rush. But eventually they all had their turn.

The only time none of the Valverdes got the *cabezón* was when there was a *rosario*. If you were preparing for a *rosario*, you saved the *cabezón* for the *rezador*. During those times Old Nacho or Vicente Jiménez always got the best.

The first shots of *guaro* were always free. They never sold it until it had trickled into the jugs. So a lot of fellows hiked down to the still to drink in the forenoon. Of course, Andrés was always there. He got his free drinks and then took off with half of the jugs.

Saturday night was time to party again. Then the cycle began all over. Though they made some money selling drink and vegetables, there never seemed to be enough. Actually, the deeper they got into drinking, the less money they had. As their poverty and problems worsened, their need for drink grew.

Sin works like a whirlpool. It spins its victims around and around in what seems like a funny, lively, bubbly pool of pleasure. At first. But it slowly sucks them down until they begin to swallow water and choke. By the time they realize it and want out, they are caught in a very serious trap. Satan smirks. Jesus weeps. And unless the sinners turn to the greater power that longs to reach down and rescue them, sin's victims are surely bound for Hell.

The Valverde family was sinking slowly, but surely. And Hell was waiting.

* * *

A year after Lidier's wedding, Luis married Manuela. Again there was a lively *tope* on Cerro Pelón, this time with fireworks. A bottle was being passed around before they even got to the house. Luis had eaten the Host too, and the priest had warned him not to take drink that night. But by the time they left Cerro Pelón, Luis had forgotten. Intentionally.

Manuela frowned when she saw him take the first swig. She was afraid for the evening fiesta. And rightly so.

Later that night the fiesta was in full swing. Vicente Jiménez was playing his guitar, and Luis and Manuela were inside dancing. Standing to one side of the room was a young man who had liked Manuela. Carlos Quesada was one of many boys in the Quesada family. They had moved into the area recently and were drinkers and fighters, just like the Valverdes. Carlos had tried to convince Manuela to marry him instead of Luis. But now that Manuela had chosen Luis, the two men were enemies.

Carlos watched for his chance to dance with Manuela. According to Zapotal custom, a woman couldn't deny anyone a dance, so if Luis's rival asked her, it was he who was being bold. Carlos sidled up to her and asked her to dance, a clear challenge to the newly married Luis. Luis was too intoxicated to notice. But his brother Ángel wasn't. Angrily he stepped outside and told Lico, "Dad, Carlos is dancing with Manuela."

"He can't do that!" Lico growled. He staggered up the steps and into the living room. Sure enough, Carlos was just finishing a slow dance with Manuela. As soon as the dance was over, Lico grabbed him by the waist, dragged him to the door, and threw him down the several steps to the ground. Carlos fell, twisting his ankle. He screamed in pain. The crowd heard him, and a cry arose. "Carlos is dying! Carlos is dying!"

Luis ran for the door to see what was going on. He saw Carlos getting to his feet and Durando, Carlos's father, lunging for Lico's throat. In no time flat a whole pile of Valverdes and Quesadas were fighting tooth and claw with whatever they could find.

Even Gelo was fighting, hopping around on his right foot and his left crutch. The other crutch, clutched in his strong right hand, became a dangerous weapon.

Most of the fighters were so drunk that all they did was wrestle and holler. But Moncho, the oldest Quesada boy, was alert enough to notice Luis stealthily looking for a weapon. Before Luis found one, Moncho whacked him with a stick. Luis keeled over with a gash in his forehead. His friends hauled him inside to clean him up. Then they hid Luis in the coffee patch until things quieted down. It took all their strength to keep him from running back into the fight.

Men stood on either side of the fight. Some were friends of the Quesadas, but most were loyal to the Valverdes. One of these men was Marina's husband, Luis Elizondo, who had come from Guanacaste for the wedding. When he saw what Moncho had done, he slipped quietly behind the house and returned carrying his sharp *cutacha.* Everyone knew that meant big trouble. Fists bruise. Sticks make gashes on foreheads. But *cutachas* kill. The watching men grabbed Luis Elizondo from behind, took his weapon away, and calmed him down. Slowly the pileup unraveled and the fighting stopped.

Fifteen minutes later Lico was laughing and handing out *guaro* from a new jug. But the rivalry between the Quesadas and the Valverdes was set in stone.

16

Don Lico's little coffee patch was his pride and joy. Several years after they had moved from Tajo Alto, Lico had planted some coffee plants for their own use. People said the elevation at Zapotal was too high to raise coffee, but Lico felt sure that he could. So he had chosen a secluded glade behind the house and planted several hundred plants in the sun. The coffee did not grow nearly as well as it did in Tajo Alto or Miramar, but for several years the grove had produced enough for their own use. The plants were covered with moss, just like the trees, but the coffee was good.

Lico tied a basket to his waist, just like he had back in Tajo Alto. He jerked away some of the unhandy moss and then carefully picked the bright, wine-red berries, leaving the green ones for the next picking. The basket was filling slowly, and Lico's stomach was reminding him that it was almost time for lunch.

Just as he filled his basket, little Aurelio darted through the coffee patch, gasping for breath. "Papito, Gelo and Mamita want you to come quickly. Leandro is here and claims the *resguardo* were at his house asking about a still up here in Zapotal."

Lico plopped his basket on the ground and hurried to the house. When he got there, he found Gelo, Teodolinda, and Leandro in a huddle behind the house, talking in low tones.

"What's going on?" Lico asked.

"At the crack of dawn," Leandro whispered, "the *resguardo* came to my house. They wanted to search my house. I said they could, but they never did. They asked a lot of questions. They seem to know there is a still up here, but they don't know who has it. I totally denied that there is a still and tried to convince them that all the *guaro* comes from Tajo Alto, but they didn't believe it. At the end they asked about you, Lico. You'll have to be very careful."

"Where did they go after leaving your place?" Lico asked, nervously looking up the trail as he spoke.

"They went back the way they came. But that doesn't mean they returned to Miramar; it could be a trick."

Leandro left, and Lico and his family got busy. Gelo collected the bottles and the one jug that still contained *guaro.* Lico hid the bottles and jug in the high grass behind the house. Next he and Gelo tried to cover the well-worn trail to the still. Desperate, Lico cut down a small tree and made it fall right onto the trail, giving it an unused look.

Sitting around the light of a *canfinera* that night, the boys and their father discussed their predicament.

"Obviously La Cuesta del Tubo didn't stop the *resguardo* after all," Gelo grumbled. "They do care what happens up here, eh? They are determined to stop all stills, even way up here in Zapotal."

"We need to talk to Andrés," Ángel growled. "That crook gets his full half of the *guaro;* then he drinks a quart of ours before he leaves. He doesn't do a bit of the work. All he does is bring the *dulce.* That's not fair. Maybe if we get caught, he can go to jail."

"Andrés is way too smart to go to jail," Lico threw in. "I caught that from the very beginning. He made it clear that we should be careful, because if we get caught, we pay."

"Who would go to jail if they caught us?" Luis asked.

Everybody looked at each other. They knew the *resguardo* first had to find proof, and an empty bottle was no proof. They had to find the real stuff or the still itself. Then they usually took one person and put him into jail for several years.

"I will go," Teodolinda offered.

Everyone was shocked. "Not you, Mamita!" Gelo answered. "Never!"

"Let me explain," Teodolinda continued. "First of all, we won't get caught. The *resguardo* always hits in the wee hours of the morning. We will always be prepared. If they come to the front door, you run out the back and hide in the coffee patch. If they insist on taking someone, I will offer myself. You know good and well that they won't take a woman to prison!"

Everyone cheered. They admired their mother's courage and resourcefulness. The *resguardo* would never find their still in the jungle. They would never find proof in the house. And if they ever did get caught, Mamita would be the hero!

No one even considered giving up the still.

Hiding became a way of life for the Valverdes. Gelo was cautious when he made his *fermento*. No one just walked down to the still as they had before. They had secret trails. The liquor was always hidden in the woods or in the grass behind the house.

Nights when they drank, they hid the bottles under something—at first. But the more they drank, the more careless they grew. At the end of the drinking spree, if someone was sober enough to remember, they would throw the bottles into the high grass behind the house. Teodolinda often ended up performing this nightly ritual.

Figuring out how to sell the stuff was harder. Did they have to go to the weeds to get the stuff every time a customer came? Wouldn't someone notice where they always went?

But the Valverdes' lifestyle had to change. The *resguardo* were like bloodhounds. Once they caught scent of a trail, they never gave up until they treed the coon. So now it was the hound's nose against the coon's cunning. Who would win?

*   *   *

In spite of the fact that the family drank more and more, the *socolón* survived. The men were still hard workers, and they did not drink quite every day. When they did work, things got done.

The *socolón* vegetables were becoming popular at the market. Lico continued going to market with one of the boys, and his crops sold well. But Lico drank up all the profits, and the money they made selling liquor was never enough to make up for it.

Once Aurelio was big enough, Lico started taking him to market. He was excellent at figures, so Lico turned him loose, since he had other business to attend to. Monkey business.

One fine market day Lico had an extra large load of fresh vegetables. He loaded down both horses. Once they got to the market, Lico helped Aurelio set out the radishes, cucumbers, cabbages, pumpkins, carrots, and chayotes. Soon people flocked around and started to buy. Aurelio handled the money, and Lico grinned. As soon as they had made several pesos, Lico disappeared, as usual.

After about three of Lico's trips back to the vegetable stand for money, Aurelio tried something his mother had asked him to do. In his gentle, high-pitched voice, he reminded Lico to get the groceries before it got late. Then he threw in for good measure, "And buy us something good this time, Papito."

Lico's heart was happy. He took the next batch of money and Teodolinda's list and bought a bunch of groceries. For once he bought everything she asked for. Then he asked Aurelio, "And what shall the special thing be?"

"Meat, Papito. Get us some meat."

Lico took the next batch of money and headed for the meat stand. Soon he staggered back with a big grin on his face. He walked open legged, a cow horn in each hand, the cow head out in front of him. He was so drunk he could hardly carry it.

"Oh, Papito, we will make a good soup out of that head!" Aurelio beamed.

"Right!" Lico hiccupped. "And I want to eat the brains fried! We will make your Mamita happy, won't we?"

Lico hid the head behind the market stand, and Aurelio covered it with a sack. By late afternoon the flies had found the head, and they nearly drove Aurelio crazy with their buzzing as he tried to chase them away.

The next morning Lico wanted to drink some more. Aurelio begged him to not get started. "What about the cow head, Papito? It's starting to stink!"

But Aurelio's pleas fell on deaf ears. Lico drank all forenoon, and Aurelio was bored stiff. The vegetables had all been sold the evening before. Finally, at noon, Aurelio convinced Lico it was time to go.

It was four o'clock when Lico and Aurelio topped Cerro Pelón, Lico leading the big bay mare and Aurelio following on Jabón. It had rained while they climbed La Cuesta del Tubo. Lico still staggered, and he carried a little bottle of spirits in his pocket just in case. Now the weather had changed and steam rose from him as the sun dried his rain-drenched shirt.

Little Aurelio was drying too. His black hair was plastered to his face. He held his nose part of the time, but his father did not notice. He was walking up ahead, singing at the top of his voice,

"Con dinero y sin dinero,
hago siempre lo que quiero,
y mi palabra es la ley . . ."
(With money or without money,
I still do what I please,
and my word is law . . .)
—José Alfredo Jiménez

The mare did not seem perturbed. Her load was not heavy. The groceries were tied tightly under plastic and rode nicely. On top of the whole load, a set of glassy eyes stared lifelessly straight up into the heavens, but the horse did not know that. The cow head Lico had bought was tied tightly, the huge horns spread toward the sky. If the glassy eyes could have seen what Aurelio saw, the cow might have grinned too. A pair of turkey vultures soared above them. What stank to Aurelio smelled delicious to them.

But Lico saw none of this. He was still singing at the top of his voice,

> *"No tengo trono ni reino,*
> *ni nadie que me comprenda,*
> *pero ¡sigo siendo el rey!"*
> (I don't have a throne or a kingdom,
> and no one to understand me,
> but I am still the king!)
>   —José Alfredo Jiménez

Aurelio struggled with knowing what he should do—laugh, cry, or vomit. He held it in until they got home. Then his mother helped him decide.

As they rode into the yard, Lico was still optimistic. "Hey, Teodolinda! Come see what we got! Aurelio and I brought you a cow head to make soup. And I want the brains fried."

Aurelio watched his mother closely. The other children flocked around. Teodolinda stood in the doorway and stared. Lico's clothes were filthy; his unshaven face wore the dumb look of the doped. The flies buzzed around the stinky cow head. Blood had oozed down over the groceries. Teodolinda found herself holding her nose too. Then she burst out crying and fled for the bedroom. Aurelio jumped off the horse on the opposite side and ran into the coffee patch and cried his heart out too.

Lico went straight to bed. The boys threw the cow head down over the hill for the dogs to work on in the days to come.

That was one of the saddest Saturday nights the Valverde family ever had. The older boys did not mind; they had been drinking all evening anyway. In their state it didn't matter that the cow head stank. It didn't matter if the children went to bed hungry. It didn't matter if Mamita cried until her heart broke in disappointment. But it did matter to the rest of the family, and to the Father who loves children and has compassion on suffering souls. It mattered an awful lot!

The next morning Lico and Teodolinda had the biggest fight of their marriage. It ended as usual: Teodolinda would not leave Lico after all. Lico knew he had won in two ways. Teodolinda shut up, and he was able to convince her to take three shots of his firewater instead of the two she sometimes took. Lico was proud that he had won again. But neither he nor his wife understood who the real victor was—Beelzebub himself!

*   *   *

The next morning Aurelio, who'd had such hopes for the cow head, was still hungry for meat. "Let's go hunting for peccary, boys," he suggested to his older brothers. Soon a plan formed. Belén, one of the younger Valverde boys, went to the neighbors' place to borrow their two dogs. Old Duke only ran pacas, and they were scarce lately. Peccaries were getting scarce too, but if they hiked an hour or two back in, they could still find groups of them running wild.

By ten o'clock Marcos, Marino, Belén, and Aurelio were on their way. Pancho, who owned the dogs, went along for the fun.

By noon they were far enough back in that they turned the dogs loose and waited on a jungle-covered hilltop. Sure enough, they soon heard one of the dogs baying as it hit a trail. The second dog soon joined in. Excitement ran high as the boys stood in a huddle, waiting to see which way the peccary would run.

"Listen to those dogs bay!" exclaimed Pancho. "Isn't that music to the ear?"

"It sure sounds nice," Belén agreed. "But it's better yet when the dogs sing, 'Treed!' and we know we will have meat!"

"There's nothing more fun than hunting with a good pair of dogs on a Sunday morning, is there?" Marcos added.

"Let's go," Pancho urged. "The dogs have set a course. It's time to run."

When a dog hits a peccary trail, the peccary runs. A peccary can easily outrun a dog, but a persistent dog can easily follow its trail because when a peccary gets upset, a gland right above its tail opens and emits an awful odor. As the animal brushes against leaves and branches, the smell clings so strong that any hound can almost follow a peccary with his eyes closed.

The peccaries were running hard. The dogs followed, and the boys ran after the dogs. If they did not run fast enough, the dogs would soon work their way out of hearing distance and the hunters would end up alone in the jungle with nothing to follow. So the five young men raced after the dogs, yelling and urging them on. Though they could not see the dogs through the thick jungle, their baying made them easy to follow. So, jumping over or crawling under logs, wading streams, climbing huge hills, and traversing wide valleys, they ran. They took turns leading out, because the leader had to slash the worst of the weeds as he ran and tired quickly.

An hour later the boys were almost as tired as the dogs, but neither the dogs nor the hunters gave up. It was the peccaries that finally gave up. All of a sudden the baying changed from a long wail into shorter, wilder yelps. "They have them cornered!" Pancho said. "Let's be careful now. A charging peccary is no fun!"

Soon they approached a huge stand of heliconia plants. "The peccaries are in there," Pancho hissed. "They can keep the dogs at bay in the thick plants. Let's sneak in to see if we can get a shot at one of the big ones."

The dogs made a terrific ruckus, barking and lunging into the weeds and dashing back out, avoiding the razor-sharp tusks that protruded from either side of the peccaries' snouts. Aurelio had never been on a peccary hunt before, and so far he was enjoying it immensely. The running part was especially fun. But now he could only imagine what the angry animals looked like or what he would do if they suddenly burst out in their direction. Nervously he began eyeing the closest trees to see if there was one he could climb.

Marcos sneaked in toward the heliconia stand. He held the twenty-two ready on his shoulder, the safety unlatched.

Suddenly there was a harsh scraping sound as if a great wind had slashed into the heliconia patch. But it was not the wind blowing in—it was the animals stampeding out. They tore through the thick heliconia stalks and raced through the jungle again, the dogs in hot pursuit.

"Aw!" Marcos complained. "I wasn't able to get a shot!"

This time the peccaries did not run far. Two of them hid in a huge hollow log in a gully. The others ran on past. But the dogs found the ones in the hollow log and yelped again.

Aurelio's hair nearly stood on end as he made his way to the log's entrance. He heard a fierce snapping sound coming right out of the hollow log's middle. One of the dogs burst into the log, and the snapping sound grew louder. Soon the dog backed out, blood spurting from his face where a peccary had ripped him with his tusk. Pancho found some tough vines and tied the dogs. Then he stationed Marcos at the hollow log's opening, his gun aimed and ready to fire. He and the other boys looked for holes along the log's trunk. They examined the whole area, whacking away with their machetes. Pancho had obviously done this many times before.

"The pigs won't be apt to try to escape again," he assured them. "They're so tired they're willing to fight it out rather than risk another run."

That made Aurelio feel better. He had been wondering what he would do if they burst out of the log at him.

Suddenly Pancho cheered. Almost at the end of the hollow log he had found a knothole the size of a grapefruit right where the two animals were holed up. As Pancho cleared the vines and trash away from the hole, Aurelio could hear their teeth snapping inside. Pancho climbed up on the log and stuck the gun down into the hole. Aurelio shuddered when he saw the peccary snap at the barrel, chewing at it, and smearing it with saliva.

Pancho took his time. He waited until he was sure. Then, *Bang!* Then a little later, *Bang!* again.

"How are you going to get those creatures out of there?" Marino wondered after the silence proved the two animals were dead.

"Just watch and see," Pancho answered, searching among the trees for some strong vines. After finding what he wanted, he approached the hole carefully. "First of all, make sure they're dead. Imagine me sticking my hand into that dark hole and being impaled by one of those horrible tusks!"

Pancho took a sharp pole and stuck it into the knothole. He prodded the animals and made sure they were not just pretending. Then he made a noose on the vine, reached in slowly, and lassoed a dead peccary by the head. Then, reaching deep into the hollow log, he flung the rest of the coiled vine out toward the hollow log's entrance. "Now, Aurelio, it's your turn. You're the smallest. Crawl in there until you find the tip of the vine I threw; then haul it out to me."

Aurelio dropped to his hands and knees and began the careful crawl into the log. *Yuck!* he thought. *It stinks in here! It's dark and smells musty and very much like peccary. What if there's a snake back in here? Maybe the peccary won't get me, but what about a snake? I'm not sure which is worse.*

Just about the time Aurelio was ready to panic, he felt the vine resting on the damp floor of the log. He grabbed it and backed out fast.

Pancho and Marcos pulled the big male peccary out and examined the bullet hole right through his forehead. Next they lassoed the female. Pancho quickly took his sharp knife and cut out the stink glands right above their stub tails. "That's so the meat doesn't smell like peccary," he explained.

He turned the dogs loose and they hiked down to the river to clean the animals. When they got to the river, Aurelio hollered, "Boys, look! Right here is where we crossed hours ago when we first got into the area."

"That's right," Pancho chuckled. "I was waiting to see who noticed. Peccaries often run in big circles. That makes it awfully nice, because we won't have to carry the meat so far."

Soon Pancho and Marcos were butchering the peccaries. They gutted them, tied their front feet together, and flung them across their shoulders for the long hike home. It was just getting dark when they got to the Valverdes'. The children ran out and cheered to see the abundance of meat. Little Hugo jumped up and down in glee. "Meat for supper! Meat for supper!" Their mouths watered at the thought of the delicious, tender peccary meat. It was not quite as tasty as paca, which was the best wild meat, but peccary came in a close second.

Teodolinda was glad for the meat, but she knew it would attract neighbors who would drink and party way into the night. She dreaded the long night ahead.

Just as Teodolinda feared, the neighbors flocked in. There was plenty of meat, thanks to the boys. And there was plenty of drink, thanks to Gelo. At ten o'clock the Jiménez brothers dropped by and played some music. Fernando even convinced Teodolinda to dance a few rounds with him. The last people left at 2 a.m., and most of the Valverdes went to bed, though some of the boys just fell asleep on the floor, stone drunk. For all their sinful fun, the family felt strangely empty.

Early the next morning Teodolinda rose and washed her face. She was still tired from the late party, but she knew Lico would soon want his coffee. And Gelo would want to get an early start on the *fermento*. Groggily, she started the fire and put on a kettle of water.

Lico got up and staggered around the sleeping boys in the living room. They had forgotten about hiding the bottles. Several lay around, and a gallon jug, half empty, perched on the table.

Lico stumbled into the kitchen.

"The coffee is about ready," his wife assured him. "Watch the kettle while I go outside."

For some reason, Teodolinda walked into the living room instead of out the back door toward the latrine. As she reached the front door, she heard a sound right outside, as of someone clearing his throat. It was still dark. A slight tint of pink showed toward the east, but the day had not yet dawned. She opened the door a crack and peeped out. Right in front of the door stood a man dressed in olive green and carrying a gun. Teodolinda's heart froze, and she slammed the door in the man's face and jammed the security rod back into the hole.

"Open up," the man barked. "We are the *resguardo*."

But Teodolinda tore into the kitchen, hissing as she ran, "The *resguardo!* Run!"

By the time she opened the back door, Lico was ready. He slipped out into the dark coffee patch as quietly as a mouse. Behind him crept all the big boys except Gelo, rubbing their eyes, trying to wake up. As soon as they were gone, Teodolinda ran back to the front door and opened it. Two of the *resguardo* burst in and immediately searched the house. They found two bottles of liquor and the gallon jug on the table. Evidence enough.

"We know you own the still," the leader spoke with authority.

Gelo protested, "No, we don't own a still. We bring our *guaro* from Tajo Alto."

"Ha!" the other *resguardo* laughed. "Don't try to act innocent. We already found the still and have it packed up and ready to take along to Miramar to court. Don't lie to us, young man! We have plenty of evidence. The still, and now two bottles and a jug of the real stuff right here in our hands. One of the men needs to go to jail. Where are the men?"

"The men are planting beans in Tajo Alto right now," Teodolinda lied. "Only my crippled son is here, and you can't take him."

"Well, someone has to go with us. Who shall it be?"

At that moment Marcos popped in the front door, entirely unaware of what was going on. He had left home some time before and moved in with the Quesadas' daughter Nena. Now, of all days to come home to visit, Marcos had chosen this Monday morning, hoping he would be in time for the early morning coffee.

The *resguardo* questioned him next. "Are you related to these people?"

"Yes, that's my mother."

"Do you own a *fábrica?*"

"Of course not!"

"Yes, you do. We found it this morning and have it packed away and ready to go to Miramar with us. Don't you dare lie to us!"

"I'm not lying. I don't own a *fábrica*. I don't live here anymore. If they have a *fábrica,* it's theirs, not mine. I have nothing to do with it," he lied. Then he marched off and left his little mother to deal with the two armed men.

No one expected the *resguardo* to take a woman. Teodolinda figured that after arguing for a while, they would leave, and the men could come home and life could continue as normal. But they did not leave. They told Teodolinda to pack her bags. Still not believing they would take her, she obeyed. Aurelio looked pale and followed her around, wondering what would happen. Gelo tried to act businesslike and answered the *resguardo's* questions. The big girls were up, trying to get some breakfast going. The little children hid in the bedroom.

Finally there was nothing more to be said. They marched Teodolinda out of the house and onto the trail. Gelo was crying softly. Sure enough, there was the cutoff barrel securely tied to a horse and the other paraphernalia tied to the pack. The smaller children were shocked to see the *resguardo* take off with their mother. Little Hugo started crying as Mamita disappeared over the hilltop and down the jungle trail.

After the *resguardo* left, the men gathered in the coffee patch. They were all upset. "Surely they will let her go before they leave Zapotal," Lico groaned. "They can't just take the woman of the house like that." They knew they should have been men enough to offer themselves instead of letting Teodolinda go. Ángel, however, was sure the *resguardo* would let her go if they just waited it out.

Marcos returned and joined the conversation. "I think we should get tough with Andrés. Look at what he does. He gets us deep into this stuff; then when things get rough he takes no responsibility at all. He's sure got it nice. He should go turn himself in and let Mamita loose."

Nobody suggested that Lico should be the one to do that. They decided to just wait it out and see what happened.

Teodolinda was shocked when she realized they really were walking her all the way to Miramar. As she walked hour after lonely hour, she did a lot of thinking. She knew her family was in a real mess. The men were fast becoming alcoholics. Even she was beginning to take shots of *guaro* whenever she needed strength. And it was nothing new to see her daughters tipsy from too much firewater.

One good thing might come out of this, Teodolinda mused. *Maybe we'll stop drinking so much. Maybe we can finally make some money from the vegetables and catch up financially.*

But even as Teodolinda was crossing Cerro Pelón thinking these thoughts, Lico and the boys were draining the last hidden gallon jug of *guaro* back in their living room.

"I know one thing," Ángel swore angrily. "Someone reported us. Those guys didn't find that still by themselves. I know good and well who it was too!"

"That's right," Lico frowned, glancing at Marcos.

Marcos was quiet, but they could all see that he was troubled. He probably knew something, but he refused to talk. The next hour of conversation was long and loud. Someday, they fumed, the Quesadas would pay for this. Especially if Teodolinda was not released right away.

The whole community was shocked when word got out that the *resguardo* had taken Teodolinda. Andrés stopped in the next day, trying to make up with the angry Valverdes. "Look," he said, "you somehow settle this predicament. I will settle with you later. I will bring you a gift."

The Valverdes were not happy. Andrés' voice was too smooth and his eyes were too shifty. Though they said nothing, they knew their friendship with Andrés was over.

The *resguardo* took Teodolinda all the way to Miramar and straight to the police station. They did not put her into a cell, but let her have a room at the police station where she could lie on the floor. But she hardly slept a wink the whole night.

The next morning one of the policemen who knew Lico and Teodolinda slipped into the room to talk to her. "Listen," he advised, "pretend you are expecting. Tell them about all your babies. You have to make them pity you. They are really hard on *contrabando* right now, and you could end up in jail for two years. But if you're smart, they will let you loose."

When the police came to get her the next morning to take her to the judge, she sniffled and cried, "I miss my babies." Sure enough, she could see that the policeman was starting to pity her. "I have had sixteen children, and I am expecting my seventeenth," she lied, rubbing her stomach. She had put on some weight recently.

At the preliminary hearing, the policeman whispered some pitiful things to the judge. He looked at the little wisp of a woman. She stood there humbly, her oversized, calloused hands folded on her stomach, her unkempt hair hanging in her sad face, her shoulders stooped.

The judge shook his head. "You can't keep her in prison. She has sixteen babies, and you can easily see she's expecting another one. I suggest that you let her return to Zapotal and give her house detention. She should come back to the police station to report every six months until she proves that they won't make moonshine anymore." Then he nodded them out of the room. As they left, he shook his head again and muttered, "What a life those poor people must face up there in that wild place! I'd probably make moonshine too, just for my nerves."

That evening they turned Teodolinda loose. She went and slept at a friend's place. Early the next morning she climbed La Cuesta del Tubo alone, arriving home by mid-afternoon. Her children rushed out to meet her. The big girls came shyly, wondering how it had gone. The little ones cried with joy, especially little Hugo, who clung to her for the rest of the evening.

That night she told the family the whole story. Everyone listened carefully. Afterward she announced, "This happened so we would stop drinking. The still was not good for us. All we did was drink and get poorer. The *socolón* is all grown up, and the vegetables are going to waste. We can't go on like this. I am going to pray to the Holy Virgin and ask her to help us stop drinking. This was the best thing that could have happened to us."

No one answered. The men hung their heads. They knew it was all too true, but could they stop drinking? It was Wednesday evening, and they were already thirsty. They had finished the last jug on Monday. Every one of them knew that by Saturday they would find some liquor, somehow. So they were silent. Mother was right . . . maybe. But men were made to drink. And drink they would.

18

One Saturday evening most of the family was sitting on their porch when Andrés Rodríguez stopped in. There was no *guaro* to pick up now, but Andrés often stopped in anyway. The Valverdes had never scolded him for the unfair financial arrangement with the first still. They hid their resentment because he was always nice and brought news and, as usual, a bottle of *guaro* from who knows where.

After talking awhile, Andrés pulled out a brand-new twenty-two that had cost him 150 colones. The Valverdes accepted the gift, but growled in their hearts, *How can a measly gun make up for our mother going to jail?*

After they had all quenched their first thirst, Andrés started to tell a story. Five-year-old Hugo sat on his father's lap. As Andrés's story grew, so did Hugo's eyes. The wilder the story became, the larger his eyes grew.

"See," Andrés said loudly, "back before your Daddy Lico moved here to Zapotal, the *león* was much more common. A big one roamed these hills all the time. One night a man named Simón was traveling home from San Buenas with his oxcart. It got dark on him coming over El Roblón, the highest mountain in Zapotal. He was walking ahead of the oxen carrying a copper lamp, and his little five-year-old boy was sitting at the back of the open cart."

Little Hugo stared out into the dark. The crickets were chirping their evening song. The leaves of the avocado tree that hung over the house moved slightly as the evening wind passed by. The dripping leaves made funny shapes and shadows in the light of the candles. Hugo shivered and snuggled in closer to his father's chest.

"As Simón traveled up the hill in the dark, his boy sat back in the oxcart, facing the darkness behind them. Suddenly the boy yelled, 'Papito! Papito! An animal!'

"Simón stopped and ran back to see what his son wanted. Pointing into the darkness, the boy told his daddy that a big animal was following them. 'I saw him, Papito!' The boy was obviously shaken, but Simón didn't really think it was anything to be scared of, so they kept going.

"Soon the boy screamed harder. 'Papito! He's getting closer! I'm scared!'

"Simón ran back again, his ox goad ready, and peered into the dark night. Nothing. Whatever it was had disappeared again. The little boy was very frightened now. Even Simón felt uneasy. But he kept going.

"Suddenly the little boy screamed loudly. Again Simón ran back to see what was going on. The boy had disappeared. Simón heard a crashing in the brush at the jungle's edge. He tried to follow, but the jungle was too thick and his light too small, and he didn't have a machete to cut a trail."

Teodolinda's pigs were sleeping under the porch. One of them grunted, and little Hugo jumped in fright. Everybody laughed at him, but Hugo looked like he was ready to cry.

Andrés continued. "The next morning Simón and a bunch of us neighbors went to search for the boy. We took my hound dogs to follow the tracks. It didn't take them long at all to find a huge hollow tree stump that had broken off about twenty feet from the jungle floor. The dogs jumped up at the trunk opening and howled as if they had treed something. The men started to chop a hole at the bottom of the tree.

"Almost immediately a big mama mountain lion jumped out on the tree trunk's edge. Simón shot her on the spot. *Bang!*"

Little Hugo jumped again.

"Once the big mountain lioness fell to the ground, we could see that her tummy was bulging. We were afraid we knew what that meant. We men listened closely and heard tiny meows from within the tree trunk. We opened up the trunk some more and found three little cougar babies. Their tummies were also bulging. Then we found pieces of the little boy's clothes strewn around the den.

"That was a sad day in Zapotal. From then on everyone respected the *león* highly. That's the only time I have known a *león* to actually eat a person."

After the story finished, even the adults sighed with relief. The men worked on Andrés' bottle again with more fervor, and before long almost everyone had forgotten the sad story. But not Hugo. The scary story was seared into his little brain forever—and so was his fear of the *león*.

* * *

One night a few weeks later, Lico came home just after midnight. The dogs barked fiercely and woke the household. Marcos, who had lingered after his evening visit, opened the door and held high his *churuca*. There stood Lico in the rain with Teodolinda's mare loaded high with paraphernalia. Looking over Marcos's shoulder, Teodolinda saw a cutoff barrel, a copper pipe . . . She could hardly believe her eyes—it was another still!

After everything was unloaded and hidden in Lico's bedroom, they sat around and talked. "What does this mean?" Teodolinda asked sternly, her hands on her hips and her eyes spitting fire.

Lico shrugged and mumbled, "Marcos found a good deal on a still. I wasn't sure if we should, but he was."

"Why didn't anybody ask me?" Teodolinda snapped.

"I forgot." Lico's voice was so quiet she could hardly hear him.

"You did not. You didn't ask because you knew I'd say no. Haven't we had enough problems with drinking and stills? Will we never learn?" Teodolinda was crying now.

"Luis agreed," Lico argued. "We're setting it up on shares."

Turning to Luis, Teodolinda asked sharply, "Does Manuela know about this?"

"Yeah, she knows. She doesn't mind."

"She doesn't mind? She will mind once the *resguardo* hauls you off to jail for two years! I will not go to jail again. Do you hear? This time the *men* go to jail!"

Young Marino spoke up. "Mamita, we will not let this still be found. And if they do get it, I will offer to go to jail. If we make *contrabando* without having to give Andrés half, we will make money."

"And," Gelo beamed, "if Andrés comes every Saturday, he will have to pay for every drink he takes! Dad, can you build me a box for the *fermento* tomorrow? The *resguardo* busted the last one to pieces."

Teodolinda never stood a chance. The boys started planning with Lico. Even young Aurelio was excited. Maybe by drinking a little he could be as important and fearless as Gelo. As Teodolinda left for the kitchen to brew some coffee, the men were planning a trapdoor in the floor where they would hide the still.

The very next day everybody pitched in. A long box had to be made, and a trapdoor in the bedroom. Once again, the *socolón* was forgotten.

The house was set on low stilts. In the back, they took out the floor and dug a pit. Then they stacked firewood around the pit. Anybody searching for anything could look under the house and see Teodolinda's pigs and stacks of firewood, right where all the Ticos kept their firewood. Then Lico made a neat trapdoor in his bedroom, and they placed the still parts in the pit and closed it up during the week it took to make the *fermento*.

About fifty yards behind the Valverdes' house was a little clearing in the jungle. The creek trickled around a bend for a perfect setup. Lico and Gelo put the box there. If the *resguardo* found the box of *chicha*, they would be very suspicious, but it was not illegal to make *chicha*. Saturday mornings they would set up the still before daylight and stoke the fire. By noon the *guaro* would be ready, and that night after dark they would store the gear away. The risk of being caught was only during those twelve hours. No one would suspect them of operating so close to the house.

The men also decided to hide the jugs better. They would never have gallon jugs in the house. They would only bring it inside in bottles, and they would always hide the bottles when they were not in use. They came up with dozens of good hiding places where the *resguardo* would never find them.

Luis showed up to help. He and Aurelio went to one of Don Tilo's farms to buy the *dulce* for the *fermento* and for the *guaro* making later.

Tilo's sugarcane mill was set up in a forest glade down by a small creek. When Luis and Aurelio got there, they found Conchita running the cane press with several of her boys.

Tilo Barrantes' original cane press.

The press consisted of a set of three upright bronze cylinders set up on a wooden base. On top of the cylinders a long beam was attached. At the end of the ten-foot-long beam, Tilo's spotted team of oxen walked in a circle, slowly pulling the pole, making the cylinder go around. The other two cylinders were fixed in place. Two of Conchita's sons fed stalks of sugarcane between the cylinders. The rotating cylinder pulled each stalk and crushed it against the solid ones. Aurelio was delighted to see the almost clear, yellowish, rich juice running out of a spout and into a bucket. He hoped Conchita would give him some cane juice to drink.

After Conchita stopped pressing, she gave Aurelio and Luis each a big glass full of the delicious juice. Soon the boys were draining the buckets into the huge iron kettle that Conchita already had piping hot with a roaring fire under it.

They stoked the fire under this big kettle encased in mud to cook the cane juice. Notice the homemade sieve they used to strain the trash off the cane juice as it boiled.

There the juice was cooked to make the different sugar products that people consumed in Zapotal. The first stage was called *miel* (honey), which was simply a thick cane juice used to sweeten drinks and food, or used like honey on bread. The next stage was *alfeñique,* the taffy stage, when it was pulled like taffy and twisted into funny shapes and sold as candy or sweetener.

The last stage made the most common product. Most Ticos liked it ladled into little round molds where, once cooled, it became the grainy, rich brown sugar they called *dulce.* These little brown cakes were then wrapped in dry sugarcane leaves, making a set of twin cakes called a *tamuga.*

When Conchita reached a stopping point, Luis announced, "We need ten *tamugas* of *dulce.*"

The thick cane molasses is ladled into these molds, then left to cool to make *dulce*.

Conchita immediately knew what they wanted the *dulce* for. Everybody who bought *dulce* in Zapotal bought it in small quantities, one *tamuga* at most. The only ones who bought in bulk had a still. But she did not say anything. She gladly accepted the payment, and they tied their heavy cargo onto Jabón's saddle and set out for home.

The next Saturday the Valverdes threw a huge party. True to their character, they ended up telling too many people, and half a dozen men stood at the still waiting for the *cabezón*. They had not invited the Quesadas, of course; they were enemies. But plenty of their enemies' friends were there, and the Quesadas would know the whole story by the next day.

Gelo got the boys to dump bucket after bucket of *chicha* into the cutoff barrel. Then he let everyone have a drink while he stoked the fire. Meanwhile, Marcos and Lidier brought in two chickens they had butchered and salted. They started a small fire off to the side and soon had the chickens turning over the coals on iron rods. By the time the chickens were sizzling, the steam in the copper pipe was condensing and ready to drip.

"Here it comes!" Gelo hollered, controlling the pressure with his thumb just like Andrés had taught him several years before. "Who gets the *cabezón?*"

Everyone pushed around, hoping to be the fortunate one. But as always, Lico hissed, "It's mine!"

Gelo obediently gave the best to his father; then everybody had a turn. They ate chicken and drank liquor.

Nobody really planned to start a ritual; it just happened. But from that day on, several people had an important appointment with the Valverdes every Saturday. When the chickens became scarce, they stole them from people who did not eat their chickens while drinking *contrabando.*

It had been less than three months since the first still was closed, and the second was going strong.

*   *   *

Off and on, most of Lico's children got some schooling. Usually the children between eight and ten years old walked together to Tajo Alto, since Zapotal did not have a school. School started at the peak of dry season, so it made for a nice walk to school on the dry trails. But about three months later, the rainy season started, and the Valverde children often stopped going. It took an hour and a half for the children to walk, one way, in dry season. When the rains came, not only did they get soaked in the heavy afternoon rains, but the trails got so muddy it was impossible to keep the children clean.

But there was another reason the Valverde children often dropped out of school after several months. They fought too much. Gelo had gone to school and learned to read and write before he got sick. Aurelio and his sisters had traveled together for parts of three years. Since Aurelio was small, quiet, and laid back, he tried his best to make up for it by fighting. Just like Gelo, he thought that was the only way he could succeed and be somebody. But his teacher soon got tired of it and sent a note to his parents. So, like many other mountain people, Lico just took his children out of school.

*   *   *

A howling *temporal* hit Zapotal like a blizzard, but instead of blowing snow, it blew cold, wet rain. It was December, the coldest month of the year. Amable, Leyla, and Mireya were the big girls now and did all the housework so Mamita could help make the living outside. Before, the Valverdes had worked together to plant. But more and more the married children worked on their own so their income would not be drained by their father's drinking. Teodolinda dealt with them whenever she could. Only Luis stuck with his father, not because of friendship, but because of the still. Though his wife Manuela hated it, Luis thought the still meant easy money. But Teodolinda and her wiser sons were proving that money was best earned by growing vegetables and hanging on to their cash.

During this *temporal,* Teodolinda was harvesting cabbages with Ángel, so Amable got up early and made the coffee. She saw all the outside workers off, including her mother. Then Leyla milked the cows while Mireya cooked the main meal that would be taken to the fields at ten o'clock.

While Leyla was milking, the children got up, cold and hungry. Dressed in tatters, they asked Amable for their *ponche* (punch). This *ponche* was a mighty concoction. First Amable gave them each a big plastic cup. Then she poured in several ounces of cane juice for sweetening. Next she reached behind the firewood and pulled out the bottle of *guaro.* She poured a shot into each cup before shooing them out the door.

Little Hugo was first in the line-up by the cow. While they waited, their teeth chattered in the cold air, and they wiggled their bare toes in the mud.

"Come, Hugo, you first," Leyla said. And one by one Leyla took their cups and filled them with stream after stream of milk shot straight from the teat. Then the children grabbed their full, foaming glasses and drained them before running back to the house.

The small shot of *guaro* was not enough to intoxicate the children, but the alcohol did warm them and give them a little boost that perked them up for the day. What no one realized was that they were creating in their children a thirst for liquor. If the older Valverdes feared the bottle only a little, this next generation would not fear it at all.

19

One forenoon Don Lico was relaxing on his front porch. The boys had all gone to work. Little Hugo, at home with his Papito, started for the spring for a drink.

The spring was special to the Valverdes. It gurgled out of the bank beside the creek that ran right past the house. The creek was lined with lovely woods on either side. Not only was the forest dressed in the greenest, lushest plants, but everything was swaddled in moss, some of which hung like green Christmas decorations from the gnarled branches. Birds and flowers finished off the beautiful scene.

Now as Hugo approached the spring, he paused and watched what the family called their hummingbird bush. Right where the bank dropped down to the spring was a jungle bush that for several months out of the year was decked out in white sweet-smelling flowers. It attracted hummingbirds by the dozens.

When Hugo first approached the bush, the birds all zoomed away. But Hugo held perfectly still and the hummingbirds returned. Little hermits, long-tailed hermits, fiery-throated hummingbirds, and best of all, the large violet saberwings that zoomed in and chased all the rest away. Hugo was enchanted.

Hugo turned when he heard Tachito ride in on his ugly black stallion. Tachito jumped off his horse and strode toward Lico, his ever-handy twenty-two rifle in hand. After greetings, Lico asked, "And what are you out shooting today?"

"Anything I can find," Tachito answered. Tachito was a sharp-shooter. No one in all Zapotal could shoot as precisely as he. The problem was that he knew it. "I can hit anything the eye can see," Tachito bragged, as usual.

Looking toward Hugo, he noticed the hummingbird bush. "Ah, now I know what I came to shoot. Do you think I could peck off one of those hummingbirds hovering in the air?" he asked, his eyes gleaming.

Hugo did not think he could. The little birds were so fast, flitting back and forth like little bullets. But Lico egged him on. "Do you think you could actually hit the little guys? I doubt it. You're good, but not that good."

"Well, let's see," Tachito grinned, a twinkle in his eyes.

Hugo held his breath. He did not want the man to kill his little friends.

A long-tailed hermit hummingbird flitted up to the bush. He plunged his long curved beak into a flower. Tachito was about fifteen yards away, poised and ready. *Bang!* The lovely brown tuft of feathers dropped to the ground.

Lico shook his head in wonder. Hugo picked up the little bird and ran for the house. He did not want to see more. Tachito the sharp-shooter could just keep on shooting. Hugo wanted nothing to do with it.

Out in the yard Lico and Tachito drank and talked. "Did you hear that the new saloon, La Puentera, is finished?" Tachito asked Lico.

"Yeah, I heard," Lico growled. "They say it's the Quesadas' pride and joy. I can imagine them strutting all over the place bragging about their wonderful saloon. But the truth of the matter is, they can't compete with us."

After Tachito left, Lico returned to his hammock on the porch. His thoughts clung to the news. La Puentera Saloon was a thorn in the

Valverdes' flesh. It was built well, with a tin roof and boards sawed by a nine-foot saw just like the Valverdes had. La Puentera was the first real saloon in Zapotal. *Guaro contrabando* had been available off and on, but never real whiskey, and never beer. The Quesadas bragged that they would never stoop to selling *contrabando* like the Valverdes did. Not that they had any scruples about drinking the stuff. Nor did Lico believe it would have bothered their consciences to make it.

There were two reasons why old Durando Quesada did not want to make *contrabando*. The main one was because the Valverdes made it. The other was that Durando had somehow managed to be chosen as the *oficial de paz* for Zapotal. That meant he was supposed to make peace between the people and the government. He was a sort of home-made judge that the government would back, which meant he could help close down the stills.

The Quesadas were fast realizing that as long as the Valverdes made *contrabando,* their saloon could not compete. They had to pay taxes; the Valverdes did not. The only thing the Valverdes had to invest in a batch of *contrabando* was rotting fruit, some firewood, and the *dulce*. The Quesadas knew they would have to shut down the second still if they wanted their saloon to succeed.

The Valverdes were confident that the Quesadas would not turn them in again. Wasn't everyone tired of fighting by now? The Valverdes were ready to let bygones be bygones. Or most of them were.

One Saturday evening Teodolinda's brother Ángel stopped in to visit. As usual, he was tipsy and wanted to drink with the Valverdes, where he could drink to his heart's content without having to pay. The Valverdes were already starting to work on their new batch of *guaro*. Soon they were all laughing and talking.

Teodolinda was cooking. She knew Ángel would demand food. He often wanted special morsels cooked just as he liked them, and he got violent when he did not get what he wanted.

Lico did not like Ángel. Especially since he had tried to slash Lico with his *cutacha*. But he put up with him just to avoid a scene. The Valverdes walked the line whenever Ángel Soto came around drunk.

The sky was a pale turquoise-blue, tinted pink toward the west. Hundreds of swallows darted across the azure sky catching the evening insects for their meal. Teodolinda stood at the window and stared at the sky, but she did not smile at the swallows' antics. She did not appreciate the splash of color that beautified the dome between the silhouettes of the jungle's giant trees. She dreaded the evening.

In need of some strength, she took a walk out behind the house and found the jug. *I'll just take several sips on the sly. I need to be prepared,* she thought.

Once the food was ready, Ángel started complaining. "Don't we have any meat? Hey, let's get some meat around. Sister, where are your chickens? Why didn't you butcher one? I'll pay for it," he promised, though he had never paid for one yet.

Teodolinda hesitated.

"You don't trust me to pay you, do you?" he growled.

"We can butcher a chicken," Teodolinda said slowly. "It's just that it's late, and by the time—"

"Late? What do you mean? It's just six o'clock, and we have the whole night to party! Aurelio, go catch that chicken!"

Teodolinda cleaned the chicken. The girls fried it. While the meat was being prepared, Ángel suddenly remembered that they needed music. "Hey, where is the radio? We need some entertainment!"

Teodolinda's heart fell further. This was not the first time Ángel had asked for music. And after the music started, he would want to dance. Teodolinda had danced several times in her youth, but she had never enjoyed it. She especially hated dancing with her brother Ángel.

The girls brought the radio that Gelo had bought recently. In his drunken haste, Ángel could not make it work. Cursing, he called the girls to help him. Soon a lively *ranchera* filled the air. Ángel jumped up and, knocking his chair over, began to yell the typical Latin yell. *"Uuuiippiippiiaa!* Come on, sister dear, let's dance!" he said with a burp.

Teodolinda was repulsed by her drunken brother but, not wanting to make a scene, she strode over and grabbed his arms. They began to circle and sway to the music. Teodolinda actually had to help Ángel keep his balance, or he would have crashed to the floor halfway through the song.

After the song, Ángel flopped back into his chair, sweating and panting. He was heavyset and aging, so he tired quickly. But ten minutes later another *ranchera* struck his fancy and he made Teodolinda dance with him again. The younger children thought it was big sport to see their mother high-stepping and careening around the room with a fat drunk. But the older ones pitied her, knowing how she hated these scenes.

The chicken was almost ready. The smell wafted into the room and made the men hungry. Ángel seemed subdued, but then an especially wild ranchera began, and Ángel staggered to his feet. "Where is Leyla? I want to dance with her!"

Leyla was an attractive seventeen-year-old. Lico and the boys protected her. They had never dreamed that Ángel Soto would ask to dance with her. She was already back in the bedroom, ready for bed. When she heard Ángel's request, she yelled, "I don't want to dance."

Ángel's face clouded, but not as much as Lico's and the older boys'. Ángel Valverde, the oldest son at home, cleared his throat in warning. He raised his hand, motioning to his father to just stay out of it.

"What? You mean to say that my cute little niece won't dance with me? I don't like that. I don't think that's very respectful. I'm not asking for anything bad, just a little fun."

Ángel Valverde's voice was edged with steel. "She is not going to dance." He rose to his feet, slowly and carefully.

Ángel Soto swung around, clearly upset with his namesake. "It's none of your business!"

"Hey, it's all of our business!" Lico snapped, rising to his feet too.

Teodolinda knew she had to act, or fists would fly. She was over fifty years old, but still as quick as a deer. She flew around her son and, stepping up to her brother, she sang cheerily,

"Come, my prince, come dance with me,
All evening long I've searched for thee."

Ángel's wrath abated, and they danced the tension away. As soon as the dance was over, Teodolinda cooed to her brother, "The chicken is ready. Let's go eat."

After her brother finally left, Teodolinda closed up the house. She thought everyone was asleep, but as she tiptoed into her bedroom, she saw a movement under the bed. Holding the candle low, she found little Hugo sneaking a swig from Lico's bottle. Teodolinda scolded him and sent him to bed. Before she closed the last window, she peered into the darkness. The nighthawks were silent. Only the frogs peeped and chirped. Right above the house a kinkajou whistled its distressed call as it tottered from branch to branch.

As Teodolinda listened to the night noises, she meditated on their lives. Tears welled in her eyes as she thought what a tyrant her brother had become. She pitied his wife and children. At least her Lico was reasonable, even when he drank.

Now little Hugo was already sneaking liquor. All of her men were drunkards, and even her baby was becoming one. She breathed a short prayer to the Virgin Mary asking her help for their sinful lives. But peace would not come to her sad heart for a long, long time.

20

Luis stood by the public trail and looked at his new house. He had borrowed money to buy a tiny piece of land from his father-in-law—a flat lot surrounded by trees in the very heart of Zapotal and close to the main trail. Manuela was happy because her parents lived just across the trail from their perfect spot.

After Luis and Manuela's marriage, they had lived with the Valverdes briefly. Then he had built a small shelter beside a creek on the Valverde farm. But during a terrific rainstorm, the creek had become a raging river and washed the little house away. Luis and Manuela and their first baby Lillian had barely escaped to higher ground.

Now, finally, Luis had built a real house. Luis and Ángel had sawed the boards from a tropical cedar, the best lumber Zapotal had to offer. The house was larger than most houses in Zapotal, with a big living room in the center, a bedroom at one end, and a lean-to kitchen at the other. Nestled among the trees, it had a wooden floor and a tin roof. It was Luis's pride and joy, and Manuela was delighted.

Luis told people he and Lidier were going to put in a store. In the main room of his new house he built shelves for merchandise. At first they did business through a big window right beside the door. Luis was sure he was finally going to make some money.

Though Luis did not tell anybody, from the start he had planned to sell *guaro contrabando.* The problem with selling the liquor at Lico's place was that half of the *guaro* was guzzled by family friends, and no one paid for it. And those men never bought liquor during the week. They only came around during the Saturday rituals when the drink ran free. *Now,* Luis gloated smugly, *everyone pays for his liquor.*

Though many didn't know it, Luis's store was a saloon before it was finished. But soon Luis built a bar like that of the La Puentera Saloon and invited drinkers into his living room to drink. This made the Quesadas angry. They knew they could not put off shutting down the Valverde still any longer if they wanted to stay in business.

Everyone just called the new place Luis's store. But with time, the very character of that wild place would demand a name.

* * *

Don Lico decided the family needed a larger house closer to Luis's store, since someone from home usually went to help Luis sell or to help Manuela with the housework. So Lico bought another piece of land and built a house at a place called Las Marimbas (the xylophone) because of the trail right past their house, which had an awful hill that got very muddy in rainy season. The horses' hooves turned it into a series of troughs that, from a distance, looked something like a xylophone.

After moving to their new home, they dismantled the still under cover of darkness and set it up in the woods just behind the house. Lidier also built a new house just across the creek from the still. They put in a false floor in Lico's house where they hid the still when it was not in use. The whole family carefully kept things hidden and watched for the *resguardo*, determined that no one would find their still.

At first things went well for Luis and Lidier. They made a little profit. Luis would borrow his father's horses once a week and travel to Miramar for merchandise. Gelo made the *guaro*. Manuela or someone from home helped run the store and the saloon when Luis and Lidier were away.

As the Valverde saloon drew more and more people on the weekends, fewer and fewer frequented the Quesadas' saloon. The Valverde *guaro* was more potent and so much cheaper. And with the clients came the wild parties and the fights.

The best customers at the new saloon were the Valverdes themselves. For them the drinks were free, so after the Saturday parties at the still, the grown boys took the liquor straight to the saloon and practically moved into the store for the weekends. Manuela cooked for them, and there was plenty of room to sleep in the big living room.

Being a loner, Lico preferred drinking at home. But at home he had to face his feisty little wife, who constantly pecked at him for his drinking habit, so he started taking his liquor to the sugarcane patch. At first Teodolinda would search for him or send the children to find him. But as time went on, everybody accepted his strange habit and left him alone. That was what he wanted anyway. Often he spent his Saturday nights in the cane field, too drunk to find his way home.

What Manuela had thought would be the perfect place turned out to be utterly miserable. The first problem was the lack of privacy. Her home's main room was the store, the bar, the social room, and the dance hall. And she had never dreamed she would have to take care of all the Valverde men every weekend. Sure, either Teodolinda or one of the girls always came to help, but the party and all the work was at her house. Though fewer came during the week, it seemed that someone was always in her home. And her own husband's drunken behavior disgusted her.

One Saturday forenoon, the Valverde men were down at the still having their party. Even so, the saloon was full, and Manuela and Teodolinda could hardly keep up with the work. The men wanted food with their *guaro,* and this made them busier yet. Luis and Manuela's little Toño, their second child, was in the bedroom sleeping. Manuela was in the kitchen at the opposite end of the building with Teodolinda. Lillian, the oldest child, was sleeping in a hammock beside her. With the record player going, Manuela could not hear Toño. Every time she wanted to check on him, she had to traipse through the saloon.

After not hearing from the boy for over an hour, she went to check on him again. She found him in the saloon, trying to talk with a drunk. Toño was as sharp as a tack and not ashamed to talk to anybody. Everybody liked the friendly little chap. Though he was only two, he could already say many words and was a real clown. Now the drunken man was laughing uproariously to hear Toño try to talk. For Manuela it was the last straw.

Luis came back from the still and stood in the doorway, wondering what he should do next, besides drink some more. Manuela marched over to him and complained, "Luis, I can't take this anymore. We have no privacy. If I want to go from the kitchen to the bedroom to check on my babies, I have to walk through a bunch of drunks. I can't even hear my own children cry, and then when they wake up, they go talk with the drunks. What an example we are giving them! Luis, we need to do something different."

"What can we do?" Luis mumbled.

"Why don't we close the saloon during the day, at least, so we can be alone?"

One of Luis's drinking buddies answered for him. "You are wrong, Manuela. You can't do that. This is a public place, and you can't close it. You just have to be patient. That's the way it is in a saloon!"

"You aren't a woman and can't understand!" Manuela snapped. "I wasn't talking to you anyway!"

The man laughed and turned to his buddies, who all agreed with him. They talked long, with drunken wisdom, about how wrong Manuela was. Luis was silent.

Manuela took little Toño and returned to her work in the kitchen. Teodolinda did not say a word, but she understood and pitied Manuela. She admired her for not stooping to drinking to forget her troubles. Already today, before noon, Teodolinda had sneaked several swallows to help her face the day.

Teodolinda could see that Manuela's relationship with Luis was deteriorating fast. Manuela's parents lived right across the trail from the saloon, and she was often tempted to just go home. But though Manuela was disgusted with her husband, she stuck with him and did her best to make the saloon a success.

That same Saturday afternoon, Juan Gonzales, a friend of the Quesadas, stopped by Luis's saloon. He was drunk. Jumping off his horse, he started cursing and hollering, "Luis, come out here! Today we are going to fight!" Luis was afraid. Juan Gonzales was a fierce fighter, and Luis knew he wouldn't stand a chance.

"Come on out, you coward! If you don't, I'm coming in to get you! Do you hear?"

Luis pulled a machete from under the bar. Suddenly his anger was stronger than his fear. "Come and get me! I'm ready anytime!"

Swearing again, Juan staggered up the steps. Luis stepped out from behind the counter holding his machete behind his back, but Teodolinda and Manuela were ready. They grabbed Luis from behind and wrestled the machete out of his hand. When Juan saw the machete, he turned and ran outside and found a stout pole.

Meanwhile, Lidier had arrived with a jug of fresh liquor. When he saw what was happening, he ripped a loose board off the wall and lurched to meet Juan, who was just coming through the door. Swinging the board hard, Lidier knocked the pole out of the drunken man's hands. The two tumbled down the steps into the yard, grabbing at each other and rolling in the grass. The fight ended when Lidier caught Juan's little finger between his teeth and bit down, hard, ripping it open and breaking the bone. Juan screamed and turned Lidier loose.

The fight was over—for the moment. But the fighting in Zapotal was not over. As long as the devil had free reign, as long as the *guaro* ran freely, as long as men did not meet with the Prince of Peace, there would be fighting. More—not less.

21

The sun seemed reluctant to wake the world that sad Sunday morning. It was still a little ways below the horizon when the birds began to sing, softly at first, then louder. Soon more birds joined in the chorus. Outside, the world seemed a happy place.

Inside the saloon, between the bedroom and the kitchen, several forms were slumped over in a doped sleep. It was very dark inside the building—in more ways than one.

Luis was sleeping in the bedroom. Manuela had hauled him in at midnight. Ángel Valverde was on the saloon floor, sleeping hard. Lidier had also spent the night there, his wife at home with her family and the babies. For once, Marcos was missing. He happened to be at his father-in-law's place, though he was as drunk as the rest. Gelo was lying in a corner, his crutches beside him. Marino was sleeping flat on his back on a bench. Belén was there. Even young Aurelio was drunk.

Teodolinda was sleeping in the kitchen in a hammock, exhausted after helping Manuela sell *guaro* all evening long. She was not as drunk as the men, but she was groggy and wrapped in the deep sleep of the intoxicated.

Suddenly the *resguardo* burst through the saloon door and found the sleeping bunch of drunks. The birds in the surrounding trees hushed their cheerful songs. The drunken men rubbed their eyes and sat up groggily.

"We are the *resguardo!*" the men dressed in green barked. "We are here looking for the still. We know you Valverdes own it."

The drunken men were suddenly wide awake. Aurelio, knowing that even one bottle of *guaro* could condemn them, grabbed a half-full bottle and slammed it against a corner post. A broken bottle was not evidence. But the bottle did not break, and the police grabbed it before he could try again.

"Too late, buddy! We have plenty of evidence. And we also know your still is hidden under the floor of your house. Take us there and open it up!"

Lidier stared at the *resguardo*. Looking up a shotgun barrel has a way of taming the toughest. He slowly rose to his feet and led the *resguardo* and the half-drunken Valverdes over to Lico's house. In no time the police had hauled all the junk out into the yard. One *resguardo* stood guard, making sure no one tried any tricks.

Soon it was over. They had a bottle, a jug of liquor, and the still itself. Plenty of evidence.

"Who goes with us this time?" the *resguardo* barked. "I won't take the old lady again!"

Marino remembered his promise. He grabbed one of the bottles the *resguardo* had missed. It still had a little guaro in it. He guzzled it down in one big draft. Then he staggered over to a rock in the yard and smashed the bottle against it. Holding the broken bottle by its neck, he announced, "I am going with you. No one else is going, just me. Do you hear?"

The *resguardo* smiled. It seemed funny that the fellow offering to go to jail would be defiant.

Marino was only twenty years old. He seemed pretty young to be going to jail, but no one else was willing. Filled with new courage, he continued, "Don't bother these people. I will pay the penalty. I am man enough!"

The *resguardo* loaded the still equipment, handcuffed Marino, and left. The women and even several of the men were crying as they watched him leave. Once the *resguardo* dropped into the green jungle surrounding the saloon, everyone started talking at once.

"This time the Quesadas will pay!" Lidier hissed. "The last time we let it pass, but this time we will take our revenge!"

"That's right!" Belén growled. "They aren't making any money at all since we opened our saloon. If we start up another still right away and keep liquor prices down, their saloon will go under."

Luis slunk out of the bedroom and joined them. All the men agreed to Belén's plan. First they would beat the Quesadas until they were afraid of the Valverdes, then they would break their business. Only then could the Valverdes reign supreme in the Zapotal booze war.

They all looked up when they heard a noise at the kitchen door. There stood Teodolinda, crying. Manuela stood right behind her. "Boys," Teodolinda pleaded, "what are you saying? Are you planning to keep on in your wickedness until you get killed? Isn't this enough of a lesson? A twenty-year-old has been hauled off to jail for who knows how long. Don't you understand a mother's suffering? What will stop you? Will you fight the Quesadas forever? Will there never be peace in Zapotal again?"

"Aw, come on, Mamita," Gelo pleaded. "The Quesadas are determined to break us. We can't allow them to run over us!"

"These things happen so we will stop drinking and reform our lives," Teodolinda argued, "but you want to get right back into it again. You never learn. I am tired of this life. Look at you lazy bums. The *socolón* is all grown up in weeds, and you can't even find time to go clean it. We are poorer today than we have ever been, yet we have a huge crew of workers who should be happily raking in money. I am sick of this lifestyle."

The boys did not answer. Some knew Teodolinda was right, but no one was ready to pay the price of peace. Not yet. Most were determined to rebuild the still and show the Quesadas what was what.

Lidier shook his head. "Mamita, do you realize what the Quesadas are doing? I don't think you know what all happens. Yesterday I sent my son Lalo to buy bread at La Puentera. He had ten colones in his pocket. As he walked along the trail through the strip of jungle where the banks are high, two boys jumped down over the bank and stole his money. Then they beat him up. You know Lalo is not a boy to get into trouble. Can you guess who the boys were?"

"I don't know," Teodolinda admitted.

"Nelson and Uriel, Marcos and Nena's boys. Your grandchildren! Now, you know good and well that if the parents didn't agree, the boys would never do something like that. If my boy came home with ten stolen colones, I would tan his hide until he couldn't sit for a week. I'd make sure he never did it again."

Everybody nodded. Even Teodolinda. Would the problems with the Quesadas never end?

*　　*　　*

The first night, the police held Marino at the station in Miramar. The next day they sent him to the Puntarenas jail. He endured that horrible place for two months, stuck in a cell with other drunks and druggies. He had to sleep on pieces of cardboard on the hard cement floor. The whole place was rampant with bedbugs and other creatures that tried to eat him alive and kept him awake at night. The latrine was a cement box over a stinky hole, right out in the open.

After almost losing his mind in the Puntarenas jail, Marino asked to be moved to the national penitentiary. Instead they sent him to San Lucas, an island off the coast of Puntarenas that was once a grand nine-hundred-*manzana* ranch. It was a spacious old place with dilapidated ranch buildings. Years before Marino was born, the Costa Rican government had taken the island and converted it into a prison. Though no one had ever dreamed the island was close enough to the mainland for an escape, over the years several prisoners had swum the few kilometers to shore and to freedom. Several had also drowned in the attempt.

When Marino got to San Lucas, ten big cement bunkhouses were perched on the hilltop with a grand lookout over the dock and the gulf beyond. The bunkhouses sheltered the normal prisoners. Marino got stuck in the ninth bunkhouse with nineteen other men. Right in the center of the bunkhouses was a special cage for the worst prisoners. It was a circular arena covered with mesh. All around this strange arena were cement cells, half buried in the hillside. The worst prisoners lived in these horrid cells and were loosed on occasions into the arena to get sunlight and exercise.

One of the first things Marino learned at San Lucas was to defend himself. Even the guards enjoyed watching the many fights, and they generally closed their eyes to the inmates' wicked acts. The first day, Marino gained the respect of the inmates in bunk nine when he fought off four men who wanted to humble him and make him their servant. The message was clear: Watch out for the young scamp from Zapotal.

A big dark fellow called El Negro (The Black One), from the east coast of Costa Rica, befriended Marino from the start. He taught Marino how to sharpen a kitchen spoon by rubbing it for hours on the cement, making a weapon as keen as a knife.

Marino was also determined to build up his body like El Negro's, so he started playing soccer with the other inmates and lifting weights. Soon the skinny Zapotal fellow had put on muscle, and he grew darker from spending so much time in the sun. But not only his body grew tougher and blacker; so did his soul. Marino took to San Lucas's wickedness as a duck to water. If he had been bad when he came, he was many times worse when he left five months later.

San Lucas had several programs for inmates. They cultivated large gardens, raised cattle, milked several cows, and kept chickens. The place actually looked like a real farm. Though Marino got into scraps with his fellow inmates, he tried his best to be friendly and respectful to the guards. Once a friend visited him and gave him forty colones. He shared it with one of the guards. Such actions soon earned him privileges many others did not have.

Toward the end of his stay, Marino got a cooking job in the kitchen. With plenty of food and exercise, his body filled out even more. Marino looked better than any Valverde ever had.

One evening Marino walked to the edge of the hilltop overlooking the gulf toward Puntarenas and sat on one of the old cannons cemented into the hill. He felt lonely. It had been seven months since he had left home, and he missed his people. He gazed up into the mountains. Though the weather was hot and dry on the island, he knew it was cool and wet in distant Zapotal. Big white clouds hung over the continental divide. The thought of Zapotal's cool, wet climate made Marino's skin tingle. Oh, how he longed for home!

*   *   *

Back home, the Valverdes were furious. They were determined to get even with the Quesadas. Two opportunities soon arose.

Marcos approached his father about the first one. "Look, Dad, I made a bad mistake when I married into the Quesada clan. Adelia, Nena's mom, is a hag. I can't get along with her at all. And it's no secret that they all hate our family. I have several children now, and we are so poor that we often don't have enough to eat. Let's put in another still, and this time I will help you keep them out of it. I can do that, since I live with them. We will make this still impossible to discover. I will help run it for part of the profit."

"Where can we find another still?" Lico asked thirstily.

"I already have one lined up," Marcos gloated. "They offered it to the Quesadas the other day, but since they knocked you out, they want to try to make a go of it with the legal stuff. But if we make *contrabando*, we'll make them go under. I'll go get the still tonight if you give me the money . . ."

One week later the Quesadas were shocked to learn that Luis's saloon was selling *contrabando* again. This time they could not find out from Marcos what was going on. Not even Nena and her sharp tongue could get a peep out of him.

The still was very well concealed in the thickest jungle in a deep canyon, and there was no trail to it. Everything was done under cover of night. The only thing the Zapotal folks knew was that there was *guaro contrabando* at Luis's store again. And they flocked there for cheap liquor and a wild time.

*   *   *

One night a neighbor held a *rosario*. Even with a *temporal* blowing in cold fog and rain, people poured in. The night got loud and boisterous.

During the *Panadera* Durando Quesada had the nerve to plop Vicente Jiménez's hat on Gelo's head. Everyone was shocked. They knew Gelo could not dance. As soon as the hat landed on his head, the Quesadas started hooting and howling, and the Valverdes started scowling. But Gelo saved the day by surprising everyone. He leaped onto the floor and hopped around the hall on one foot and his crutches. His hair had grown long, and he wore a red bandanna tightly wrapped around his forehead. His crooked leg and foot hung shamelessly outside his pants, the leg twisted and sticking right up his back past his waist. His floppy little foot actually bumped against his lower back when he hopped.

But what really struck those watching closely was not Gelo's grotesque shape and strange hopping. It was the fierce glare in his eyes. That, and the seemingly impossible maneuvers Gelo performed, made people wonder. Someone hissed, "That wild Valverde cripple is a witch!" And soon the rumor was flying across Zapotal.

But those who knew Gelo knew he was not a witch, just a lonely young man determined to be somebody. His eyes glowed with determination—and with growing anger at the Quesadas.

Later that night Gelo and his brothers were alone, still drinking. The wind screeched at the cracks and did its best to make them miserable, but the people inside felt warm from the strong drink and dancing. Gelo had a crazy idea.

"Boys, tonight we are going to drink beer," he announced. "I am tired of drinking *guaro*."

"Where will we get beer? The only place you can buy beer in Zapotal is at La Puentera, and they are already closed at this hour," Belén reminded him.

"You wait and see," Gelo bragged, the gleam in his eyes brightening.

The three Valverdes rode out at midnight. They hunched low in their raincoats, but the wind was strong and drove the rain through the stitching and cracks. As they rode, Gelo hollered again, "We will have beer to warm us up tonight!" The others laughed. But Gelo shook his mane and roared, "You will have all you want, boys!"

When they pulled in at La Puentera, Aurelio nearly panicked. Gelo was determined to do something crazy. Franklin Quesada, the bartender, was fast asleep. There was no way he would open the saloon at midnight. But Gelo motioned to his comrades, and they tied their horses to the fence and draped their raincoats over their saddles. Gelo pulled his *cutacha* from the sheath tied under the stirrup.

At the door of the saloon, Gelo shouted, "Franklin, open up! We want some beer."

Silence.

"Franklin, it's Gelo Valverde. Open up if you don't want any trouble!"

A rooster crowed in a tree behind the house.

"Franklin, open quickly before I get mad. Hurry!"

The silence seemed loud. Inside, Franklin whispered to his wife, "If it's only Gelo, I am not afraid."

Suddenly Gelo and his brothers lost patience. His brothers kicked the door as Gelo beat it with his crutches. The door gave way in splinters and pieces.

Gelo hobbled inside, his *cutacha* in one hand. Franklin crouched inside the door with a piece of hose in his hand. His wife was behind him, holding his machete. Up until tonight Franklin had been sure he could handle Gelo. But now he wasn't sure. In the light of the *canfinera*, Gelo's glaring eyes and dripping hair gave him a menacing appearance.

Gelo pointed at Franklin and hissed, "No tricks, okay?"

Franklin took a small step backward. Gelo pointed to a bench by the wall and barked, "Sit right there and behave! We are going to drink beer!"

Turning toward Franklin's wife, he ordered, "Get back into the kitchen with that machete!"

Franklin and his wife obeyed.

Gelo and his brothers gathered at the bar and drank beer and laughed and talked for almost an hour. They hinted at how they were going to get even with their enemies someday—especially those who always turned them in to the *resguardo*. But Franklin did not open his mouth.

After drinking all they wanted, the boys stumbled outside, and Gelo hobbled over to Franklin. "Okay, give me the bill."

Franklin quoted a price and Gelo handed over the money. Then he hobbled out into the night.

Later Franklin told his family what had happened. Glancing at Marcos, Franklin continued. "Boys, I feel trouble in the air. Gelo and Luis are angry enough to do something drastic. I am not scared of any of them if they would fight fair. Don Lico and Lidier won't try any tricks. But Gelo and Luis and Belén are another story. I just don't trust them at all."

*   *   *

One night after work, the whole Valverde family had gathered around the fire in the kitchen to ward off the cold. "I really wonder how it's going with Marino since they moved him to San Lucas," Teodolinda said. "Shouldn't someone go visit him?"

"I'll go," Lidier announced. "I have some money from cabbage I raised."

"That's good," Lico agreed. "Who knows what that poor boy faces in a wild place like that? We don't even know if he's alive."

They agreed that Lidier would go see Marino the next Sunday, and the conversation moved on to other matters, some serious and some light. Little Hugo was sitting at his father's feet, hoping someone would tell an interesting story. No dramatic story was told that night, but Lico did talk about something Hugo never forgot—the *Sagradas Escrituras.**

Hugo gazed intently at his father while he talked. Don Lico's face was unshaven and boney thin. His expression was serious in the candlelight. His hollow eyes seemed to glow.

"See, when I was young, my dad used to own a *Sagradas Escrituras,*" Lico began. "And do you remember how we borrowed one from Uncle Tino from Tajo Alto? Thousands of years ago, God sent us that book," Lico continued. "He inspired the saints to write it. It is also called God's Word."

"But the priests say we can't understand it," Teodolinda threw in. "Only people who have studied can understand it and teach it."

"That might be true," Lico continued. "But remember when we had Uncle Tino's Bible in our home? I read from it every night, and even the children could understand the stories. And during that time we felt God's blessing on our home. We don't anymore. All we do is drink and fight.

"The book tells about the end of the world. It says Jesus will come again, and that a great fire will come and burn up this world. It says good people go to Heaven, but bad people get burned up with Satan. That's what my dad used to tell us."

Hugo glanced at his mother and noticed tears in her eyes. She agreed with his father. *That must be one powerful book,* Hugo concluded. And a longing arose in Hugo's breast to someday see and read the *Sagradas Escrituras.*

---

* sacred Scriptures

22

"Mother, I want to move to a place called Chachagua," Luis told Teodolinda one day. She was cooking in the kitchen, and he was leaning on the *molendero*, enjoying a rare chat. Visiting was something no one had much time for anymore because of the saloon. But today was Wednesday, and they were not as busy as during the awful weekends. Manuela was at home with her mother, and Luis took advantage of the opportunity to talk to his mom.

"When Manuela and I went to pick coffee in San Ramón last month, we met the Solanos. Do you remember them?"

"Yes," Teodolinda said. "They used to be Zapotal people but moved to some place far away, right?"

Luis nodded. "After we were done picking coffee, they invited me to go home with them. We walked down the mountains on beyond San Ramón. Chachagua is a little town in the foothills of the mountains. It's hot as a firecracker, but it's nice land. They invited me to move there. It is not as cold as here, and things grow well. I could sell the saloon and buy some land."

"You say stuff grows well there?" Teodolinda asked. "Stuff grows well here too, but you don't plant anything. Why move?"

"Mamita, you know the real reason I have to move."

"Why?" she asked, though she already knew the answer.

"I have too many enemies here," Luis answered hesitantly. "The Quesadas and I are at the point where someone is going to get hurt badly. And now old Juan Gonzales is going around saying he's going to kill me. Mamita, I didn't tell you, but I just bought a pistol. It was that, or get killed."

"Luis! I wish you wouldn't have! And yet I know what you are saying is true. Maybe you should move. What does Manuela say?"

"She doesn't want to move, but she knows we have to. Why don't you talk to Dad about it and give me some advice? I really don't know of any other option."

"Who would buy the saloon?"

"Ángel says he will buy part of it. I have been making payments ever since I got that loan from the bank in Miramar. He will give me the money he has and finish making my payments. That's not enough, but I thought maybe you would buy a share."

"I'll think about it and talk to your father. I just bought that cheap piece of land across the hill and don't have much cash right now, but I know you have to move, and the sooner the better. Maybe in Chachagua you can change your ways and stop drinking."

"That's exactly what I want, Mother. I can't go on like this. Manuela is threatening to leave me, and you know how I love my children. This could be the last chance I have with Manuela."

Teodolinda noticed the tears in her son's eyes. At that moment she knew she would buy the saloon. But in her heart she longed for the same chance Luis had. Oh, if she could just forget all her troubles, pack her bags, and follow her son to that far-off place called Chachagua! Surely then she could make a new start! Maybe someday she could also move to Chachagua.

*　　*　　*

The next Saturday, Luis's saloon was filling up fast. A drunken man named Edgar was hollering at him from outside. At first Luis did not pay any attention to him, but the man continued yelling until Luis stepped to the door to see what was going on. Edgar kept on cursing and swinging his machete. He marched up to a small itabo tree that stood in front of the saloon and whacked it off with all his might. Luis retreated behind the bar, but soon the big fat man stumbled into the saloon, hollering at Luis to come out and fight.

Luis was shaking. In his pocket he had the pistol, but he was sober enough to know he should not use it. He was so close to closing a deal and moving to Chachagua. He would just have to beat this man up and forget it.

Luis met Edgar at the door and swung his fist, hitting him in the face and knocking him backward down the steps. Then he jumped down the steps himself. In a moment they were rolling in the dirt. Luis forced Edgar to the ground and bit his chest. But Edgar wrapped his big arms around Luis's neck and pulled his face into his chest until Luis couldn't breathe.

Beto and Juan Gonzales were among the spectators. Beto had married Luis's sister Leyla, but his brother Juan had been Luis's enemy since the recent fight when Lidier had intervened and bitten his finger. They both saw what was happening. Luis was thrashing his legs desperately.

Beto hissed, "Hey, we have to help Luis. Edgar's choking him to death!"

"Aw, just let him go," Juan laughed. "Dying a while would do him some good."

Luis knew Edgar would not let go until he was dead. His thoughts raced. If I could get to my pistol, *I would kill this beast . . . but there's no way. This man has a grip of iron. I never thought I would die this way, and I am not ready to die! I can't breathe! I am going to faint! I am going to die!*

"He's killing him!" Beto shouted, running to help. About half the crowd was glad he did. The other half was sorry. Beto jerked the big man's arms off Luis's neck and turned him loose.

Luis sat on the ground, weak and gasping for breath. Should he pull out his pistol and shoot the guy? Or . . . yes, Luis knew what he needed to do. He got up slowly and staggered toward the saloon. His saloon. Suddenly he hated it with all his heart. Once he reached the top step, he turned and looked the crowd over. He was overcome with emotion. His friends were there. Several of the Quesadas were there. Juan Gonzales was there. It was time to tell them the truth.

Taking a deep breath, he started. Luis had never been an orator, but he spoke sincerely. "I am going to leave this place. I can't live here anymore. I don't want to have to leave Zapotal on my way to jail or be carried out of here to my grave. I am leaving on my own accord. I am selling the saloon to my brother Ángel and my mother." Then Luis turned and escaped into the saloon.

Manuela was crying. She did not want to leave Zapotal, but under these conditions, she would. As soon as possible.

Teodolinda was not crying. She was proud of her son. Lico had never been impressed with Luis. She knew his weaknesses too, but suddenly she felt that Luis would change. He would move to Chachagua. He would stop drinking. He would reform. Oh, if only she could go with him! But no, she had to take the saloon on so he could leave. She was willing. She knew Ángel could never make it work on his own, so she would help him. Then maybe someday, after Luis changed, she would go live with him.

Luis moved the next week. It did not seem soon enough, but he got out of Zapotal safely. Teodolinda and Ángel took over the saloon, with Teodolinda in charge. And as things usually did when she ran them, it flourished. But it also doubled her already heavy workload. Because of the stress and strain, more and more she turned to the bottle for strength. Occasionally she even found herself puffing on Lico's cigars.

People flocked to the saloon on the weekends. And with the crowds came the fights. And with the fights, the fame. And with the fame, the name.

Nobody knows who first called Teodolinda's saloon La Peligrosa.* But somebody did, and it stuck. All over the Zapotal hills and throughout the surrounding towns the name became well-known. Its fame sped

---

* The Dangerous One

down the mountain until it reached Miramar, where it was known in homes, in churches, in schools, and even in the police station. Its fame reached all the way to San Ramón. And it reached Heaven's gate, where the heavenly Father looked down on the sad, wild saloon called La Peligrosa and knew it would not always be thus. No, the saloon would die, and its death would bring glory and honor to His name.

*　　*　　*

Nena Quesada, Marcos Valverde's wife, hated the Valverdes with a passion. Her husband, though he had married into her family, was still loyal to the Valverdes. Recently she had discovered that no secrets could be told in his presence, because he would tell his family everything. He had told them when the Quesadas turned them in to the *resguardo*. Not only that, he had started complaining to Teodolinda about his horrible marriage. And that really made Nena angry.

One day Teodolinda decided to talk to Nena. They lived just over the hill from each other. Through Nena's smart son Nelson, Teodolinda was able to choose a day when she knew Nena's parents were not at home.

Teodolinda hiked over the hill to the Quesadas' shack and politely asked to talk with Nena. Nena met her out on the porch and heard her out, scowling all the while, her smaller children clinging to her skirts. Teodolinda pitied them. She had heard that things were deteriorating in their home, but nothing had prepared her for the dirty, tattered little babies that clung to her filthy daughter-in-law.

"Nena," Teodolinda began, "I hear that you are having marriage problems. I know it's hard to be patient with a husband who drinks and carouses. But Marcos was like that when you married him. You knew that, didn't you? You should be patient with him and love him anyway."

"Yeah, I knew it," Nena snapped, wiping her baby's nose with her blouse. "But I didn't think he'd be a mama's boy and run home and tattle about everything that happens in his marriage."

"He comes home to get away from your sharp tongue," Teodolinda said. "And the last time he showed me the bump on his head where you hit him with a piece of firewood. How could I help but find out?"

"Well, I guess he'll just have to choose who he'll be loyal to—me or his little mama. If he lives here, he has to hear me out and do what pleases me." Nena's eyes were bright with anger.

"Well, I just came to give you some advice, that's all. I am concerned for my son and these five dear little grandchildren—"

"Well, you don't have to be so concerned, okay? It's really none of your business. You stay on that side of the hill, and we'll stay on this side, and we won't have any more trouble. The Quesadas and the Valverdes will never be friends. And I don't want your advice. I have my own mother to listen to."

Teodolinda was already walking away. Her daughter-in-law's tongue was too sharp for even her. As she hurried across the yard, she pitied her son and her grandchildren. The last thing she heard was Nena speaking to Nelson. "I don't ever want you to go back to that witch's house again, do you hear?"

Teodolinda was weeping when she walked into her house minutes later. Lico wondered what was wrong, but Teodolinda did not want to talk about it. Later she told him the sad story. Lico just shook his head and sighed.

*   *   *

One morning Gelo was riding up the long hill past the Quesadas' house, which was set in a ways from the trail, but was easily within shouting distance. Gelo's previous experiences at that spot made him speed up old Jabón and ride on the far side of the trail without glancing toward the house. Nevertheless, he heard Nena's voice.

"Hey, cripple, where are you going? To the moon?"

Gelo stole a glance toward the house. As usual, Nena stood at the window watching him ride past.

"Hey, horse!" Nena shouted. "Aren't you afraid of having a *león* on your back? Poor horse!"

Gelo looked away and rode on, determined not to argue with a woman, especially his sister-in-law. But then she started again. "When will you come fight with my brothers? They can lick you any day. You're a good-for-nothing cripple!"

Gelo shook his head like a *león*, spurred his horse into a gallop, and disappeared over the mountaintop. Long after he was out of earshot, the hate in his heart still burned hot against Nena and her brothers. Gelo vowed that he would get even. He hoped his opportunity would come soon.

It did.

The following Saturday morning, Gelo rode to a farm past El Roblón to brand some cattle for his father. He took eight-year-old Hugo along, riding double. On their way home they passed La Puentera. Against Hugo's protests, Gelo stopped for a drink. He tied Jabón to a tree and told Hugo to sit out in the shade until he was ready.

As soon as Gelo entered the saloon, the atmosphere thickened. Gelo tried to act totally at home. The others eyed him cautiously. He was not just the crippled boy from Zapotal anymore. Now he was a man—a desperate, unpredictable man who had a gripe with life, and especially with the Quesadas.

"Give me a beer!" Gelo demanded, hobbling to the bar. "Isn't this a good place to quench one's thirst?"

Nobody asked him why he didn't quench his thirst at La Peligrosa, where his *contrabando* ran free.

The saloon was nearly empty. Franklin Quesada was tending the bar, and his brother Alcides sat drinking not too far from Gelo. The Quesada-Valverde feud was at its peak. Gelo had bided his time and chosen this day to finally get even with the people who had sent his mother and brother to jail.

After enough drinks to get his blood running hot, Gelo took the plunge. "Alcides, what's the deal with that mare you stuck in my dad's field?"

Alcides swung around and looked at Gelo, his eyes full of drunken fire. "And why is that your business?"

"Well, if you sponge off my dad like that, I think I have a right to get involved. I'm here today to tell you to get that mare off our land, do you hear?"

Alcides was surprised. When not drinking, Gelo was usually quiet and timid. Alcides was bigger than Gelo, and he had always assumed that Gelo was scared of him. Jumping from his bar stool, he stood towering over Gelo. Gelo did not flinch.

"Since when can you tell me what I can or can't do?" Alcides barked. "Why don't you go home to your mama!"

Gelo sat still, his body tense. "You foul-mouthed Quesada," he said slowly, "today I give you solid warning. Get that mare off our farm, or else!"

Alcides swung his fist at Gelo's face. Gelo's twisted hands grabbed Alcides' forearm, warding off the blow. Gelo yanked the surprised Alcides toward him; then he pounced.

Though Gelo's legs were weak, his arms and chest were powerful. All Alcides could do was roll around on the ground with him, cursing and swearing. Gelo silently vented his hatred and rage toward the Quesadas for all the times they had mocked him and taken advantage of his family. His weapons were his teeth and his specially manicured fingernails, which were more like claws. All Alcides could do was howl and pound at him, but at such close quarters, his blows did little harm.

Hearing the ruckus, little Hugo flew to the saloon door and saw the men rolling on the floor like a pair of dogs. Fearing for Gelo's life, Hugo turned and ran the whole mile home as fast as his bare feet could take him, up the steep hill and down the other side. He raced into the house screaming, "They're killing Gelo down at La Puentera! They're killing Gelo!"

Fortunately, only Teodolinda and the girls were at home. Teodolinda asked no questions. She grabbed a machete and ran, her daughter Victoria running along beside her and Hugo racing behind.

Meanwhile, Gelo and Alcides rolled until they were exhausted. The other men, for once true to Zapotal rules, did not interfere. Finally, Alcides yelled, "Get this beast off me before he kills me! Help!"

Franklin walked around the bar and looked at the two. They were drenched in sweat and blood. Alcides's shirt was ripped to ribbons and his chest was a mass of chewed flesh.

"Franklin, get this beast off me!" Alcides screamed again.

Franklin grabbed Gelo by his hair and flung him toward the door.

Gelo landed on his back, gasping for breath. Alcides lay in a heap at the other end of the hall, bleeding and blubbering quietly. Franklin walked behind the bar, thinking the fight was over. But he froze when he heard Gelo speak in low, icy tones. "Boys, this is the day you die."

Gelo rolled over and dug into his pocket. His hand emerged with a small twenty-two revolver. Everyone froze.

There was often blood shed in Zapotal, but seldom was anyone killed. It was an understood rule. They beat each other up and occasionally used their *cutachas,* but they did not carry guns and shoot each other. No one had ever been shot in either saloon.

Franklin and Alcides stared helplessly. Gelo lifted the gun, aiming toward Franklin. Slowly, deliberately, Gelo talked on. "We Valverdes have been watching for this chance. You have tried to finish us off, but today I am finishing you off. Even if I go to jail for the rest of my life."

Franklin stood still as a statue, pale as a ghost. Alcides cried and cowered on the floor. Gelo aimed.

Teodolinda and Victoria approached the saloon noiselessly. Victoria reached the door first and took in the scene at a glance. Pouncing, she grabbed Gelo's forearm. Franklin leaped and jerked the gun from Gelo. He stuck it in his own pocket and stepped back, making way for the powerful little lady who burst through the door.

Teodolinda had seen Victoria tackle Gelo. Out of breath and almost crying, she lit into the drinking men, starting with Gelo.

"Gelo, where did you get that gun?"

"I borrowed it."

"Why did you do that?"

"To shoot these critters!"

"That would have gotten us all into big trouble. You don't even think of that, do you? All you do is drink and ruin your life. Gelo, shame on you!"

Then Teodolinda turned to Alcides. "And you, why do you lie on the floor and cry like a baby? You're the one who is always picking fights with my men. Your whole tribe delights in mocking my crippled son. You have made a fiend out of him!"

Brandishing her machete for emphasis, she addressed them all. "What do you get out of fighting, anyway? Can't you let bygones be bygones? Will you fight until you've all killed each other? Stop it all and let's be friends and neighbors, okay? You're all a bunch of drunkards and fighters. Cut it out and get on with life! Franklin, hand me that pistol. And Gelo, get up off the floor and go home."

With that, Teodolinda stalked across the floor, grabbed Gelo's crutches at the bar, and took them to him. The men watched in guilty silence. With one more disgusted glance around the room, Teodolinda turned and stalked home. Victoria and Hugo, who had been watching from the door, followed. Gelo got up slowly, hobbled to his horse, and rode home.

Alcides stood slowly and stumbled to the bar. "Franklin, look what that beast did to me!" he sobbed.

"You'd better leave Gelo alone, do you hear?" Franklin said. "You'd better be glad Victoria came when she did. He would have shot us both."

Alcides shuddered. He knew it was true.

The Quesadas finally gave up. La Puentera went broke and closed down. There was no way to compete with the cheap liquor La Peligrosa produced, and they were too afraid to go to the *resguardo* the third time. Besides, it would not help anyway. The Valverdes would just find another still. Old Durando tried to take legal action against the Valverdes once, but Lico traveled to Miramar and had a good talk with the head of police, who was a personal friend. It was not hard to convince him that Durando and his sons were as rotten and crooked as the rest. The law never took action, so Durando and his sons decided to take Teodolinda's advice to let bygones be bygones.

They tried it. But it never really worked. They just did not know when to quit. More strife would stir up the family feud. But this time the women would fuel the fire.

23

"Mamita, I'm hungry for something good," Gelo announced one day. "What is there to eat?"

"There's not much here, son," Teodolinda answered. "Just beans and green bananas."

"I'm sick and tired of beans and bananas," Gelo groaned. "I could almost throw up just thinking about them!"

"Well, I'm sorry," Teodolinda retorted. "That's all the men have brought in for me. If you bring me a paca, I'll fry you some really good meat."

"Aw, Mamita, don't blame us. You know the hunters in Zapotal have killed all the pacas. Meat is scarce these days."

Teodolinda felt like telling Gelo that if they would drink less and go to the *socolón* to work, they would have more food. But she held her tongue. She herself was drinking more and more, just to kill her discouragement, though she knew in her heart it only made it worse. Now she could not even rebuke her lazy, drinking sons.

Then Teodolinda remembered something that was growing in the *socolón*. They had not planted any decent vegetables that rainy season. They had not even had enough money to buy seed. But pumpkin and chayote seeds were free for the asking. So she and Aurelio and Belén had planted row after row of pumpkins and fixed up the chayote bowers. They should be growing well by now. It was too soon to expect fruit, but there would be plenty of *quelites*.

"Gelo, I know where there is something good to eat, but it's too far for you to go get them."

"Nothing's too far for me, Mamita. Just tell me where and I'll go get the food. I'm as hungry as a *león* for something new!"

"Well, it's not exactly new, but we haven't eaten any for a long time. I wonder if you even know what *quelites* are?"

"Nope."

"When we first moved here to Zapotal and faced hard times, we ate *quelites*. The tips of pumpkin and chayote vines fried with eggs or meat are very healthy and tasty."

Gelo looked doubtful. "That sounds strange, but I am hungry enough to go all the way to the *socolón* to get them. How many would it take?"

"You have to get plenty, because they shrivel up when you fry them. It would take a lot to feed the whole family, but it would sure be worth a try."

"It's still early, and if I leave right away, I could be back by dark."

"Take one of the boys with you, Gelo. I think Aurelio would go. Are you sure you want to try it? It's far, and your crutches get hung up in the roots on the trail . . ."

"Don't you worry; I can do it," Gelo said, hobbling out of the house.

Aurelio was busy, so Gelo decided to go to the *socolón* alone. He had been there before, but never so late in the day, and never alone.

The trail was well-worn, and since rainy season had just begun, the mud was not too deep. First he walked through their cane field. The tall cane stalks shot up on either side of him like a tall green wall. Next he crossed their cow pasture and worked his way through two ditches and small creeks. His first half-mile went smoothly.

Soon he left the flatland. From there on, the trail was a mile-long climb through virgin jungle. As Gelo left the open field and entered the jungle, it was like slipping into a dark tunnel. Immediately the ground was more soft and wet. His crutches sank into the soft black soil, and it was a job to pull them back out again. Fifteen minutes into the jungle he was sweating profusely. The climb was difficult enough for someone in good physical condition and nearly impossible for someone on crutches. Gelo had to crawl over logs, jump up steep banks, and stop repeatedly to free his crutches from the tangled roots. By the time he arrived at his destination, it was getting late, and he was exhausted. He sat in the shade at the jungle's edge and rested.

The end of the *socolón* before him was a huge tangle of lovely pumpkin vines. Down where the old potato tree had been, the chayote bowers were patched together and covered with new green growth. *It won't be hard to find shoots, that's for sure,* Gelo mused.

Gelo got up from his resting place and cut several jungle vines. Then he hobbled down to the pumpkin field. He plucked the new shoots and piled them neatly. He did the same at the chayote bower. Not knowing how many he needed, he cut until he had a huge stack. Then he stretched the jungle vines around the whole pile and tied them tightly. Making a loop with the extra vine, he strung the bundle across his shoulders like a backpack, and away he went.

Gelo was now not only tired, but he carried a bulky load. Nevertheless, he hit the jungle with all the strength that was in him—and he needed every ounce of it.

Teodolinda had discovered that Aurelio had not gone along with Gelo. So she found herself thinking often about Gelo as the long day crept by. She could not help but wonder how he would fare on a trail so wild and long.

At four o'clock it started to rain. The jungle grew dark and windy. The tall trees moaned and groaned, and every now and then a branch fell. Once, just as Gelo slipped and fell for the hundredth time, a branch fell right across the path ahead of him. Gelo was so tired he just lay on the trail where he had fallen. The vines still held his bundle, but the shoots were tattered and frazzled. It hardly mattered anymore. All Gelo wanted to do was rest a little and then fight on.

At dusk Teodolinda was getting worried. "Valverde, please go meet Gelo. He left five hours ago and still isn't back. Maybe something happened to him."

Lico looked out the window, dreading the drenching he was sure to get if he went. Just as he looked out, Gelo stumbled into view. Teodolinda looked over Lico's shoulder and stammered, "My poor little boy!"

Gelo was splattered with mud to his waist and bathed in sweat and rain. His whole body sagged on his crutches from extreme fatigue. He made it to the porch and sat down. Then he flopped onto his back and lay down. "There are the *quelites*," he whispered. "They'd better be good."

His family stood and stared, all imagining the trip to the *socolón* and back in his condition. Two and a half miles of some extremely rough terrain. Lico was proud of his son. Now, that was being a man!

Teodolinda quickly washed the shoots. The water helped freshen them up until they almost looked edible. Then she broke them into smaller pieces and cracked several eggs over them. As they fried, she prepared a hot cup of black coffee with plenty of sugar and took it to Gelo. He sat up and grasped the cup with a whispered, *"¡Gracias!"*

That night the whole family ate *quelites* and beans with cooked bananas. It was not the finest food in the world, but to the Valverdes it was food for royalty. Gelo especially enjoyed the greens. "They sure are delicious!" he exclaimed as he downed the largest portion.

*   *   *

Teodolinda felt sick. Sick and tired. More and more she was making their living, and they rarely had enough to eat. Most of their income came from selling *guaro*. Teodolinda hated the saloon and all it represented. And she and Lico were fighting more. She was constantly scolding him because the men did not work—they just sat around and drank. He could get back at her now, because she drank too. But at least she worked. Besides, who had gotten her started drinking in the first place?

Teodolinda knew she needed a break, or she would lose her mind. The whole family would suffer, but at least it might wake Lico up to what she did for the family. So one day she announced, "I'm going to Guanacaste to see Marina. I don't know when I'll be back."

Everyone was surprised, but no one dared contradict her. Lico was especially quiet. Only little Hugo showed his emotions. He cried and cried, and when the time came for her to leave, the girls had to carry him back into the house by force.

The morning Teodolinda left, the weather was sunny and clear. She began the walk to Miramar with just one small bag on her back. When she topped Cerro Pelón, she walked over to the lookout where she and Lico had eaten breakfast on the way to Puntarenas before Hugo was born. As she sat there in the grass, her mind filled with many memories. All by herself, her head on her knees, she cried. She cried because she did not know what else to do. She cried because way down in the gulf she saw the island of San Lucas. Lidier had visited Marino, and in spite of it being a wicked prison, Lidier claimed that Marino was well and happy. She cried as she thought of what Marino was going through. She cried because she was partly to blame.

Teodolinda also cried because of her lost relationship with Lico. His lazy, drunken ways repulsed her. He had been such a good worker—an ideal husband for a woman like her. Now he was reduced to a lazy bum, all because of the awful curse that came with drinking. She cried because she wished so much that she could have her old Valverde back—the one who had walked her all the way to Miramar and had shared a sweet breakfast with her on this very spot many years ago.

Teodolinda cried for her children, who suffered from their poverty and sin. As she thought of Hugo at home—maybe hungry, maybe sneaking a drink from the jug to forget—it was almost too much for her. And Aurelio, the loner. And ·Gelo, her crippled boy. And Luis, who had moved far away because he was afraid of himself. She thought of her grandchildren. Little Nelson, her favorite, who had to live with that shrew for a mother.

But most of all, Teodolinda cried for herself. What had she become? She had never dreamed she would drink and dance and party. But more and more she was being sucked in. It was almost as if she had no choice. *Either I join the crowd and survive or isolate myself and shrivel up and die,* she thought. She was especially ashamed of her drinking and smoking. But she was afraid that, without those two boosters, she could never survive the Zapotal headaches and heartaches. Her harsh life demanded some kind of buffer.

As she cried, she decided she would soon go to San Ramón to confess her sins to the priest. Maybe that would bring her peace.

After an hour of weeping on the mountaintop, she let the wind dry her tears. Her heart felt cleansed. She would go to Guanacaste for a month and then come back and face harsh Zapotal again. She would do it for the sake of her children and her drunken husband, whom she loved. She got up and strode down toward Miramar with a purpose.

*　*　*

A month later, on the way home from Guanacaste, Teodolinda stopped at Miramar for the night. The next day she stopped at a store to buy something for little Hugo, whom she had missed more than anybody else. Christmas was just around the corner. What could she buy for him? Noticing some nice light-blue fabric on the shelf, Teodolinda decided to buy some to make Hugo a shirt.

When Teodolinda got home, everyone was glad to see her. But, as she had feared, little Hugo seemed distant. He resented that she had abandoned him. So she called him to her and whispered, "I bought you something for Christmas. I got some fabric to make you a new shirt."

Hugo brightened immediately. "A new shirt for Christmas! A new shirt for Christmas!" he shouted.

Teodolinda made the shirt before Christmas. It took her a long time to sew all its seams by hand, and she had to do it on the sly so Hugo would not see it. To her dismay, she had miscalculated and did not have enough fabric for the sleeves. She searched high and low for another piece of fabric of the same color, but all she could find was a piece of tan material with red squares on it. So she finished the shirt with that and hid it until Christmas.

On Christmas Eve Teodolinda sent Hugo to bathe and get ready for the party. Then she handed him the new shirt. He did not mind a bit that the sleeves were checkered with gaudy red. In fact, he liked it all the more. Though they were extremely poor and the shirt was not at all fancy, few eight-year-olds were as happy as Hugo was that night.

Teodolinda had prepared plenty of good food for their Christmas Eve celebration. They had killed a pig and made two hundred tamales. Hugo was happy that Mamita took the holiday off and let others run La Peligrosa, but no one else seemed to be. People followed her to her house as if she were a magnet. Where Teodolinda was, the fun was—and the best food, and the best service. So Christmas Eve did not turn out to be fun for Hugo after all.

Old Nacho came in for a *rosario* that night. After the *rosario,* people started drinking, as usual. About the time the crowd got rowdy, Hugo crawled up on his bamboo bed and banana leaf mat and covered himself with his burlap blanket. Although it was a poor bed, it felt cozy to him. Outside it was windy and cold. Though it was not raining, the winter cold made him shiver. He still wore his new shirt. He curled up in a ball, and his shivering subsided as he slowly warmed up. He was almost asleep when a noise startled him and made him jump. Somebody was fighting outside again.

Hugo lay in his bed trembling, though now it was not from cold. The drunken, angry screams terrified him. The good memories of the evening and his new shirt were forgotten as wave after wave of fear washed over him.

Several days later Hugo was hungry. They had eaten all the food from the Christmas party. Now they were planning a big fiesta for New Year's Day, but in between the two special dates there was hardly any food in the house and no money to buy any. The day before, food had been scarce and he had gone to bed hungry. Now this morning all Hugo had gotten for breakfast was a cup of coffee and a piece of bread. By midmorning he was famished.

His mother had sent him to borrow some *dulce* from a neighbor, and now he was on his way home. He knew he should hurry, but his belly was growling, and the hunger almost made him feel dizzy. Then he remembered the blackberry patch on the hillside. He scampered off the trail and ran up the hill. In among the thorny bushes grew the small wild blackberries, almost more sour than sweet. But they tasted good to a hungry little boy.

It takes a lot of berries to fill a boy's tummy, and it takes time to pick that many berries, so Hugo spent almost an hour picking berries and popping them into his mouth.

When Hugo got back to the house, his mother scolded him. "Hugo, where have you been?"

"Mamita, I was so hungry that I stopped on the way back to eat blackberries."

Teodolinda studied Hugo closely. He was not lying. The purple edging around his mouth and his scratched hands confirmed his story. "You should have brought me the *dulce* first and then gone to pick berries. That way I would not have worried about you. Besides, I needed the *dulce* right away."

The next morning, just before noon, Marino walked in. Teodolinda hardly recognized him. He had been a gangly teenager when he left, but tough prison life and daily exercise had filled him out, and his muscles bulged. Physically he was in much better shape than when he had gone to prison. But his heart and soul had grown even harder than his muscles.

After several months in San Lucas, Marino had been sent to the state penitentiary near San José for several more months. There he had also made friends with the cooks, and soon he was cooking and making friends with everyone. His sentence was shortened, and altogether he spent only eleven months of his two-year sentence in jail.

* * *

Tilo Barrantes' fame grew in Zapotal as his wealth grew by leaps and bounds. He now had twelve farms, and each farm was run by a mistress. Tilo's idea was to raise boys to run his many farms for free. Though the method was perverted, it seemed to be working.

As Tilo grew richer, the Valverdes grew poorer. Tilo did not drink up all his income. Then news came to Zapotal that Don Tilo had gone to Rome. He had become rich enough from selling cattle that he could travel anywhere in the world. But the main reason Tilo had gone to Rome was not tourism. He wanted peace of mind. He knew he was living wickedly. He wanted to get absolution for his sins straight from the Vatican. A priest there told him that as long as he was willing to support his mistresses and their families financially, everything would be all right. His conscience soothed, Tilo returned from Rome and told many fantastic stories about his trip, but his heart remained unchanged. Don Tilo was still Don Tilo. His projects flourished, but his soul was lost.

24

"Ouch!" Aurelio screamed in pain and frustration. Sharp pains often jabbed his head like a knife. He slowly rubbed his aching, itching head. He knew a zoo of lice lived in his long hair. That was normal. But this pain was not normal. Under his hair his skin was bumpy. And, oh, did those bumps smart!

Aurelio sat behind the house on a stump, forlornly rubbing his head. He longed to ask Mamita what was wrong with him, but lately he could hardly get her attention. If he tried to talk to her at the saloon, she usually hushed him and told him to scat. She was always busy either running the saloon or cooking food or washing clothes or a thousand other things. And the older girls, Leyla and Mireya, were the same way. Everybody was too busy to help a young teenager with his struggles.

"Ouch!" he fussed again. "What can I do?"

After dark Aurelio slipped outside. He knew where his brothers kept a gallon jug of *contrabando* behind the house. They often sent him to get it. Now he crawled into the weed patch. It was only Tuesday evening, and there was still a quarter of a jug left. He unscrewed the lid and lifted it to his lips. Every swallow burned like fire as it washed down his throat. His face contorted as he forced it down.

After a couple swigs, Aurelio knew he would be able to sleep. The pain in his head would go away and he would find relief. As he worked his way through the high grass in the dark, he suddenly heard a rustling noise ahead of him. Someone was entering the grass patch. Frightened, he cried out.

"What are you doing in here?" Lico barked.

"I-I-I was thirsty, and my head hurts so. I needed a drink so I can sleep . . ."

Lico should have acknowledged to his son that he was in the exact same dilemma. But he didn't. He just growled and pushed on past. He had caught Aurelio sneaking a drink, and Aurelio had caught him, and they were both too embarrassed to fight about it.

That night Aurelio was sad when he went to bed. Sad and angry. His heart hurt more than his head. Why didn't Mamita care? Why was she always so busy? Why did she spend more time at La Peligrosa than at home? Sometimes he felt that he did not really have a mama at all.

A week later Aurelio awoke with his head hurting worse than ever. He seldom bathed, and since Mamita was so busy, none of the children's general appearance was good. After helping his sister milk the cows, Aurelio headed for the house to find some breakfast. He felt like screaming, his head hurt so much. In desperation he reached up and grabbed at his scalp as if to catch whatever was eating him. And he did. When he opened his hand, he held some strands of straight black hair and several ripe cattle grubs that had popped out from where he had clutched at his scalp. Aurelio stared at his hand in horror. Now he knew what was hurting him and why his head was so swollen and stinky. He felt like throwing up, but instead he found little Hugo and asked him to go bathe with him.

After Aurelio bathed in the creek and washed his hair in a fury, he asked Hugo to help him squeeze out the pus from the biggest bumps on his head. He laid his forehead on a rock, and Hugo found the bumps and squeezed. They were able to squeeze out several more grubs, but mostly what came out was pus. That night Aurelio had a fever from the infection.

The next day Hugo told Leyla about the grubs. Aurelio was embarrassed, but he knew he needed help. Leyla was horrified and promptly took her mother's scissors and cut off all his hair in uneven, jagged lines. Some of the exposed bumps were swollen to the size of golf balls. Leyla squeezed the bumps until Aurelio cried. Then she rubbed his scalp daily with a rag drenched in kerosene. In a week his head was back to normal.

Teodolinda only found out about Aurelio's grub problem after she asked about his awful haircut. But by then, he was better.

* * *

For once the morning dawned bright and clear. The world was still wet from rain during the night, but now the early morning winds snatched the clouds and sent them scurrying toward the southwest. The whole world seemed fresh and clean.

It should have been a happy day, but Teodolinda knew it would not be. She had been up since 4 a.m. preparing food. Now she needed to get a little washing done before the first customers came to the store. A few thirsty Zapotal men would drop by for their first drinks by nine o'clock. And since it was Saturday, men would be drinking there all day long and into the night.

She was fifty-five years old, yet she jumped nimbly down the bank toward the creek, where the clothes were soon receiving an awful beating on her stone. Her graying hairs slipped down into her face, and she pushed them back with the backside of her gnarled, soapy hand. Her thoughts were not happy. Many things troubled her and knit her brow, but just now two stood out.

Teodolinda knew Gelo was already at the still. He always went down early to get a head start on the *contrabando*. The rest of the men would follow later. Several of the youngest boys had left the house at ten the night before and not returned until after midnight. Although they never told her, she knew what they were up to. They were stealing chickens for the party at the still.

Teodolinda always worried that someday the men would get caught at the still with *guaro* and stolen chickens. There would surely be a fight, and someone would get hurt. It was bad enough that the men all lived at the saloon over the weekends, but that was not as dangerous as the jungle. She could help keep things under control at the saloon, but at the still . . .

The other thing that bothered Teodolinda was her own behavior. She had never dreamed that she would become an alcoholic. Never! In her mind she still screamed, *I'm not an alcoholic!* But in her heart she knew that if she wasn't one, she was certainly acting like one. Even now, at 8:30 in the morning, she felt as if she needed a drink. Her head hurt from her constant lack of sleep. The work at the saloon was killing her. And more and more she needed a drink to be able to go on.

It had started when Lico urged her to drink. He always claimed that a little would not hurt. But now she realized that Lico was just like all other alcoholics—he hated to drink alone. They always wanted others to drink with them so they would not feel as guilty. Lico did not have to urge her anymore. She found the bottle herself. And not just a sip or two before a delivery for strength. Every day seemed to offer a reason.

By ten o'clock Marino, Belén, and Aurelio were preparing the chickens. After chopping their heads off, they heated water on Gelo's fire to scald them. Then they plucked them. At first they had been careful about hiding the chicken feathers. They had also been more careful about hiding the still. But recently they had become careless again.

At eleven o'clock Don Lico strode into the small clearing. He stood to one side and took it all in. Gelo had the *chicha* boiling away and the fire spitting hot. Marino and Belén were roasting the chicken pieces on iron rods over the coals. The whole area around the still was a muddy mess from all the rain and the many men stomping around. Otherwise, everything was green and lovely. The jungle always impressed Lico, even when, like now, he was more concerned about his awful thirst than the blooming flowers in the trees above him. But there was one thing in the scene that Lico hated. The stealing.

He walked over to the three boys. "You are a bunch of *sinvergüenzas chicheros* (shameless drunkards)!" he shouted angrily.

The boys stared back sullenly. They seemed embarrassed, but only a little. They just looked away and waited.

Lico started again. "Why do you steal? I don't care if you drink and all the rest, but don't steal! That will only make you more enemies than you already have. I am ashamed that my sons steal. If you were a little smaller, I'd lash your hides!"

"Aw, Dad," Belén muttered, "it's just chickens."

"Yeah, but that's the way all robbers start. They swipe chickens, then cows, then money. You are *sinvergüenzas chicheros* for sure!"

Just then Gelo yelled, "It's coming! It's coming!"

Everybody forgot everything else and ran. Lico got the *cabezón*. And everybody ate chicken, even Lico. They spent the whole afternoon there, eating and getting soundly drunk. It was dark by the time they staggered into the saloon, and the partying continued long into the night.

That evening Aurelio was frightened. He felt strange. His staggering was not just drunkenness. Something else was wrong with him. He had been feeling it a lot lately, only tonight it was worse—a strange dizziness he had never felt before. When they had run for the *cabezón*, Aurelio had run with the rest, but he had stumbled, overcome with dizziness. And that was before he had drunk anything at all. He did not tell anybody about the strange experience, but he knew something was wrong with him. Something besides his drinking problem.

25

Victoria and Hugo walked slowly along the rough jungle trail. The jungle canopy spread over them like a wide green tent. All around them immense trees stood like straight, strong guardians. Vines adorned with moss, orchids, and bromeliads hung across the trees' shoulders like garlands. The bright morning sun peeped through the canopy, drawing golden dappled patterns on the brown leaf-covered forest floor. Butterflies, birds, and an occasional animal provided amusement for the children in the green world of the Zapotal cloud forest.

The children enjoyed their leisurely walk as only children can. At times they chatted and laughed. Other times they walked in silence, thinking their own private thoughts. Sometimes they noticed the beauty that surrounded them, but mostly they ignored the exotic display. What would have seemed like paradise to others was commonplace to them.

For two whole hours they traveled, sometimes through the jungle and sometimes through the fields. Then the two children burst out into a huge clearing.

In front of them lay an open field, slanted on a hillside. Sprinkled through the field were trees of different sizes and shapes. The early pioneers always left a few standing to make shade for the cattle and housing for the birds. And, like this morning, they just plain made the field beautiful.

In the middle of the field was a line of men—Lico, Marino, Belén, Aurelio, and Ulises—swinging their machetes. Lico took the lead, choosing the right speed for the younger boys. Each worker chopped down all the weeds in his two-yard reach, making a ten-yard swath. Most of the field already looked clean and orderly. But one section was grown up in weeds as high as Hugo's head.

Lico had taken a contract to clean a big field on one of Tilo Barrantes' many farms. It took two hours to walk there every day. By Tuesday morning everybody was sober enough to go to work early.

On this day, a week into their contract, Victoria and Hugo were bringing lunch to the men. Both carried an *alforja* full of little plastic bowls with lids. Each bowl was full of rice and beans, a hard-boiled egg, and fried plantains. Victoria's *alforja* held things to make coffee once they arrived.

Upon bursting into the clearing and seeing the men engrossed in their work, Victoria grabbed Hugo's hand and pulled him back under

the jungle's edge. "Let's surprise them and make the coffee right away," she urged. Hugo quickly found some dry sticks, and Victoria started a small fire. While the fire heated up, they cut two forked sticks with their machete and pushed them into the soft black dirt on either side of the fire. Then they laid a stick across the forks and hung a little kettle of water on the stick.

Once the water was boiling, Victoria pulled the little teapot out of her *alforja*. Next she found the pouch of coffee. Her older sister had measured the coffee grounds into the little cloth bag. Now Victoria hung the little bag in the teapot and poured the boiling water through the coffee grounds. The rich aroma almost made them dizzy. They were so hungry! They could hardly wait.

Victoria sent Hugo to call the men. Hugo ran out into the field and called, "Papito, lunch is ready!"

Ulises called Hugo over to where he was working. "Look what we killed this morning," he announced as he led Hugo over to a huge stump. "It almost bit Papito. When it struck at him, Belén ran over and cut its head off."

Hugo shuddered. Right in front of him lay a huge headless fer-de-lance, one of the most dangerous snakes in the world. It was all of six feet long, and its head, lying off to one side, was as big as Hugo's two fists held together.

Ulises and Hugo joined the other men at the makeshift camp. Victoria had laid out a piece of colorful plastic on the ground and placed the little bowls of food on it. The little teapot was perched on some leaves to the side of the plastic, steam rising from the spout. Victoria had put in just the right amount of shredded *dulce* to make the coffee sweet enough, but not too sweet. There were cups for all.

After the men had eaten and returned to work, Victoria and Hugo enjoyed their lunch. It would be hours before the men were ready to leave, so Victoria and Hugo played. First they ran back to a creek they had crossed and played in the water, but the water was so cold they soon tired of that. Then Hugo said, "Victoria, I'm hungry. I am going to cut down a palmito."

Feeling important, Hugo whacked away at the young palm tree, the heart of which he knew would be good to eat. But the palmito tree was as hard as iron, or so it seemed, though this one was young, and its trunk was not quite as tough as some. Hugo used both hands, as most youngsters do when first learning to use a machete.

After a lot of whacking, the palm tree finally fell. Hugo ran toward the topmost part where the heart of the palm lay. As he ran, his machete slipped out of his hand and fell ahead of him, the sharp tip toward him. Before he could stop, Hugo had kicked his bare foot against the machete's tip. He fell to the ground and clutched at his foot, wailing. Victoria helped him up and examined the wound. The cut was small but deep. After Hugo stopped crying, they headed back to camp, forgetting the palm heart, Hugo limping and whimpering like a puppy.

On the way home that evening, Hugo favored his hurt foot and had trouble keeping up. As they dropped off the mountain range on one side, they had to cross the Jabonal River. Every day Aurelio and Ulises intended to swim in one of its deep green pools on their way to work, but they never had time. Now they decided to run ahead and take a dip until the others caught up. They convinced Hugo to go with them and took off running. Hugo forgot about his hurt foot in his desire to swim. Lico saw what was happening and shouted after them, "It's bad to swim when you're hot and tired. It could make you sick!"

Aurelio hollered back, "We'll be careful. It won't hurt us!" And they kept on running.

They jumped into the deep pool, clothes and all. The icy water almost took their breath away, but they soon got used to it and splashed and swam like otters. Aurelio dove deep, opening his eyes as he skimmed along the bottom. He could see the forms of brown rocks and an old log that lay on the river floor. He surfaced, shook his hair that had grown back since the grubs, and swam to the water's edge.

"Let's get going, boys!" Lico barked. They all obeyed and jumped out of the pool, their skin red and tingling from the cold mountain water. They warmed as they ran to catch up with the older men.

That night Aurelio and Hugo were sick. Hugo had a high fever and his foot swelled mercilessly. Aurelio was terribly dizzy and had a fever too. Their mother was at La Peligrosa and never found out. Mireya tried to make both boys comfortable, but they had a horrible night.

The next night was dark and full of night sounds. It had rained earlier, and the tree frogs and pipers were having a grand time. A red-eyed tree frog clucked his little song right outside the bedroom window. Inside the house, almost everyone was sleeping, but fourteen-year-old Aurelio lay groaning on his bed.

Mireya was also awake. She curled herself up in a ball on the hard board bed and tried to block out her younger brother's groans, all the while fuming in her mind. *Why can't Mother take care of her own children? Why do I have to carry such a big load?*

Finally Mireya called out to Lico, who was fast asleep across the thin wall, "Papito, Aurelio is very sick!"

"Nah, he's just got a bad cold," Lico grunted. "Give him an aspirin and he'll be all right."

Aurelio heard his dad and started to cry softly.

Mireya knew Aurelio did not just have a cold, but what could she do? She lighted a *canfinera* and hunted for a pill. She finally found one, and it brought Aurelio some relief. But not Mireya. She knew Aurelio was a very sick boy.

After several days Aurelio seemed better, but he was not. Two weeks later he was out drinking with his brothers way into the night. Aurelio came in with the rest, but he felt awful. He hit the bed hard that night and did not get up for two weeks.

Those two weeks ticked along slowly. Aurelio was getting worse, but no one seemed to notice. He was in pain. His eyes hurt. His head hurt. His arms and hands hurt. His legs and feet hurt. Practically everything hurt except his hair. And he was so dizzy. Never had Aurelio been so dizzy before. Every time he opened his eyes, his small world spun. After suffering from dizziness for hours, he would vomit and feel better for a while. Then the whole thing would start over again.

But what scared Aurelio the most was that half of his body felt numb. And though he did not try to talk, he was sure he could not. He was sure he was going to die.

Most of the family just ignored Aurelio. Nobody even told Teodolinda he was sick. And since Aurelio could not talk, he never complained. That single aspirin Mireya gave him was all the medicine he ever got.

Two weeks after Aurelio got sick, Lidier stopped by. Before he even dismounted, Mireya found herself telling him all her troubles. "Mamita never comes around anymore, and there is hardly any food left to eat. All Papito does is drink. No one believes me that Aurelio is terribly sick. But he is, Lidier. Sometimes I think he is dying!"

Lidier jumped off his horse and entered the house. He marched into the dark bedroom and sat beside the bed. Then he reached out and touched Aurelio's arm. "He's got a high fever!" he exclaimed in alarm.

Aurelio rolled over and faced his older brother. Lidier was shocked. Aurelio was skin and bones. His hair was an unkempt mass. He had not bathed for two weeks, and he stank. His dark, sad eyes were sunken into his skull, yet they clung to his brother's as if appealing to a god.

"Aurelio," Lidier asked quietly, "how are you feeling?"

Aurelio's face contorted as half of it cooperated and the other half lay dead. He tried to talk, but the garbled sound that came out of his twisted mouth was impossible to understand. When Aurelio saw that they could not understand him, he started to cry.

Lidier stalked out of the bedroom. "This is awful," he said, swearing under his breath. "Is there no one around here who cares about Aurelio? He's dying!"

Aurelio heard from the bedroom. Though the words were not comforting, he appreciated that someone finally cared. He buried his face in the burlap blanket and cried harder than ever.

After talking with the girls, Lidier decided to take Aurelio and head for La Peligrosa. This was an emergency. He would talk to their mother and see what she would do with her dying son. He went back into the bedroom, picked Aurelio up, and carried him out to his horse.

Mireya held him while Lidier mounted; then she handed Aurelio's skinny frame up. Lidier put him on the saddle in front of him and held the limp form so he would not fall.

Twenty minutes later he marched into the saloon and barked, "Mother, one of your sons is dying!"

"Which one?" she asked.

"Aurelio!" Lidier exclaimed. "If something isn't done soon, he will die!" Lidier scolded her for her negligence.

With a sad look on her face, Teodolinda tried to defend herself. "I didn't know how sick he was! No one told me!" she claimed. "I thought he only had a bad cold . . ."

Dry season had just come to Zapotal, and the community people had fixed the ox trail through Tajo Alto with picks and shovels. On this day, for the first time ever, a four-wheel-drive truck had driven into Zapotal to haul out the mountain people's corn. Teodolinda got ready in a jiffy, and the truck carried her and Aurelio down to Miramar on the new road. Lidier promised to help at the saloon until Teodolinda came back.

At Miramar they rushed Aurelio to the Puntarenas hospital in an ambulance. After Teodolinda was sure he was in good hands, she left for home, knowing that, with Lico's drinking problem, things would regress and there would soon be no more food to eat. Aurelio stayed at the hospital, where kind nurses took better care of him than anybody ever had in Zapotal.

During the next three months, Aurelio improved. His fever left him. His health slowly returned. But he would never be the same. At the end of the three months, he still could not walk or talk, so they started therapy. Finally the doctors decided it might be best to send him home. Maybe he would recuperate completely there. So they put him on a bus to Miramar.

Once Aurelio got to Miramar, he got off the bus and tried to walk to a friend's house, creeping slowly alongside the wall of a house so he would not fall down. But eventually he did fall, right in the ditch beside the street. Some friends found him there and sent him to the

Miramar health center. Then they sent word to Zapotal that Aurelio had been released from the Puntarenas hospital, but was still sick and waiting at the health center.

During Aurelio's three months in the Puntarenas hospital, only Ángel had visited him. Now Teodolinda came to see him in Miramar and discovered that they wanted her to take him to a children's hospital in San José.

Teodolinda was troubled that morning as she went to get Aurelio. Somehow this was all her fault. If she would not drink and was not always so busy, maybe everything would be better for them.

She helped Aurelio walk out to the street, where she flagged a taxi and asked the driver to take them to the big Catholic church in the center of town. Aurelio hung on to his mother's shoulder as they walked in the huge church door. Inside, Teodolinda set him on the nice tile floor. Then she knelt, sobbing. With tears in his eyes, Aurelio watched her walk on her knees, inching her way through the huge cathedral to the distant altar, where she bowed in prayer. As he watched his mother praying for his health, he pondered, *Is there a God? And if there is, does He hear the prayers men pray?* He looked around at the stained-glass windows, the statues that hung on the walls, the flowers, and all the fancy ornaments. *Does God really live in here?*

Another thought struck Aurelio—a thought that had haunted him often lately. *Do I really have a soul?*

Now his mother was walking back, tears streaming down her face. *She must be terribly tired,* Aurelio thought. *And I'm sure her knees are sore. I know my mother loves me if she is willing to do this for me. I forgive her for not coming to visit me while I was in the hospital and for not caring for me when she was at the saloon. It's all because she has to work so hard to make our living. And because we are so poor.*

Teodolinda did not know what her son was thinking or what emotions were going through his heart. She did not know how much her skinny boy loved her. She only knew that she was trying her best to please God so He would heal her son. Maybe he would get well now.

As Aurelio and his mother traveled to San José on the bus, Aurelio tried his best to talk to her. She was able to catch snatches of what he said. "Mother, if I get well, I promise to walk all the way to Cartago to the cathedral where La Virgen de los Ángeles lives. I will walk there and take her a gift for healing me."

His mother smiled at him. Would he remember to fulfill his promise? She would remind him, she decided.

After Aurelio was admitted to the hospital, Teodolinda explained why she had to return to Zapotal. Then she gave him a hug and disappeared down the long hall and around the corner. Aurelio stayed in that hospital for six long months, and not once did a relative come to see him.

Teodolinda returned from San José determined to reform. She tried her best to make Lico stop drinking. The first several days after she was back, she slept at home instead of at the saloon. Gelo still made *guaro*, and they still had their Saturday parties, but Teodolinda made every effort to get the men to stop drinking during the week. She started hiding the liquor and keeping it only for the store, and she watched like a hawk to make sure they were not sneaking drinks.

Several of the boys tried to help Teodolinda cut back on the drinking, but others looked for ways around the new rules. One evening Lico went out into the night. He did not go to La Peligrosa. He avoided the busy, noisy saloon with a passion. No one knew where he had gone until Teodolinda walked into the bedroom unexpectedly and found Hugo on his hands and knees talking to a crack in the wall. The door was half closed, so she sneaked in behind the door to see what was going on. She heard a hoarse whisper from outside. "Get me a drink of *guaro*, please! I'm terribly thirsty."

From her hiding place, she watched Hugo reach into the closet where she had hidden the bottle. Then he ran to a window and handed it out into the dark. Minutes later, the bottle came back in through the window, and Hugo hid it in the closet again.

That night Teodolinda gave up. Later, after everybody else was in bed, she drank from the bottle herself. She had not done it for two weeks and was as thirsty as Lico. If Lico had known, he would have joined her. But he did not. He spent the night in the sugarcane patch.

26

The night was pitch dark. Even the stars seemed small and unable to squeeze out much light. The wind was cold and blustery. It was January, when the nights were sometimes cloudless, and always cold.

In the grip of this dark, cold night a threesome walked very slowly along a mountain trail—a father, a mother, and a child. The father walked with a stagger, for he was very drunk. In his left hand he carried his bottle. The mother held his right hand and tried to keep him steady, but it was getting harder and harder to keep him on the trail, or even on his feet.

A nine-year-old boy walked on the other side of the woman and clung to her right hand. He was afraid. He knew they were heading straight toward El Roblón, and that name made his little heart tremble.

El Roblón was a lonely place where the trail ran right over the crown of one of the highest mountains in Zapotal. Recently the huge tree that had reigned supreme on the mountaintop and given it its name had uprooted and made a natural bridge for wild animals to cross from the jungle on the one side of the trail to the other. No one tried to cut the huge log. It was far too large for their primitive tools. So everybody just circled around the big root mass and rejoined the trail on the other side.

But the main reason every boy feared El Roblón was because it was a cougar crossing. Many Zapotal people told stories of having seen the *león* cross the trail in the evening or early morning. Hugo had never been able to forget Andrés Rodríguez's terrible story of the *león* that had fed the little boy to her cubs.

Now Hugo's teeth chattered. They were destined to walk over El Roblón right around midnight, the worst hour of the night. And they would have to cross at whatever speed Lico could manage to stagger.

Lico could hardly walk at all now. Every so often he would stop and take a draft from his bottle, which fortunately was almost empty.

A farmer who lived out toward Barranquilla had asked Lico to take care of his farm for a month. Lico had taken the job, taking Teodolinda and Hugo along to live with him. They cared for the man's cows, fed his animals, and took care of his place. Since it did not take much work to keep things going, Lico got bored. So every Saturday he went home for the weekend parties.

Now as they stumbled along toward Barranquilla after one of their weekend visits, Teodolinda wondered what she could do with her alcoholic husband. But Hugo's head was filled with *león* stories, and his poor little brain could think of nothing else.

Now they were climbing the huge Roblón mountain. Lico had finally finished his bottle, but the bottle sure hadn't finished with him. To Hugo's horror, just as they crowned the mountaintop, Lico stumbled and could not walk anymore. Even Hugo tried to help him up in his desperation to move on. Together, he and his mother managed to get Lico around the huge root mass and onto the main trail again. Now they were going downhill. That would surely speed things up a little. Maybe they would get back to the house soon.

Lico picked up a little speed weaving down the hill. Teodolinda held his hand. Hugo pulled on his sleeve. Then Lico slipped and fell in the mud, where he lay like a felled ox. Even Hugo knew he would not be getting up for a long time. They dragged him off to the side of the trail, where Teodolinda grimly prepared for a long night's watch. But Hugo was nearly panicking.

Hugo looked back up the hill. It was too dark to see clearly, but in the distance he could just see the outline of the big tree hanging over the trail. Trembling all over, he quickly looked away, sure he had seen something slinking along the huge trunk. He curled up as close to his father's breast as he could. His bare feet stuck out of his short pants, and soon the cold of the night had him shivering.

Even cuddled up close to his father, Hugo could not help but think of how the *león* had snatched that little boy from the oxcart. His father was too drunk to protect him. Maybe his mother . . .

Hugo peeped over at his mother. What he saw almost made him smile. Teodolinda crouched on her haunches right beside Hugo. To

protect herself from the cold, she had pulled her heavy skirt up over her head. The lower part of her body was protected by her thick white slip. Hugo felt better. Mamita was apparently not afraid. And he was right between her and Papito. Surely he would be safe if the *león* came.

The wind whistled through the branches that hung over the trail. Fortunately, it was not raining. But, oh, the wind was cold! Now Hugo trembled not only with fear, but also with the cold. Time ticked on ever so slowly. The león never came. Finally and mercifully, Hugo fell asleep.

After huddling in that position for nearly two hours, they heard shouts. Hugo woke with a start. Teodolinda yanked her skirt down. Three men rode by, looking like ghosts in the dark. They were the last drinkers from La Peligrosa. They pulled their horses up, and one of them hollered at the huddled threesome, "Who is it and what's going on?"

Teodolinda quickly answered, "It's me, Teodolinda. Old Lico got so drunk he couldn't walk anymore. He fell here, and we are waiting until he wakes up."

"Well, this is no place to spend the night! Do you think he could walk if we helped you get him up?"

"I'd say so," Teodolinda answered hopefully.

The three men, drunk themselves, tied their horses and staggered over to the scene. Hugo was standing now, trembling all over. "I pity the little boy," one of the older gentlemen whispered. But Hugo heard. It warmed his heart to know somebody suspected what he had suffered.

Two men grabbed Lico, who was as limp as a rag, and hauled him to his feet. "Don Lico!" they shouted. "Here comes the *león!*" The news did not scare Lico at all. His limp legs still just hung. But Hugo's heart was pumping fast again. Could it be true?

The men cursed and swore. Gradually Lico woke up. Once Teodolinda could handle him again, they jumped onto their horses and took off for their own homes. "*¡Muchas gracias!*" Teodolinda hollered after them.

It was shortly after two o'clock when the threesome finally arrived at their Barranquilla abode. Lico barely found out when his wife tucked him into bed. Teodolinda was very glad to be home, and the bed felt better to her than to her husband. But of the three, little Hugo was the most glad to be out of the cold weather, and his warm bed felt better than any he had ever known in his life.

27

The young man walked slowly up the steep mountain. His ragged blue pants had been patched many times and were too short for his growing legs. His tan shirt was missing a button, and its tail was hanging out. His shoes were torn and too tight for his feet. His long wavy black hair was unkempt. He trudged along, dragging one leg, too crippled to travel, yet determined to climb the mountain. Though the morning air was chilly, his shirt was already moist with sweat from the great effort.

At the top of the first hill, the trail ran along a ridge. An old, rundown fence flanked the trail on both sides. Loose strands of wire hung from live fence posts, some as straight as arrows and others leaning over as if they were as weary as the young man hobbling past. Along the fencerow the weeds grew high, often blocking the view. At other places the young man could look into the steep fields that clung to the side of the mountain and the deep chasms beyond.

Suddenly a white-winged dove burst out from the underbrush right beside the traveler. The sudden, loud flapping of wings startled him, and he jumped. Then he stopped and chuckled at himself, his face twisting out of shape as only one side grinned. The dove took no notice as she flew off and landed in the shrubbery farther from the trail.

The young man stopped to catch his breath. Squeezing through a damaged place in the fence, he struggled into the field and sat on one of the millions of rocks that adorned the meadows. He stared down at the lowlands he had left behind. Far below he could see the gulf. The Puntarenas peninsula looked like a toy city. Beyond Puntarenas he could see the island of San Lucas, where his brother Marino had lived for five months.

The gulf at sundown from a Zapotal mountaintop.

As he gazed out to sea, tears flooded his eyes. He imagined telling his family all he had been through in the past year. Would they listen, now that his face was all twisted when he talked? Would they recognize him? Did they even remember him? Did they care that he had stayed alone at the children's hospital in San José for six long months? Not one of the family had come to visit him. In his heart Aurelio knew it was not because they did not love him. It was very hard for the mountain people to leave their homes and brave distant cities and strange places. And the Valverdes never had enough money for traveling.

Aurelio examined his surroundings. Right in front of him stood a large tree that had shed all its leaves in dry season, replacing them with thousands of bright yellow flowers. Down over the hill a naked Indian tree thrust his tall red branches up toward the heavens as if the Indian were raising his hands, invoking a blessing on the valley below. Among its bare branches hung a white wasp nest three times as big as Aurelio's head. A flock of brown jays spotted the young man sitting on the rock and began to warn all living creatures with their "peeah, peeah, peeah, peeah!"

Aurelio smiled his twisted smile again. He picked up a small rock and threw it at the birds, but his poor, weak arm could not propel the rock more than twenty feet into the valley below.

Aurelio slowly got to his feet. He noticed a stick nearby. He had been watching for a stick all morning, but none was the right size and shape. This one was perfect. He would use it to help him inch up the mountain toward home.

He came to La Cuesta del Tubo with its eight steep switchbacks. They seemed to go almost straight up. Aurelio took the hill with fortitude, even though he was getting thirsty and carried no water. He was also getting hungry and had no food. He would have to be tough and take the trail inch by inch.

It helped that it was dry season and the trail wasn't muddy. In places he clung to the large rocks along the trail and pulled himself up with his good arm. At other times he clung to the trees that loomed over the path. He was so tired that he actually crawled up the steepest places, and his knees were raw by the time he reached the top, where he crawled into the woods beside the trail and flopped onto the dry leaves. He was too exhausted to think of the rattlesnakes that abounded in the area. He just needed rest.

He fell asleep immediately and slept for an hour. When he woke up, the sun told him it was about two o'clock and that the worst heat was past. Aurelio lay there a while. *Is it worth it?* he wondered. *Why can't I just lie down and die? I dread meeting my family and my friends from Zapotal. What will they think of me? I'm a cripple like Gelo, and I can't even talk . . .*

Aurelio crawled out of the woods and, using a rock for support, pulled himself shakily to his feet. With the help of the stick, he traveled on, even more slowly than before.

By the time Aurelio topped Cerro Pelón, he was crying softly. His face was covered with dust, and his tears drew patterns on his cheeks as they ran down and dripped off his chin. He could barely take another step and was almost fainting from fatigue, thirst, and hunger. After struggling across the flat top, he arrived at the first farm on the Zapotal side, where Miguel Badilla lived.

Miguel hardly recognized Aurelio. He had grown taller, paler, and much thinner. He hardly looked like a Valverde anymore. "So you are on the way home from the hospital all alone?" Miguel asked after giving Aurelio food and water.

"Yes," Aurelio nodded humbly. He did not really want to talk, because he knew his face twisted to one side and looked a fright.

"You were very sick," the man concluded. "Very sick."

Aurelio nodded again and drank thirstily from the cup.

"Now you're on your way home, eh?"

Aurelio nodded.

"What kind of sickness got you?"

Aurelio tried his best to talk, and his face distorted as he hissed, "I 'ad a stroke."

The man nodded kindly and dropped the subject. He had not understood, but he knew it was useless to persist. The poor boy obviously couldn't talk.

It was almost three o'clock when Aurelio left Miguel's farm. It was cool now. The Zapotal mists wrapped him in their sweet embrace and mercifully cooled him. He could travel faster downhill, and he did not fall as often. Aurelio hobbled on. Each step was a battle, and every step taken was a victory won.

The deep hoof troughs at Las Marimbas were dry. But try as he might, he could not step from one crest to the other as he had when he was well. He used to run along the steps, as agile as a mountain goat. Now he had to climb down like the horses in rainy season. He would step up on the crest with his good foot, putting most of his weight on his stick. Then he would drag his bad foot up. Then he would let his bad foot slide down into the trough and plop down his other foot. It took him over a half hour to inch down the whole row of steps to the bottom and the welcome entrance to their home.

Aurelio hobbled into the yard just at dusk. Teodolinda was at the saloon, as usual. Lico saw Aurelio first. He walked out to meet him, hiding the emotions that surged through his heart. He started asking questions about his stay in the hospital. Aurelio dragged his useless foot the last couple of yards. He sat down on the porch and wiped the dust and tears from his hot face. Then he tried to answer his father's questions. But he was so ashamed of his twisted face and garbled words that he burst out crying instead. Lico blew his nose and tears welled up in his eyes.

By now the family had gathered. Gelo understood Aurelio's tears. He sat beside Aurelio and cried too. Lico called Hugo aside and whispered something in his ear. Hugo ran.

Aurelio made his way into the house, and the girls fed him. He was so happy to be home. He sat at the table and felt like a king. Those long months had seemed like an eternity.

Many kind folks at the hospital had befriended him, but he could not talk. He could only listen and use signs to try to explain what he wanted. Now his tongue was loosening, but he was still too ashamed to speak. So he lowered his head over his plate and gobbled down the home cooking he loved so much—rice and beans and cooked green bananas. It was the best meal he'd had in months!

Teodolinda rushed into the living room and crossed the floor as if airborne. She stopped by Aurelio's side and threw her arms around him. Aurelio cried again. His mother did too. Even Lico cried now. Hugo hid behind Gelo and cried with the rest.

Aurelio smelled the *guaro* on his mother's breath, and he knew nothing had changed at home. He would end up drinking too, he knew.

Later, as the nighthawks sang their mournful songs in the darkness, Aurelio caught up on the news. There was talk about moving to

Chachagua. A man had tricked Lico into signing some papers while he was drunk. Lico had come home and announced, "I sold the farm."

Now, weeks later, the family laughed when they told the story. Lico just grinned.

"Yeah," Gelo chuckled. "First he sold the farm for a song. Next he took a small down payment. The man promised to pay the rest in payments, but we know he won't, especially since he already has the signed papers."

"That's right," Ángel added. "That man sure is happy. He got two hundred *manzanas* of good land practically free!"

"At least we still have the house," Gelo said. "And Mamita was smart enough to keep her bit of land separate."

Teodolinda turned to Aurelio. "We're more and more convinced that the time has come for us to move out of Zapotal."

Aurelio did not know what to think. But as his thoughts cleared, he decided, *Nothing could be worse than our life here! We may as well move.*

28

Little Nelson stepped as fast as he could without breaking into a run, a heavy sack balanced on his back. He was in an awful hurry. Whatever he carried in the sack wiggled, and that worried him and made him walk faster.

Nelson was climbing the steep hill from Las Marimbas toward his home where he lived with his mother Nena and father Marcos and all the rest of the Quesadas. They all lived together in one house, almost piled on top of each other. That morning his mother had sent him on a strange errand, and now he was on his way home.

Just before Nelson reached the top of the hill, he saw the last person he wanted to see—his grandfather Lico Valverde. What would he do if Grandpa asked him what was in his sack? He would act as if nothing were wrong and just be friendly. Maybe his grandpa would not ask, and maybe the chickens would not squawk. So when Lico got close, Nelson gave him a big smile and said, *"Buenas,* Grandpa."

Lico returned the smile, and Nelson saw that he was not drunk. That made matters worse. When Lico was sober, he noticed things. Lico returned Nelson's *buenas* and then asked the fatal question: "And where were you, my son?"

"I was running an errand for my mother," Nelson answered, still smiling.

"That's good. You'd better hurry home, or she will scold you," Lico admonished; then he continued down the trail toward his home.

"And where were you?" Nelson asked on impulse.

Lico paused and looked around. "I was also running an errand for the woman of the house," he replied with a chuckle.

Little Nelson sighed in relief and hurried up the hill toward home. After topping the hill and running down the other side, he ran into the living room, breathless. "Mama, I made it!" he gasped. "But I just about got caught. When I got there, just like you said, no one was home. I hollered to be sure. Everybody was either at La Peligrosa or down by the still. The girls must have been over at Lidier's place. After I was sure no one was around, I took the corn you sent and ran into the kitchen calling the chickens. The dumb things followed me in, and I closed the door. I caught these two fat ones and stuck them in my sack. Then I ran."

"Great! Good job, son. We'll get more later. They won't know the difference. That horrid woman has too many chickens anyway."

Nelson liked his spunky grandmother, and he did not like hearing her called a horrid woman. But he was used to hearing the Quesadas talk about the Valverdes, and he liked it when his mother praised him for a job well done, even if the job was stealing from Grandma.

"But, Mother, wait until I tell you what happened. When I was coming back, I met Grandpa Valverde. I was so sure he was going to ask what was in my sack."

"Did he ask you?" Nena wondered.

"No. I just acted friendly. When he asked where I had been, I told him I was running an errand for you."

"I wonder where Don Lico was," Nena mused. "That sure was a close call."

"He said he was running an errand for the woman of the house too."

"I don't know where he was," Nena laughed, "but I can sure tell you where he was going. He was on his way to the still. Today is Saturday.

That's why I sent you today. I bet Don Lico missed the *cabezón* because he was running an errand for that hag."

Nena, heavy with her sixth child, turned to her mother. "I'm glad you are a midwife, Mama. I couldn't bear it if Teodolinda had to deliver my babies."

"Yes," Adelia agreed. "People claim Teodolinda is the best midwife in Zapotal, but I think she uses witchcraft."

"Mother," Nena said firmly, "even if I have complications, don't ever let that woman touch me. Do you hear?"

"I won't, don't you worry. I will be your midwife. And it looks like it will be soon," Adelia chuckled.

*　*　*

One day the Quesadas were having a party. Since they did not sell liquor anymore, they had to buy *contrabando* from the Valverdes. They would not go themselves, but would send someone else.

Toward evening the youngest uncles started coaxing Nelson to take a drink of liquor while Grandpa Durando was not around. Luis Quesada, the youngest of Durando's sons, handed him a whole glass full. "Come on, Nelson. You can do it. Just guzzle it down, and you will be a man."

"Not a whole glass the first time," Nelson snapped. "That's way too much. Just give me a half glass and I'll do it."

Luis dumped half of the firewater back into the bottle. Nelson stared at the glass. He had always seen how even the bravest drinkers twisted up their faces when they took a swig of *guaro*. He had concluded a long time ago that the stuff must be horrible. He almost wished he had not accepted the challenge. But there was no backing out now. He grasped the glass bravely and downed it in one big gulp.

Nelson was horrified at the way the stuff burned its way down his throat. It burned all the way up under his scalp and down to the bottom of his innards. It was as if his whole body were on fire. Poor Nelson coughed and gasped for breath. His uncles laughed uproariously. But a boy taking his first drink of liquor is one of the saddest of sights, because though it is the first, it is seldom the last.

That young boy will spend years lamenting that he took that first drink.

Nelson expected strange aftereffects, but nothing like what happened. He ran out of the house and into the yard, feeling as if he needed to vomit. His belly churned, and it felt like creatures were crawling up his throat. The next thing he knew, he was partly vomiting and partly gagging and pulling strands of something from his mouth and nose and flinging them aside. Suddenly he realized what was happening. The strong drink had disturbed his parasites, and the worms were fighting their way out. Nena's chickens ate them as fast as Nelson flung them into the grass.

*   *   *

Aurelio was feeling much better since he was back from the hospital. Except for a stutter, he was almost back to normal. One day he decided to go watch a soccer game. Right up the newly built road from La Peligrosa was a flat field where young people often gathered to play. Aurelio was not strong enough yet to join them, but he wanted to watch.

Everybody thinks I am worthless because of my sickness, he thought, leaning against the fence. *I want to show everyone I am a man now . . .*

He saw Luis Quesada among the players. Luis was his age. Suddenly Aurelio got the urge to fight Luis. He was sure he could whip him, and people would realize he was growing up. He had always admired Gelo for being strong and fierce. No one wanted to fight Gelo anymore. Aurelio wanted to be a hero like him. And today was his chance.

When the game broke up and people began to leave, Aurelio yelled from the road, "Luis, you s-s-s-stinking Quesada, why don't you c-c-c-come up here and f-f-fight with me."

Luis was startled, but undaunted. "Hey, I ain't scared of you. If you want to fight, come down here!"

The crowd egged Luis on. "Go get him!" one of the men challenged. "He's mocking you! You can do it!"

"I p-p-prefer f-f-fighting on the road," Aurelio shouted back. "I think the road is where the b-b-brave g-g-guys f-f-fight. Only the ch-chickens f-f-fight in the f-f-field."

By now the crowd was pouring through the fence onto the road. Luis was not about to stay in the field looking like a coward. He crossed the fence down a ways from Aurelio and swaggered up the road, taunting the loudmouthed Valverde. The crowd cheered. Since Aurelio had picked the fight, the crowd was on Luis's side.

Aurelio flung himself at Luis, fists flying. The crowd went wild and cheered them on. To everyone's surprise, including Aurelio's and Luis's, they were a perfect match. They both ducked and dodged punches, but both also landed a few. The crowd was enjoying it immensely.

But Aurelio quickly tired. As soon as he slowed down, Luis punched him harder and aimed more viciously. Aurelio knew he would not be able to hold his own much longer.

Aurelio suddenly gasped, "Let's f-f-f-finish this f-f-f-fight another d-d-day." Then he swung around and ran for home.

The crowd hooted and laughed. Luis's voice rose above the din. "Coward! Run home to your mama!"

When Aurelio got home he downed his third drink for the day, then his fourth, burying his shame in the bottle. He was quickly learning how the Valverdes coped with life's troubles.

*   *   *

Teodolinda was proud of her sow. The sow had already had a litter of twelve piglets, and now she was due again within several weeks. Piglets were cold cash, and Teodolinda needed the cash very much right now.

Like all the Zapotal hogs, Teodolinda's ran loose. Penned pigs required too much food to make them fat. If they ran loose, they found fruit, roots, and other goodies in the wild to supplement their diet. Teodolinda's special sow got whey from the milk from their several cows, and they also fed her corn. But she grew fat on all the stuff she picked up in the wild.

This sow also had a sweet tooth. Her weakness was sugarcane. Lico's cane field was close to the house, where they could watch it. The dogs and the children ran the pigs off if they tried to sneak some cane. So the sow went up over the hill to Durando Quesada's patch. Their cane patch was so big that there was no way they could see when the sow sneaked in. Several times the Quesadas had caught the sow ripping down the cane and chewing out the rich juice. They always ran the sow off, whacking her with sticks.

One day Nena and her smaller children and her siblings were watching her father cut cane to make *dulce*. He had peeled a piece of cane for each of his grandchildren, and they were chewing to their hearts' content. On her way back, Nena heard a noise deep in the cane patch. Pushing quietly through the tall cane, she came upon Teodolinda's sow chewing on a broken cane. Nena felt her blood rise. How she hated that sow! She sneaked out and returned home without the sow being any the wiser.

She arrived at the house all sweaty and panting. "Nelson, quick!" she gasped. "Your grandma's sow is in the cane patch right now. Go beat her up! Where's Luis?"

Soon Nena had the two boys all excited. "She's right in the middle of the patch. Sneak in with your sticks and machetes ready and then chase her and beat her all the way to the top of the hill. Since she is big and fat, she can't run very fast. Give her a beating she won't forget so she will never want to come back again. Run, boys!"

The boys did not hate the pig. They did not even hate Teodolinda. But they did love to be ornery, and this promised to be an adventure.

The boys got their machetes and cut nice-sized sticks to whack the pig. Thus armed, they sneaked into the cane field like mighty hunters in the jungle. They ambushed the sow, which ran for her life, the two boys in hot pursuit through the tall cane, whacking the poor animal as they ran.

When they burst into the open field, the sow figured the boys would give up as usual. But this time it was different. The sow started up the long steep hill toward her home, but her tremendous weight and her tummy full of piglets slowed her down. The boys took advantage of her weariness. They had been using their sticks on the sow, beating her right on her back. But when she slowed down, they started using their machetes, smacking her with the flat sides again and again.

When the sow slowed down more, the boys got rougher. In their carelessness, their machetes did not stay flat. All of a sudden Nelson gasped, "Luis, you cut her all along her back!" Sure enough, blood was trickling down her ribs.

"It doesn't matter!" Luis laughed. "This pig will never come back to our farm!"

Nelson decided to help make sure she did not. He ran alongside and beat her ears with the flat side of his machete. Once the machete caught her ear and almost cut it off.

By now the sow was so exhausted that she stopped altogether. Her breath came in quick, short gasps. Nelson and Luis noticed that she was shaking all over. That frightened them. Nelson muttered, "We done killed this pig!"

"No, we haven't," Luis said. "But we can tell your mama that the pig will never come back here again."

The boys returned home. The pig finally topped the hill and stumbled blindly down the other side. She crashed into the yard at Lico's and flopped down right in front of the house. Teodolinda came to the door to see what was happening. She found Gelo on his hands and knees checking the sow. She joined him in the yard and stared.

"Look what they did to my poor sow!" she gasped. "They've killed her for sure!"

"You're right, Mamita. This is the Quesadas' doing. They are the meanest beasts around. How did they dare do this to your sow?"

By now the girls and the rest of the children had joined the solemn circle. They shook their heads as they saw the ear hanging on by a sliver, the huge gash across her back, and her white skin turned purple all along her back where she had been beaten.

"The people who did this are more animals than this beast!" Teodolinda fumed. "It's not even the animal's fault. Animals are animals. We didn't pen her up, so it's our fault. But instead of coming and beating us up, those cowards took it out on the poor pig. Look at that poor sow, trembling all over and hardly able to breathe."

Just then Lico and the boys came home from work. They joined the rest of the family and stared. The sow was a gruesome sight. All of Teodolinda's dreams of what she would do with the money from the piglets popped like bubbles. Anger surged in her heart.

Lico shook his head slowly. "I am sure the Quesadas did this. I suspect Nena was behind it. Marcos keeps telling me that she hates us with a passion. She probably got a couple of her younger brothers or her own children to do it."

"Those people will pay," Marino swore vehemently. "There is a penalty for something like this. We could make them pay us for the hog and more. They are supposed to warn us if our animals are doing damage. But these people take the law into their own hands. It's not right."

"That's true," Lico agreed. "But if we think we can put Durando in jail, we're dreaming. First of all, he has legal authority in Zapotal. Second, he would go to the Miramar judge with a story so twisted that we'd end up in jail for their crime. No, we'd better not ask for more trouble with the Quesadas."

The boys were angry and cried for blood. They wanted Lico to go with them to the Quesadas' house to force them to pay for the pig. But Lico refused.

Teodolinda finally spoke up. "Boys, what they did to this pig is awful, I agree. But it won't make the sow better to go and beat them up. It will only make matters worse. It's my sow. I will take the loss. Let's let God punish those people if He wants to. I vote for no more problems with the Quesadas.

"Victoria, go put the big kettle of water on. Aurelio, go get the knife to cut her throat. The rest of you go get firewood. She is almost gone already. Let's forget about revenge and have a party with plenty of pig meat."

Everybody agreed, mostly because all of a sudden their mouths watered at the thought of fresh pork and lots of *guaro*.

*   *   *

"Mother, something is wrong," Nena panted. "This baby can't be born. Something is different this time. Please, can't you do something?"

"I'm sorry, daughter. I have done all I can. Something is very wrong. I don't know what more to do but wait."

Adelia walked out to the yard and talked to Durando. "What can we do? Nena is very sick. I'm afraid for the baby. She says she hasn't felt any movement all day. That's a bad sign."

"Why don't you go get Teodolinda?" Durando asked. "She's the best midwife in Zapotal."

"Humph! I don't trust her. Besides, Nena won't let the woman touch her."

"So you two are too proud to go call her," Durando said. "That's too bad."

"Durando, stop it!" Adelia snapped. "Teodolinda's not an option, and you know it! Will you send for Doña Chepa?"

"Doña Chepa lives over in San Buenas. That's far away, woman! Teodolinda lives just over the hill!"

"Well, be prepared then," Adelia retorted. "Things don't look good for your daughter."

Durando sent Luis to San Buenas for Doña Chepa. Two hours later Doña Chepa entered Nena's room. It did not take her long to draw her conclusion. "The baby is dead," she told Adelia and Durando. "I am not sure why she is unable to deliver it. The only person around here who can help is Teodolinda. Get her right away, or the mother might die too."

"We didn't want to call Teodolinda," Adelia whispered.

"Why not? She's the best—"

"We don't get along."

"Well, tonight you'd better forget your differences and send for her!"

"I told you," Durando told his wife. "We are wasting precious time."

"Wait," Adelia groaned, running into the bedroom. Doña Chepa followed.

Nena lay still on the bed, her face pale and drenched in sweat. Her arms were flung back, and her thrashing had stopped. Her breath came in quick gasps. Suddenly Adelia noticed her face changing color. She was turning slightly blue.

"I am going to die," Nena groaned. "Help me, quick!"

"Nelson," Adelia screamed, "come! Nelson, your mother is dying! Run get your other grandma right away. Tell her your mother is dying in her delivery. Hurry!"

Nelson's feet hardly touched the ground as he flew up the hill toward Grandpa's house. He often went to Grandpa's—sometimes to visit, sometimes to steal. But never on an errand as important as this one. He ran faster, sure that Teodolinda could save his mother's life.

After Nelson left, Adelia shook her head and started to cry. "I can't take this," she sobbed. Pointing to Doña Chepa, she choked, "You take over. I'm leaving. I can't stand Teodolinda!"

To Durando's horror, his wife slipped out of the house into the darkness. *What a proud woman I married*, he thought, and sighed. He and Doña Chepa were on their own.

At Lico's place everyone was ready for bed. For once Teodolinda had come home and left one of the girls at the saloon. She desperately needed rest. She was sitting on a chair, just about falling asleep, listening to her husband talk when someone yelled at the door. Lico opened it, and little Nelson burst in.

"Mama is having her baby and is dying and she needs you right away." The words tumbled out. "Please, can you come?"

Teodolinda was glad Lico was sober for once. "What shall I do?" she asked him in low tones. "Do you think this is a trick?"

"No, I don't think so. I think you should go help her," Lico answered slowly. "She is your son's wife, and even if she weren't, she needs you."

"But she hates me. And Adelia hates me even more."

"Well, it goes to show that hate doesn't get us anywhere, and we do need each other. I say go."

"You are right," Teodolinda said. "I will prove to them that I don't hate them. If I don't go, they will think that I do, and she might die." She turned to her grandson, still waiting at the door. "Wait, Nelson. I'm coming."

Teodolinda ran into her room, grabbed her bag, and put on her rubber boots, since it was raining hard. Then she remembered. "Lico, I need a . . . you know what."

Lico grinned. He found the bottle and served his wife. As they parted at the door, they did not give any sign that little Nelson could see, but they shared a moment of closeness that they had not felt for a long, long time.

Once she got to the Quesadas' house, Teodolinda was all business. "Good evening," she said to Durando and Doña Chepa; then she marched right into the bedroom. Doña Chepa followed. Teodolinda stood at the bedside briefly, taking it all in. Nena barely opened her eyes. Teodolinda could see why they had called her. Adelia was gone, and Nena was too near death to care. She was turning blue. There was no time to lose.

Teodolinda quickly went to work, her fingers carefully probing Nena's abdomen. "Yes, the baby is dead," she said quietly. "There is no movement. It may have been dead for a day or two. It is also breech. The baby will have to be turned."

Doña Chepa watched as Teodolinda worked. This woman had never studied midwifery. She had only gone to grade school for parts of two years. Yet she was obviously skilled. She had a gift Doña Chepa herself did not have.

Nena was so far gone she barely responded. Every now and then she flung her head from one side to the other and groaned. "Please help me," she whispered once. "I'm going to die!"

"Not if I can help it," Teodolinda murmured, wiping sweat and strands of hair from her forehead.

When Teodolinda left the Quesadas' house several hours later, the dead baby was prepared for burial and Nena had fallen into an exhausted sleep.

Teodolinda's enemies, including Adelia, would still curse her and say it was witchcraft. But one enemy never said that again. Although Nena did not say anything good about Teodolinda, she stopped cursing her. The Quesada-Valverde feud was still far from dying, but the fight between Nena and Teodolinda was over forever.

29

Teodolinda felt her life was spiraling down into a bottomless pit. One morning she felt especially blue. She'd had a fight with Lico because there was never enough money and he never planted anything anymore. He had long ago stopped raising cattle because he claimed he never had any luck with them, but the problem was partly due to his temper. One day he beat a wayward cow so badly that he broke her horn off. The cow got screwworms in her head and died. That and his drinking problem constituted most of Lico's bad "luck." So he sold his last cows to Teodolinda and encouraged her to make a go of it.

Now Lico was constantly asking her for a calf to sell for cash. That was what they had argued about that morning. Teodolinda felt rotten for getting so angry and unreasonable.

Gelo had been in another fight. Aurelio had gotten drunk and picked another fight too. Even her girls were getting wilder all the time. And to top it all off, at noon she had found out that Marcos and Nena were threatening to break up again.

That afternoon she started drinking. She was serving at the bar, and almost no one stopped in during the long afternoon. Teodolinda never drank to get drunk; she just drank enough to forget. But this afternoon she went beyond that. Like Lico, she felt she needed to drown herself and her sorrows in *guaro*.

Toward evening her legs felt so weak that she knew she had to sit down, so she just plopped on the floor behind the bar. Then, feeling the false, stupid happiness of the doped, she started to sing.

"Hay un llanto que atraviesa el espacio para llegar a Dios,
Es el llanto de los niños que lloran en desesperación . . ."
(There's a cry that flies through space to reach God,
It's the cry of the children who weep in desperation.)

Little Hugo heard his mama singing and went to see what was going on. When he saw her sitting on the floor, eyes closed, singing at the top of her voice, he giggled and called Aurelio. Aurelio did not think it was funny. He stood and stared. He had never seen his mother so drunk before.

Teodolinda bellowed on with her song.

"Violencia, maldita violencia,
¿Por qué te empeñas a cubrir de sangre la tierra de Dios?
¿Por qué no dejas que en los campos nazca nueva floración?"
(Violence, cursed violence!
Why do you make it your job to cover God's earth with blood?
Why don't you allow the countryside to burst into bloom?)
—Chaclón/Lorenzo Palacios Quispe

"Mamita," Aurelio reproached her, "get up and go to bed. Soon the men will come for their drinks and find you in this condition. I am ashamed."

Teodolinda threw her head back and opened her mouth to sing again. *"Violencia, maldita violencia . . ."*

Aurelio shook her shoulder. "Mother, wake up! We have to get you to bed before the men come."

He soon saw that it was hopeless. He ran into the kitchen to find Victoria. "Quick, Victoria. Come look at Mamita."

Victoria was as shocked as Aurelio, but she grabbed one arm while Aurelio grabbed the other. Fortunately, Teodolinda did not weigh much. Together they hauled her to her feet, dragged her across the hall, flopped her onto the bed, and covered her with a blanket.

They were barely done when they heard someone yell, *"¡Upe!"* Don Rufino, the first customer, marched into the hall and sat at the bar. "Hey, where is everybody? I'm thirsty."

Aurelio stepped behind the bar and tended it for the evening.

"Where's Old Mama?" Rufino bellowed. "I ain't used to not having her here with her smiles and jokes."

"She's sick in bed," Aurelio answered quickly. "She needs some rest."

"That's right," Rufino agreed. "We all do sometimes."

About then the next customer strode in. The night had begun.

The next morning Victoria and Aurelio told their mother how she had acted. Teodolinda had the most serious look on her face they had ever seen. She was ashamed. Suddenly she felt a great revulsion for the saloon and all it stood for. She wished she had never bought her share. She hated the dances, the fights, and the wicked rosaries. She knew they were all wrong, and they disgusted her. Something had to change.

*   *   *

Juan Gonzalez was the Valverdes' archenemy. He especially hated Marcos. One day he and his cronies decided to give Marcos his dues. They knew which day Marcos rode through their area on his way to La Peligrosa. Laughing and plotting, they set their trap.

At a lonely place on the trail was a high bank with a cluster of trees on its crown. Juan and two of his buddies hid among the trees on their horses. As they reined in their mounts, Juan chuckled, "Now we'll see what that monkey is made of. He thinks he's tough stuff, but today we will prove that he's just a bunch of hot air."

"How will you stop him?" his brother Beto asked.

"Just wait and watch," Juan admonished, loosening his lariat from the saddle's straps. "I'm a cattleman, and I can handle a lariat better than you handled your spoon this morning when you ate your *gallo pinto!*"

Juan hushed as he heard the voices of men riding down the trail just over the crest. Juan sat loosely in the saddle, his lariat unwound and ready. As the riders came into view, he saw Marcos riding double with his son Nelson on the back. Hugo was riding alone on his own mount. They were talking animatedly, riding toward the saloon, totally oblivious of the three wicked men high on the trail's bank.

When the two horses were about even with the hidden men, Juan urged his horse forward gently into plain sight. Marcos heard the noise of the horse's feet in the tall grass and looked around abruptly. Juan was riding toward him on the bank, faster now, his lariat circling over his head. The other two riders followed.

Marcos knew it was too late to escape. He was well within reach of the rope. He spurred his horse, which leaped forward in a wild dash. Hugo's horse followed. Then Marcos ducked, bending way over his horse's neck, burying his face in its mane. His horse was galloping fast when the lariat hissed through the air like an angry rattler striking at its prey, but since Marcos was bent over, the rope missed him. To everyone's horror, it caught Nelson squarely around the shoulders. Juan's horse was trained to slam to a stop as soon as the rope left his master's hand. Marcos's horse had just put out a powerful burst of speed. The result was logical and horrible. Before Nelson even had any inkling what had happened, he was jerked off the horse and plunged onto the trail right where the mud was deepest. He fell on his back in the mud.

When Marcos heard his son scream and felt the saddle lighten, he reined in his horse, cursing and swearing. A galloping horse does not stop on a dime, but Marcos loved his son, and in a matter of seconds he and Hugo had turned their mounts. Marcos drew his *cutacha* and raced back toward the fallen boy with a bloodcurdling cry.

Juan, knowing he was in trouble, frantically jerked the lariat loose from the saddle's horn. Abandoning rope and child, all three men took off, spurring their mounts fiercely.

Hugo and Marcos wanted to follow the three bandits until they caught them or their horses fell dead, but Nelson was moaning and groaning in the mud. So Marcos and Hugo slid to a halt and jumped off their horses to help the poor boy.

Nelson was sure he was dying. Mud covered his head and filled his ears. But his only injury was a rope burn around his shoulders. Fortunately, the lariat had settled onto his shoulders and not his neck, which would have snapped with the jerk of the rope.

By the time they had Nelson ready to travel, they realized it was senseless and even dangerous to pursue a ruffian like Juan. So Nelson crawled back onto the horse, carrying the rope as his trophy from the awful experience. Marcos was furious, but he decided to bide his time.

Several weeks later Marcos had his chance. He met Juan at a *rosario* and beat him soundly.

* * *

Nobody remembers what started the last fight between the Valverdes and the Quesadas. They just know it happened one Sunday night after a dance. It started in La Peligrosa and then moved out into the dark yard, as if they naturally fled for the dark as they fought.

The Quesadas and the Valverdes were all involved. Even old Lico and Durando were in it, and a whole bunch of the boys. Fortunately, Luis Valverde was far away in Chachagua. But the rest were all there and going strong. At one point even Adelia jumped in. She got knocked down under the men who were hitting and biting each other. Someone shouted, "Hey, they're crushing Mother!" They stopped fighting long enough for her to get up and run; then they went back to rolling, scratching, biting, pinching, hitting, and cursing all over the saloon's yard. They fought until they were too tired to fight anymore. Then they finally got up, and the Quesadas all went home.

Everyone went home bragging that they had won. But in a far more real sense, they all lost.

* * *

The little wisp of a woman tiptoed quietly through the door the boy pointed out to her. She was dressed poorly, but her clothes were clean. Her gray hair was bound back in a modest bun. She wore simple rubber sandals. Her hands were work-worn and rough. Her eyes were sad.

The room she entered was tiny and dark. Right beside the nearest wall was a chair. She knew she must sit there, so she did. Right beside her, a little below her face, was a set of tiny holes drilled through the thin plywood wall. There, she knew, she must crouch to confess her sins. It seemed so strange to confess your sins to a wall. She had not done it in years. It would seem so much better to sit right in front of a real person and confess your sins to his face. But she knew a priest waited just across the thin wall, ready to hear her confession.

For a moment she was overwhelmed with what she was going to do. She was going to confess her sins to a man God had chosen to mediate between Him and her. That man would decide what she must do to atone for her sins. And she knew her sins were many.

The woman leaned toward the tiny holes. She felt shy. Her breath came in quick little gasps, and her heart was beating hard. She felt like she needed a stiff drink. Then she rebuked herself under her breath. She was here to get rid of her sins, and yet she desired them at the same time!

Quietly she whispered to see if anyone was there, "Good day."

"Good day," a gruff voice answered. "What are your sins?"

The voice sounded cold. It suddenly occurred to her that this priest had probably heard so many sins that very day that he just wanted to get this over with. She blushed deeply.

"Lately I have been drinking some . . . I have been dancing . . . I have been enjoying the dances . . ."

Suddenly the voice on the other side of the holes changed its tone. "Where are you from?"

"I'm from Zapotal," she answered, confused. *Why does he want personal information? He's not supposed to know who I am.*

The voice across the wall grew husky. "Listen, it would be nice if you came to my house, and you could tell me about yourself privately. I would serve some wine, and we would have a wonderful time . . ."

She was shocked. His tone and message were clear—way too clear! Her heart turned cold as ice. She fled the room, her emotions switched from repentance to anger. As she fled the huge San Ramón cathedral, she vowed under her breath, "I will never enter a Catholic church again!"

Teodolinda kept her word.

On the way home Teodolinda stopped at her mother's place and told her the whole story. "Oh, yes, I could have warned you," Angelina said. "That priest has several children with some of the church ladies in his parish. He's got a bad reputation."

Later, after her anger cooled, she told Lico, who only chuckled. "That old priest had no idea you were a fifty-seven-year-old grandma!" he said.

That night Teodolinda lay in her bed tossing as several hours ticked by. Sleep seemed as far away as the wicked priest down in San Ramón. How could a man, supposedly a leader of God's people, be so wicked and ungodly? All her life she had trusted in her parents' religion. She, like many Catholics, had sworn to live and die in the Roman Catholic Church.

But now what? Were all the leaders of the church fake? Was the whole church rotten to the core?

Her religion did not satisfy. Neither did it help her overcome her sin. And with that acknowledgement, a new question arose: Was there something better out there?

One more question haunted her as she finally drifted to sleep. *How can I get hold of God so my life can change? Is there a better way?*

Though her thoughts never found their way into words, the small cry of her heart leaped high into the heavens and reached the throne of the Father. The Father did not answer in an audible voice. But, in response to her cry, a measure of peace crept into her soul. And as the little woman fell asleep, a calm answer touched her heart. *Yes, there is a better way. Someday you, the little woman who runs La Peligrosa, will find Me. That's the kind of woman you are, and that's the kind of God I am!*

30

Las Marimbas was a flurry of activity preparing for the next day's big *rosario*. Teodolinda knew this would be their last one, and she wanted their leaving to have a religious touch, so they were going all out to make this *rosario* memorable. They invited lots of people. Gelo was preparing a double batch of *guaro*. Teodolinda and the girls were making more food than they ever had before. Old Nacho was going to lead the *rosario,* and Vicente Jiménez would provide the music for the dance.

Almost everyone was busy. Gelo and the boys were at the still. Teodolinda and the girls were at La Peligrosa. Lico was in Miramar buying supplies. The children were here and there. At one point, Hugo was alone at home. He felt important guarding the house.

He sat out on the porch watching the road to see which of the family would come back first. While he waited, a little old gentleman walked into the yard. Hugo recognized his face but did not remember his name, though his father would have known it was Rafael Herrera from Palmital. The little man was friendly and soon was sitting on the porch in deep conversation with Hugo. Hugo felt important to be able to take care of the visitor until Papito returned.

"Where is everybody?" Rafael asked, looking around suspiciously.

Hugo explained carefully where they all were.

"Is Gelo down at the still?" the little man probed.

Soon Hugo was telling the man all about the still. "Today," he reported, "Gelo is keeping the *cabezón* for Old Nacho, who will be coming to the *rosario* tomorrow."

"Do you have any *guaro* here at the house?" the man asked slyly.

"You bet! We are making two batches, one right after the other, so there's plenty for the *rosario*. I know where they hide the stuff!" Hugo boasted.

"Hey, let's you and me have a little party right now," Rafael suggested, his eager eyes betraying his great thirst.

After some convincing, Hugo finally parted the tall grass and brought out a gallon of the firewater. Rafael thought it would be best to get Hugo to drink a bunch; then he could make off with the rest of the jug. So he took a swig; then, smacking his lips, he gushed, "That was so good!"

Hugo was used to drinking, though he had never been drunk. But Rafael made sure he got drunk this time. He convinced him to take swig after swig. As soon as Hugo showed signs of getting high, Rafael picked up what he wanted to take home. Just as he grabbed the jug, Leyla popped through the gate by the road on her way back from La Peligrosa, where she was helping butcher a pig for the next day. Rafael saw her coming. He dropped the jug and scooted around the back of the house.

Leyla caught sight of someone disappearing from the porch and escaping around the back. She sprinted up the steps to see what was going on. What she found appalled her. There sat Hugo, his eyes gleaming dumbly. Beside him was the jug of *guaro*.

"Hugo!" Leyla shouted, grabbing him by the shoulder. "Who was here with you?"

Hugo looked up at her and did not answer. Instead he started giggling and slumped over on the floor. There he started laughing as if Leyla were the funniest thing he had ever seen.

Leyla swung around in time to see the little man run out through the gate and up the road. She was shaking with anger. It would be foolish to run after the man, but oh, she wished she could! Who had dared come to their house and make their youngest boy drink himself into a stupor?

Leyla grabbed the jug and hid it in the house. What could she do for Hugo? She decided to put him to bed, but when she got to the porch she found him vomiting. She ran back into the house and burst out crying.

Later Hugo was sober enough to describe the culprit. The family was furious when they figured out who it was.

Rafael Herrera did not show up at the *rosario* the next day.

* * *

The next morning dawned with rare and delightful weather. The air was nippy, and for once the Zapotal sky was as blue as the deepest, clearest tide pool in the Pacific Ocean. The many Zapotal birds sang joyfully.

It should have been a wonderful day. Teodolinda almost got caught up in the feeling of the morning, but she soon forgot any trace of joy as she slaved the day away with her family preparing for the evening *rosario*.

Once, during a short pause, she looked at her kitchen. The big kettle with the corn mush for the tamales was full and bubbling. Victoria stirred it with a huge spoon hewn out of a one-by-three. It looked more like a boat paddle than a spoon, but it worked.

Mireya was preparing the banana leaves that Aurelio had brought in. She pulled each leaf briefly through the fire burning on the hearth. The big leaves wilted in the heat and became pliable and soft for wrapping the tamales later. Mireya then sliced the stem out of each long leaf with a sharp knife.

A big pot of meat cooked over the end of the hearth. Later, when they made the tamales, they would put a chunk of meat in each one. Extra meat hung in strips over the fire. It was raw, but salted. The smoke and the heat would preserve it, and Teodolinda would use it in her cooking for weeks to come.

Teodolinda had been cutting up the vegetables on the *molendero*. Now she ran out into the yard and cut a handful of cilantro to flavor the tamales. On her way back in she stopped in the doorway for a moment to catch her breath. She smiled as she watched Hugo in the yard chopping dry branches to size for the earthen cookstove.

Teodolinda knew she should hurry, but she leaned against the doorjamb thoughtfully. For some strange reason she remembered the day, years and years ago, when she had leaned against her favorite tree back in San Ramón, daydreaming to her heart's content. Back then she'd had time for that kind of thing, but hardly ever anymore.

As Teodolinda watched her tribe working, she knew she should be happy. It was a lovely day, and she had raised all these children. Her husband was healthy and still helped provide a little bit. Yes, she should have been happy. But she was not.

Somewhere deep in Teodolinda's heart lurked a nameless dread. It was always there whenever she stopped and checked how she really felt, but sometimes it grew into a monster and almost choked her. Today, though everybody else seemed happy, Teodolinda felt the monster clutching at her throat.

Suddenly she knew. The monster was fear. Right now she was afraid of the evening. It was all one big drama, and she knew the ending before it began. This was just the opening scene. It would end tonight at about midnight.

The dark being who seemed to be directing the play had a hideous grin on his face as he focused on each member of the family. He, too, knew how the evening would end. Not the details. Teodolinda did not know the details either. But they both knew there would be a *rosario*, then some food, then some music, then some drinking, then the fights. And the fear that even now clutched at Teodolinda's heart was, *Who will be hurt tonight?*

*   *   *

Hugo and Ulises rode double on a new horse Lico had raised since Jabón had died. Ulises sat in front and held the reins. Hugo felt very important, for he was carrying El Niñito (the little child). He clutched him tightly. Old Nacho had warned him sternly, "I will let you use El

Niñito, but you must be very careful. The trails are muddy, and if you let him fall into the mud, it will bring a curse on you."

Hugo took it all very seriously and clung to El Niñito and to the horse so he would not fall off. But the horse slipped as they trotted into a mud hole, and Hugo almost fell. He hugged his older brother and resettled himself as soon as the horse's pace evened out. As he did, he noticed that the door of El Niñito's box had flung open.

El Niñito, a plaster of Paris sculpture of baby Jesus in a wooden box, was an object of worship in the Zapotal community. Old Nacho usually kept it at his house, but it really did not belong to him. It belonged to anyone who was Catholic. So whoever wanted to could borrow El Niñito for a *rosario.* All he had to do was take care of him and bring him back as soon as he was done.

On top of the box was a little slot in the wood. During the *rosario,* everyone was expected to drop in a peso or two. Then Nacho would collect the offerings and take them to Miramar. Usually the little door had a lock on it, but the lock had gone bad, Old Nacho had explained, so he just expected Lico to send him the money collected that night.

El Niñito stood upright in the little box lined with white cloth and flowers. The baby was dressed in a purple robe, his hand raised as if waving, his sweet face smiling. All this Hugo saw at a glance when the little door in the front of the box was flung open. He closed the tiny door again, never noticing that the baby's purple hat had fallen into the mud.

Hugo and Ulises delivered El Niñito to La Peligrosa. By then Teodolinda was there to receive him and carefully place him on the bed. He would rest there until evening.

*   *   *

It was seven o'clock, and the hill between La Peligrosa and Las Marimbas danced with dozens of tiny lights like fireflies. The candlelit procession chanted as it made its way up the trail, *"Gloria al Padre, al Hijo y al Espíritu Santo . . ."*

---

* Glory be to the Father, to the Son, and to the Holy Spirit.

A nighthawk glided ahead of the procession, its eyes glowing red in the light of the candles. It landed on the trail and bobbed up and down as if nervous. Then it held still and whistled its mournful song.

The crowd started singing a song about El Niñito Dios (the God child). El Niñito was carried on a wooden structure between four men, each grasping a corner. The frame was decked out in wildflowers, picked fresh from the Zapotal countryside. The baby's cathedral was perched right in the middle among the flowers.

Old Nacho walked right in front of the frame, setting the pace and leading the chants and songs. Teodolinda and Lico, who had planned the *rosario*, walked right behind the frame. The rest of the crowd surrounded them. At the tail end came the Jiménez brothers. They carried their instruments and played whenever the crowd sang.

It took the crowd almost an hour to walk the mile from La Peligrosa to Las Marimbas. Teodolinda felt a special joy when they carried El Niñito into the house. Oh, she hoped it would somehow bring peace and forgiveness and blessing! In her heart she feared it would not, because she had tried it so many times before. But maybe, just maybe . . .

They placed the little box on a small table in the center of the room. Then Old Nacho called the people in and announced, "We will now start the *rosario*."

Suddenly Nacho stopped and studied the little idol. Then he turned and asked Teodolinda, "Where is El Niñito's hat?"

"I don't know," Teodolinda stammered. "Does he wear a hat?"

"Yes, and it's gone!"

"I will check with the boys," Teodolinda promised fearfully.

"Well, it had better show up. He always wears a little purple hat."

The *rosario* lasted an hour and a half. The living room was full and running over. People stood outside, mostly men with their hats off, reverently trying to follow Old Nacho's prayers. The Jiménez brothers were outside too. They would come in when the atmosphere changed. And that would be soon.

As soon as the *rosario* was over, Don Lico emerged from the bedroom with a big smile, a big bottle, and a little cup. Teodolinda frowned as she watched him give everyone a free shot of the best Zapotal *guaro*. She was surprised when he even gave Durando Quesada a drink.

Old Nacho moved the table to the wall where the *estampas* hung and carefully turned El Niñito toward the wall. Next he took the sheet Teodolinda brought him and covered the special wall. The end of the sheet draped over the table and the little box the baby was in.

After Lico generously doled out his best, it was Teodolinda and her daughters' turn. They gave out the best tamales anyone there had ever tasted and the best coffee, according to the best Zapotal hospitality. Never had a Zapotal rosario been so well attended. Everyone knew it was probably the last the Valverdes would ever host.

The Valverdes' friends were there. And also their enemies. And every stripe of folks in between. Most of their enemies stayed outside. The house was packed. The yard was full. The kitchen was running over with children and ladies helping out with the food. Everyone got a tamale and all the coffee he could drink. Some people even got two tamales.

Most of the men noticed early on that Ángel Soto and Ángel Valverde were not happy with each other. By the time the Jiménez brothers started their music, the bomb was ready to explode.

The last thing Teodolinda wanted at this *rosario* was a fight. She watched closely, determined to stop it before it happened. She stepped outside into the dark and called her son aside. "Ángel, please, let's not have a fight tonight."

"Mother, that man has been so mean to us so often. He needs a licking tonight, and it's my turn to give it to him."

"But, son, fighting won't help. It will just make it worse . . ."

But Ángel had already ducked around the corner looking for another drink.

Teodolinda knew it was useless to talk to her brother, so she went back into the kitchen, keeping her ears open.

Though Ángel Valverde was years younger than his uncle, the more he drank, the more he became convinced that he could whip him. He waited for his opportunity as the evening ripened.

Ángel Soto was loud-mouthed as usual. Recently his wife had left him because she could not stand him anymore. So now he was out to have the time of his life. He had been throwing indirect slams at his nephew all night.

During a lull in the dancing, Ángel Soto sat at a table and demanded that Teodolinda bring him some hog meat. He had already eaten two tamales, but Teodolinda brought him a piece with a fresh cup of coffee and a tortilla. Ángel Valverde stalked up to the table and challenged his uncle. "What do you think you're doing, eating us out of house and home?"

"And who are you, anyway? Who gave you the authority to scold me?" retorted Ángel Soto, surprised and slightly alarmed at the challenge. He did not really have the energy to fight tonight, but neither could he allow this young upstart to run over him.

Ángel Valverde laughed scornfully. "You don't even recognize your nephew anymore. Maybe it's time that everybody here knows why. You're scared!"

Now Ángel Soto was angry, but he did not get up. He sat there as stiff as a statue; then he hissed, "What's ailing you, kid? I'm not scared of you. I could lick you any day! I just don't know what's got your goat. What have I ever done to you?"

"So you want to know, eh? Well, today I will tell you!"

As the two men argued, people automatically cleared the area. Everyone knew Ángel Valverde would not back down. And everyone knew Ángel Soto would never let a youngster get the best of him. So a fight was inevitable. Most of the men were ready for some action, but some were concerned about the results. Lico was one. For once he was sober enough to smell trouble. He headed for the kitchen to find Teodolinda. She was the only one who might be able to talk sense into her brother. He found her right inside the door, her eyes wide with fear. And he saw right away that she was ready. Knowing his wife, he turned around and left without saying a word.

Ángel Valverde had longed for this opportunity ever since his uncle had gone after his dad with his *cutacha*. Teodolinda had been expecting

Hugo at the time, and as a result of that fight, her health had deteriorated and little Hugo had had to be born in Miramar. Ángel reminded his uncle of these things; then he continued slinging Ángel's sins to his face—all of the horrid things their family, and especially his mother, had suffered at his hands. Ángel Valverde laid it all out in one long train of insults, standing before the seated man and wagging his finger at him.

But Ángel Soto was more concerned about another man at the *rosario* than all the Valverdes put together—Juan Gonzalez. Ever since Juan's brother Beto had married Leyla Valverde, Juan had been slowly making up with the Valverde family, though he and Marcos were still enemies. As the two angry Ángels foul-mouthed each other, Juan Gonzalez edged closer. Ángel Soto noticed and kept sneaking glances his way.

Ángel Soto's oldest son Douglas stood protectively beside his father, his face red with indignation. Several of the Valverdes were edging closer too. Gelo hobbled into the room and sat on a bench right inside the door. Lidier and Lico stood just outside the door in the dark, ready.

After Ángel Valverde ran out of steam, Ángel Soto rose from his chair. He started to defend himself on all the issues his nephew had brought up, but he was so angry and so drunk that no one could understand his garble. The evening was not turning out as he had planned. He had an old score to settle with Juan Gonzalez, not with the Valverdes. He and his son had been planning revenge. Now he had the Valverdes to contend with too.

Ángel Soto knew the fight could get ugly, but he was too angry to hold back. He lunged toward his nephew, expecting him to run. But to his surprise, he stood his ground. Just as they closed in, fists ready, a little woman popped up between them. Both Ángels respected her and stopped. Lico and Lidier grabbed Ángel Valverde from behind and hauled him out into the yard to calm him down. There they discovered a knife he had planned to use on his uncle and took it away.

Ángel Soto also felt strong arms manhandling him from behind. Beto and Juan Gonzalez laughed as they jerked him down the steps and across the yard. He cursed them and the day they were born and threatened to kill them both, but they only laughed harder and pushed him down over a bank, watching him slide down and land in the cold creek with a splash. Then they ran back into the house, laughing all the way.

Ángel Soto had never been so humiliated in his life. He walked, dripping, to the fence where he had tied his mule. He jumped on the mule and met with his eighteen-year-old son in the dark. He handed him his six-inch switchblade and hissed, "Now's the time, Douglas! Remember our plan? Go for it!"

Juan Gonzalez was trying to look as calm as he could on the bench right inside the door, but he realized that Ángel Soto would probably be back for more. He thought he was ready.

Suddenly a young man burst in the door, stabbed Juan, and ran before anyone knew what had happened. Juan jumped to his feet, blood spurting from his arm.

Douglas ran back out to his father, gripping the switchblade in one bloody hand. He did not say a word. He just jumped on the back of his dad's mule, and they galloped off into the night. The men poured out of the house like bees out of a hive, only to hear the mule's hooves pounding the trail as Ángel Soto and his son made their escape. Juan followed, grasping his arm to stop the bleeding. Teodolinda brought a *canfinera*. Everyone talked at once trying to figure out who had done it. Most people guessed it was Douglas. Everyone knew the boy had not aimed for Juan's arm. He had aimed for his heart, but the arm was in the way.

That was unpardonable according to Zapotal rules. Suddenly Ángel Soto had more enemies than friends. And they would not forget easily.

The party broke up soon after, and Teodolinda went to bed, relieved that the awful evening had not turned out any worse than it had. The next day she sent her boys out to search the trail for El Niñito's purple hat. Old Nacho had warned her of dire consequences if the relic was not found. The boys found the hat in the mud and returned it, along with the little statue. Teodolinda was relieved. Their family had enough curses hanging over their heads.

*   *   *

Two weeks later the *resguardo* hit them again. This time the Valverdes knew the Quesadas had not turned them in. They would not have dared. Apparently the *resguardo* were just in the area searching for the still everyone knew existed, and some helpful neighbor had tattled.

This time the *resguardo* took Ángel. Once he got to Miramar, he talked to the head of police, who was their friend. He offered to pay a nice fine if they turned him loose, so they let him go and he rushed home, free on bond.

The Valverdes were not interested in another still. Teodolinda's hatred for the drinking, the saloon, and all that went with it made her desperate to move.

A year after Luis had moved to Chachagua, Lidier and his wife Gregoria had moved too. With two of their sons in Chachagua, Teodolinda convinced Lico to go for a visit. He took Ángel along. She hoped that seeing the new place would motivate her husband to move there. Maybe, just maybe, he would like Chachagua too.

Her plan worked. Don Lico never returned to Zapotal. Instead, he sent Ángel back with a message for Teodolinda. "Sell the piece of land you own. Sell La Peligrosa. Sell your cattle. You and the family come join me as soon as you can."

And she did.

31

Chachagua was a small sleepy town nestled right at the foot of the mountain range that, many miles away, wore San Ramón and Zapotal on its back. The town was small enough that any news, great or small, generally made a stir. One day a new rumor hit the town like a deluge and gushed up and down the dirt streets like high water down a riverbed.

A new family was moving in from Zapotal—a huge family with dozens of children. They were bad. The mother was a witch who delivered babies miraculously. No baby she delivered ever died, but it was born with a pact with the devil and would be evil all its life. The father was a hermit who drank every day and slept in the woods. The boys were all fighters and drinkers. One was a cripple and a witchdoctor with supernatural powers. He did not use his fists like normal fighters, but used his teeth and claws like an animal.

But the worst of the rumor was that the Valverdes were moonshiners.

Chachagua was slow in waking up, but one thing they had awakened to was moonshining. It was a thing of the past. For years the two saloons in Chachagua, the Apollo 12 and the Cantina, had sold only legal, tax-paid alcoholic beverages. Not that that made Chachagua any better than Zapotal. The liquor ran just as freely and had the same horrible effects. It was just more expensive in Chachagua, and the government smiled because it got a nice slice of the profit.

Now the townspeople of Chachagua, who had accepted Luis as one of them, started seeing an old, skinny, poorly dressed man hanging around Luis. He walked with a limp. Old Rafael Valverde had hardly been able to walk as he got older, and now Lico was feeling the effects of the family bone weakness.

Chachagua started to believe the stories about the Valverdes. Lico did seem like a hermit and avoided people whenever possible, especially new people. And he drank a lot. He hated to show up at the saloon to drink, so he always sent one of the local boys to buy his whiskey.

* * *

Back in Zapotal, Teodolinda was running the show, and things were happening. She put her cattle and her piece of land up for sale, and she offered to sell La Peligrosa at a bargain.

Tilo Barrantes bought her land and her cattle. Tilo was really booming as a landowner. The rumor was that he now had twenty farms in Zapotal. And if he had twenty farms, he had twenty women, and more children than anyone could count. Teodolinda did not mind. He was always cheerful and nice to deal with.

But no one seemed to want to buy Teodolinda's saloon. Finally Manuela's parents bought it for a song. But the saloon died, and it became a house for one of their sons. Liquor was never sold there again.

* * *

The morning of April 1, 1970, dawned clear and brisk. It was moving day for the Zapotal Valverdes. Lico was already in Chachagua with their oldest son Luis, who had moved there with Manuela two years before. Lidier and Gregoria had followed a year later. Marina still lived with her husband in Guanacaste. Marcos was still at odds with his Nena and the Quesadas in Zapotal. Leyla had married Beto and lived in Tajo Alto. Amable had moved to San José and found a job. Mireya and Victoria were the only girls still at home. The boys still at home were Ángel, Gelo, Marino, Belén, Aurelio, Ulises, and Hugo.

They needed a rig big enough to haul all their things, plus ten people and all their dogs and chickens. Fortunately, the day they chose to move was in the driest of dry season. Vehicles could drive all the way to La Peligrosa as they had a few years before. So Teodolinda hired an old jalopy truck to haul their things to Chachagua.

Neighbors dropped by the last several days to say good-bye. Even if the family was a pack of moonshiners and drinkers and fighters, Zapotal would miss them. Once the Valverde family left, life on the cold, harsh mountaintop would never be the same.

The overloaded truck pulled out from La Peligrosa just before noon. A few stragglers and the remaining family were there to bid them fare-well. Teodolinda saw it all as they drove away. She sat in front with the driver. In the yard stood Leyla and Beto, waving good-bye. Marcos stood apart, a forlorn look on his face. Tilo Barrantes sat there on his spanking mule with his cowboy hat, smiling broadly as he waved.

Teodolinda hid her face in her handkerchief and wept. Her last look at La Peligrosa was through a sheen of tears. The whole scene turned blurry and unreal. Teodolinda had lived forty years of her life in Zapotal. In a way, she wished she could just erase those years. Could she somehow start over? No, she could not change history. But she realized there could be a change. Maybe the future would be brighter. Oh, how she longed for a new life in this Chachagua she had never seen! As she sobbed into her handkerchief, she vowed that she would never drink *guaro* again. And she kept her word.

The loaded truck slowly wound down the long hills toward the lowlands. The truck created quite a scene as it roared through Miramar. Then it dropped the last several miles to the paved Pan-American Highway that led south, past Puntarenas and on to San José, perched high on the Central Plateau. Before arriving in San José, the truck had to climb the same mountain range it had almost fallen out of. The Pan-American meandered up the mountain range, making so many twists and turns that even the truck seemed carsick. Most of the Valverdes had never ridden in a vehicle before, and all were green with motion sickness.

When they reached the Central Plateau, they came to San Ramón, where Teodolinda had lived as a child. San Ramón was a much bigger city than even Miramar, and though it was not nearly as high as Zapotal, it still was fairly high on the same mountain range, many miles farther south.

After buzzing through San Ramón, the loaded truck careened down the other side of the mountain. The road was paved part of the way, but before they got to Chachagua, they hit the potholes and dust again. By the time the truck puttered into Chachagua, they all looked a mess.

Chachagua thought they were ready for the new family from Zapotal—until they actually saw them come through town. The truck was full and running over. An ox yoke stuck up out of the load, and a folded cot of the old style with a rusty metal frame. An old hound dog thrust its head up over the frame, its tongue lolling and dribbling. Seven men and boys sat around on the stuff, all of them covered with dust from head to toe. Gelo sat on the very top, a folded red bandanna tied around his head, his curly mane sticking out every which way and saturated with dust. None of the boys seemed happy. Their Zapotal scowls seemed frozen on their high-cheeked Indian features. They just wished the drama were over, and they despised the townspeople for staring. Victoria and Mireya, also seated on the back, were too embarrassed to look up as the bystanders watched the strange procession bumping down the street.

After passing the insignificant center of town, the truck chugged down yet another hill and across yet another bridge. As they roared up the next hill, a small bumpy road turned off to the right, and the old truck veered onto it, finally heaving to a stop after several more miles. It was almost dark. The trip had taken seven long, bumpy, dirty, dangerous, dizzying hours.

They had stopped in front of a small house, newly built, right by the road. Luis and Manuela stood in front of the house, their children all eagerly waiting to see Grandma and all their uncles and aunts. Little Toño was jumping up and down in excitement. As usual, Lico was hiding behind the house.

After greeting everyone, Teodolinda went to look for the husband she had not seen in a month. She found him under a guayaba tree, sitting on an old log, chewing on a piece of sugarcane. He looked up and smiled when he saw his little woman walking toward him.

Lico lowered the cane stalk. "So you made it?" he asked without getting up.

"Don't I ever look awful?" Teodolinda smiled as she sat down beside him on the log. "I'm so glad we made it!"

"Yeah, so am I," Lico said and then returned to contentedly chewing his sugarcane.

*   *   *

Soon after they got to Chachagua, Teodolinda and Ángel purchased a piece of land on Calle Rojas. They immediately built a small house for their big family. They did not have enough money to build a big house, but it was home, and they all liked Chachagua—except for the heat. The Valverdes were used to the coolest climate Costa Rica had to offer. Now they had dropped over three thousand feet to the lowlands, and it felt as though they had moved into an oven.

Soon Lico was planting yucca and papaya on their new piece of land, and the boys were finding jobs at the neighboring farms. Though they all missed Leyla and Marcos, who had stayed in Zapotal, it was good to be with Luis's and Lidier's growing families again.

The Valverdes were also finally experiencing civilization. Even if Chachagua was still a sleepy little frontier town, the Valverdes had dropped out of the mountains, and it was a novelty to join the lowland townspeople. There was a good hospital in Ciudad Quesada that was near enough to help if they got sick. And the Chachagua stores seemed to have everything anyone could ever want. There was even a meat market. Chachagua had a real gravel road, and several people owned vehicles. Children rode around on bicycles, something never seen in Zapotal. Probably the biggest difference between Zapotal and Chachagua was that they did not need their horses. Now if the Valverdes wanted to go anywhere, they just walked out to the main road and caught the bus. And, of course, the saloons were open at any time during the day. The Valverdes were part of the modern world now, and they loved the change.

As the Valverdes settled in, the people of Chachagua watched. They soon discovered that many of the wild rumors were false, but some were all too true.

Several months after moving to Chachagua, Teodolinda traveled by bus to San Ramón to visit her sister Arcilia. As soon as she arrived, she noticed a difference in her sister's family. Her sister was attending a local evangelical church, and Teodolinda wondered if that had anything to do with it.

Teodolinda had been taught that leaving the Catholic Church was a mortal sin, so she was afraid of any other denomination. But since she had been so disillusioned by the Catholic priest and had not found peace, she consented to attending a service with her sister.

The first thing Teodolinda noticed was the simple church house. She had never been in any church except the big fancy cathedrals. This church was big, but had simple benches in rows in a very simple building. The only ornamentation was several bouquets of flowers on the corners of the pulpit.

The people came in informally, smiling and greeting one another as they would have in the market. They did not tiptoe and whisper in fearful reverence. Teodolinda was not sure what to think. At least they seemed friendly. They shook her hand and made her feel welcome.

Once the folks began to sing, Teodolinda felt more at home. Several men played guitars. Soon Teodolinda was swaying slightly with the music, much as she would have at home at a *rosario*. She found herself clapping along with everybody else. But these songs were all about God, and the music was not as wild as it had been in Zapotal.

"*Hay una senda que el mundo no conoce,*
Hay una senda que yo pude encontrar . . ."
(There is a way that the world knows nothing of,
There is a way that I was able to find . . .)

—Tomás Estrada

Teodolinda wondered about that way. Was there a way? A way to happiness? A way to peace? Her eyes filled with tears. *If there is, I would sure like to find it,* she thought.

After the singing, a young, neatly dressed man walked up to the pulpit and asked everyone to stand. Then he said he would read a Scripture in the name of the Father, the Son, and the Holy Ghost. He reverently read Psalm 91. Teodolinda was familiar with this psalm. They often quoted it when they were afraid, invoking the words like a charm for protection. But this man read it as if it was meant to be understood and believed in a personal way. Teodolinda liked the feeling the simple, clear words gave her. She closed her eyes as she listened.

After the Bible reading, a row of a dozen girls dressed in pure white and ranging in age from six to ten almost floated up to the platform. They started to sing:

"¡Cuán gloriosa será la mañana
Cuando venga Jesús el Salvador!
Las naciones unidas como hermanas
Bienvenida daremos al Señor."*
—Mariano Betrán

(How glorious will be that morning,
When Jesus the Saviour will return!
The nations, united as brethren,
Will give the Lord His welcome.)

The soft, sweet music and the words of peace and blessing filled Teodolinda's heart. A great emotion rose up in her innermost being as God gently used those girls and their songs to touch her heart. It was just a beginning. But everything starts somewhere. And for Teodolinda, that was when the first little awe of God crept into her heart. Along with the new awe, a ray of His love reached her heart that evening. And love has such a wonderful way of softening hearts.

Arcilia convinced her sister to go forward after the message so the preacher could pray for her, so Teodolinda followed her up to the altar and knelt beside her. The minister prayed for her, but it was the one experience she did not like that night. He shouted and repeated things, and he held her little head in his big hands and almost jerked her neck out of place.

Later Teodolinda told Arcilia, "Sis, I really liked that singing. I was almost wondering if those little girls weren't angels. But I didn't like it when that guy jerked my head. And he didn't need to shout as though God and all the rest of us were deaf!"

After Teodolinda returned to Chachagua, she told Lico all about the service and how it had affected her. He listened; then he shook his head. "I don't think you should go to that church," he said. "Your mother taught you well in the ways of the Catholic Church, and to go to another one is sin. Nothing good will come out of it, do you hear? Don't ever do that again."

Teodolinda did not answer, but she knew she was done with the Catholic Church. Her heart was preparing for the way, whatever that was. But she did not know what else she could do now. There was no evangelical church in Chachagua. Her longings would have to wait.

32

Calle Rojas was a normal road in Chachagua, Costa Rica—just a bumpy gravel street that swung off the main road past the bridge and meandered down the mountainside toward the town of Sector Ángeles.

Calle Rojas was named after the Rojas family, who had lived there as long as most of the Chachagua folks could remember. But though the Rojas gave the road its name, the Valverdes gave the road its fame. The Rojas were just an ordinary Chachaguan family that fit in like good citizens should, so the road was known only to the locals. But all that changed drastically during the dry season of 1970.

The Valverde family moved to Calle Rojas with good intentions, planning to live changed lives in this new place. But as always when men try to change on their own, it did not work.

There were some changes. For one thing, the Valverdes did not own a still. They tried to set one up, but *contrabando* was a thing of the past in Chachagua. The *resguardo* were vigilant, and no one wanted to get caught buying or drinking the stuff. Besides, Apollo 12 and the Cantina were always open, so why risk it?

Lico's drinking slowed. He did not like to go to town to drink, and nobody wanted to go buy it for him, so he would often go, down a couple of drinks, and then come home and sleep it off. Life at home became much more peaceful.

Teodolinda did not drink at all, in accordance with her vow. But it was harder for her to stop smoking. After several months in Chachagua, however, she managed to quit.

But for the rest, the drinking kept right on. The boys seemed worse than ever.

Luis had slowed his drinking since moving to Chachagua, though he still drank too much. Manuela was helping him reform. He also made an effort for the sake of his children, Lillian, Toño, and Edwin.

Luis and his friend Chepe enjoyed playing guitar together. They would play and sing after dances to entertain folks as they left for home. Often the late crowd would stay and listen to their funny songs. Chepe sang soprano, and Luis always followed with a high Latino tenor. People would laugh and cheer and clap. Then Luis would stagger home in the wee hours of the morning, drunk. He also smoked cigars and chewed tobacco. His vices disgusted Manuela, and it bothered her that their children were growing up watching such an example.

Of all the Valverde boys, Lidier was one of the worst drinkers. And he did not like to drink alone. One night he convinced his dad to go drink with him. Old Lico limped badly now and did not really want to go, but his son convinced him. Lidier got him to drink so much that Lico could not make it home. When he woke up the next morning, he was sprawled by the roadside at the turnoff to Calle Rojas.

Lidier's poor wife Gregoria always worried what might happen to her husband when he left to drink. Often she would send their fourteen-year-old Lalo along to bring him home. One night Lidier drank until midnight before staggering toward home. Lalo tried his best to help his father walk, but as they stumbled down the steep hill on Calle Rojas, Lidier fell into the ditch, and Lalo could not move him. Lalo was frightened, but there was nothing he could do in the dark. It was a lovely, clear night, so Lalo lay down beside his dad and eventually fell asleep in the grass. Father and son woke up just before dawn in the ditch beside the road.

The air was often tense in Apollo 12 when the Valverdes were around. Gelo, particularly, carried a chip on his shoulder. He still sported his long wild hair. In fact, he could not even remember his last haircut. Since his hair was wavy, it did not hang down, but stacked up high and wide in tiny curls, giving him the appearance of a lion.

Gelo was a notorious fighter. He would dance on one leg and one crutch and savagely swing the other arm and free crutch. His upper body was especially strong from walking with crutches. After his opponent got too close to whack with his crutch, Gelo would drop both crutches and grab him wherever he could, usually around the chest. Then he held tight and used his teeth and fingernails. Gelo manicured his nails daily. They were long, very strong, and sharp.

The younger Valverdes had bad reputations too. Aurelio tried to reform and drink less, but the rest drank and fought as much as ever. Every evening they would drink and fight in the local bars and dance halls. In the wee hours of the morning they would lurch home and sleep off their hangovers. Weekends were even worse. After a year in Chachagua, the Valverde boys had as many enemies as friends.

At home, Teodolinda tried her best to get everybody to stop drinking. Lico slowed down, mostly because he was too ashamed to go to town and frequent the saloons, but for the most part, her efforts were in vain.

Several of the Valverdes found work at a local sawmill, where there was a lot of competition to be the toughest and the best. Several other families also boasted renowned fighters and loudmouths. And of course these men clashed with the Valverdes, causing more fights and feuds.

People who knew the Valverdes well could appreciate their good qualities. They were good workers when they were sober and loyal friends once their trust was won. Those who could overlook their arrogance and feistiness got along fine. These friends soon realized that the wild rumors that had made their way to Chachagua before the Valverdes were not nearly all true. But a lot of people did not know them well and were afraid of them. Long-haired young men, a wild-looking old man who would hide rather than meet people, women who kept to themselves . . . Some people not only believed the rumors, but added to them.

In less than a year the Valverdes had put Calle Rojas on Chachagua's map. And yet God loved that poor family, even as He watched their lives spiral down deeper into the pit of sin that leads to Hell.

In spite of the fact that some of the Valverdes had wanted to reform when they moved to Chachagua, in spite of Teodolinda's small cry to God and His response, in spite of the fact that the heavenly powers were laying the groundwork for a very great miracle, the Valverdes still lived seven long years in wickedness before it happened. It took those seven years to prepare their hearts. And during that time God carefully chose and prepared the man he would send to the rescue.

33

J ohnny Guadalupe Jesús de la Trinidad Rojas Bejarano grinned as he thought about his long religious name. But his grin was not a happy one. It was bitter and dejected. He shook his head. His long black mane undulated over his bare shoulders. His head hung low. The dim light from the single bulb dangling from the ceiling of the little room made his brown back glow. He reached for yet another cigarette. When would he ever be sleepy enough to crawl into bed so he could forget his troubles? It was midnight, Sunday evening, December 12, 1975.

Johnny puffed away on his cigarette, deep in thought. From his birth, his parents had had big plans for him. He was to be the most religious child in the family. They had wanted him to be a priest when he grew up. That was why they had given him the big religious name. By the time Johnny was six, he had been well indoctrinated in the Catholic Church, and his only desire was to be the priest his family wanted him to be.

Then his parents had converted to the evangelical faith, and everything had changed.

For the next six years Johnny had been torn between his parents' faith and his grandmother's religion. His grandmother still insisted that he be a priest, and Johnny was almost convinced. But then one day, when Johnny was twelve, his father had persuaded him to join the family for a special service in the city of San José, where they lived. During the message the Holy Spirit had touched him, and he had gone forward during the invitation, broken, weeping, and seeking his Saviour.

Now, eight long years later, a lump formed in Johnny's throat as he remembered his conversion. Tears threatened, so Johnny closed his eyes tight. He remembered well those first four years when he had served the Lord sincerely. Those were happy memories. His lonely heart longed for those days when peace was part of his life. But now his heart was hard, and peace was as foreign to him as snow.

Johnny had been sixteen and studying in college when things went awry. The influences of his fellow students and the liberal studies filled him with doubts. Slowly his heart turned cold toward his Saviour, and he followed after the world. His life slowly fell apart. Johnny shook his head again as he remembered the awful arguments with his dad when he came home in the wee hours of the night with his wicked friends, and his mother's desperate tears when she discovered that he was drinking and doing drugs. His life had become a mess as he lived with woman after woman in his selfish search for happiness and fulfillment. Now here he was, twenty years old, his life a wreck. His sinful street life was catching up with him. He had become a slave to his awful vices.

Johnny reached over to the little table, picked up a piece of paper, and grabbed a little plastic bag of green-brown powder. His hands trembled as he rolled himself another puff. More and more he turned to marijuana. It helped him think he was happy. He could forget all those memories, at least for a little while. Maybe if he smoked another round . . .

An hour later Johnny was stoned. His skinny frame slid between the sheets of his simple cot. He rested his long hair on the lumpy pillow and fell into the deep sleep of the doped. He never even knew he had crawled into his bed. The dim light shone on, as if trying to keep the demons from attacking the young man's brain. The demons were certainly there. But so were the angels.

God loved the young man who barely breathed on that cot. Not only did He love him, He had a plan for his life. He knew Johnny's tears earlier in the evening meant that he was getting desperate and that his heart was mellowing toward the God he had abandoned. The time had come for a change. In His mercy God gave Johnny a lovely dream.

In his deep sleep, Johnny saw a bright light in the distance. The light drew nearer and nearer. Was he hallucinating? No. Not this time. This was different. Johnny watched the bright object as it drew closer and closer. Suddenly he recognized a set of bright, beautiful bronze feet dropping out of Heaven and stopping right in front of him. His heart skipped a beat when he saw the round scars in the middle of each foot. Those were Jesus' feet!

Slowly Johnny allowed his eyes to travel upward, following the contours of the legs to a robe, pure white like snow. He raised his eyes to a pair of lovely hands, the palms turned outward toward him. The hands had the same round scars, right in the center of the palms. Johnny's chest felt tight, as if it could almost burst. It was Jesus!

Johnny's eyes tried to go higher, but when they came to Jesus' neck, they had to stop. Jesus' face was as bright as the sun in all its glory, and so intense it was impossible to look at it. Johnny's eyes dropped. Then he heard a tender voice say, "Johnny, why have you become so rebellious? Why have you abandoned Me? I love you, Johnny. I have a plan for your life. But you must repent and submit yourself to Me so I can make the plan reality."

Johnny contained his pent-up emotions just long enough to whisper, "How can You still love me when I have been so rebellious? I have sold my life to sin and have followed the way of the devil."

Jesus' answer was clear. "The Father's love is very big, Johnny. We are calling you in Our great love and compassion."

Johnny reached out and grasped Jesus' feet, letting loose all the feelings that were exploding in his breast. He clung to those feet and wept as if he would never stop. God's love broke his heart totally, and tears of repentance poured out, washing the feet of Jesus once again. And Jesus' blood washed Johnny's sins away.

When Johnny woke up, he was kneeling beside his bed, weeping like a baby, crying out to God, confessing his sins. Suddenly he jumped to his feet. He knew he was converted and that he would serve the Lord for the rest of his life.

Johnny reached under his mat where he hid his vices. He fished out the little bag of marijuana and his last pack of cigarettes. He crushed them and threw them out the window into the lonely alley. Then he took his knife and cut off the black shoestrings he had tied around his neck and wrist. As soon as it was daylight, he hurried down the street to the barber, where they whacked off his long black locks. Then he went back to his room and showered. Next he searched out his parents and shared the glad news. That night he went to church with his parents, and there was great rejoicing in the home and in the congregation. The lost had been found. The rebel had been converted. The gangster was now a son of God!

A year after his conversion, Johnny was ready for service. In his prayers he told God again and again, "Lord, I want to serve You wherever You would send me. May I go into some faraway place to preach Your Gospel? I am willing. You tell me where."

Johnny told his father and the church of his desire. Everyone knew that Johnny would enter the service of the King full time.

God heard the young man's longings and in due time made his dream come true. Johnny Guadalupe Jesús de la Trinidad Rojas Bejarano would serve the Lord in a very special way in a far-off place—called Chachagua.

34

One day Aurelio felt a strange urge to go back to Zapotal to visit. Teodolinda was not sure it was a good idea, but when he reminded her that he could bring back news about Beto and Leyla and Marcos and Nena, she agreed. He had a good job and had enough money for the trip, so Teodolinda got some gifts together for her children and sent him on his way.

Memories flooded Aurelio's mind as he topped the mountain and walked into Zapotal. Every mile of road held a memory. The closer he got to home, the more memories flooded his mind. Many were good, but many were very bad.

When Aurelio arrived at Leyla's place, everyone was delighted to see him and to hear about the family. But one of the first things Aurelio noticed was Marcos sitting out behind the house, dejected and sad. He did not even come in for the hot coffee Leyla served Aurelio. So he asked, "What's up with Marcos?"

"Nena ran him off and is living with another man," Leyla explained.

Later Aurelio walked out behind the house and found his brother sitting on an old stump, his head resting on his arms. Aurelio tried to get him to talk. It was hard to get him started, but once he did, he poured out the whole story. His life at the Quesadas had always been horrible, but after the Valverdes left, it got worse. Finally Marcos decided to move to Chachagua. When Nena found out, she threw an awful fit. She chased him off and took in an older man who had lived with her when she was young.

"So now," Marcos told Aurelio, "I'm stuck. I want to move to Chachagua so badly, but I can't forget Nena. I have been married to her for so long, and I love my children. I just can't let them live with that old grouch of a stepfather . . ." With that Marcos buried his head in his arms and started crying.

"I wish there was something I could do," Aurelio sighed.

Marcos suddenly raised his head. "Maybe there is," he said. "Aurelio, she has always liked you. You were always the sick kid, and she pitied you. I bet she would listen to you."

"I could try," Aurelio said doubtfully. "Maybe I could convince her to move to Chachagua with you."

"But how in the world could you get her away from the Quesadas and all the way to Chachagua?" Marcos almost wailed.

Aurelio suddenly knew he had a mission. He was in Zapotal for a purpose. "I will convince her, Marcos. I'll set a date for her to sneak out and meet us somewhere. I'm working for a rich man who owns a truck. I will tell him, and he will come here to pick you all up."

Aurelio and his brother talked for a long time, working out all the details. The plan seemed perfect—except that Nena would never agree.

"I will go tomorrow," Aurelio finally promised. "I will do all I can. We'll wait and see."

The next day found Aurelio walking up over the hill toward the Quesadas. He did not know what he would do if the men were at home. What if his old enemy, Luis, was there and wanted to fight? He had chosen mid-afternoon for his visit in hopes that the men were out working.

Aurelio paused on top of the hill and watched the Quesada residence. Sure enough, the men were gone. Old Durando sat out on the porch, and that was bad enough. But as he watched, he saw Nena and Nelson go down to the creek to wash. This, he knew, was his chance.

Aurelio came around the field from the back and surprised Nena at the creek. She acted glad to see him and made him feel welcome right away. At least her hatred for the Valverdes was not directed at him. And maybe she felt differently about them since Teodolinda had saved her life.

After visiting for a while, Aurelio started in. "Nena, I have good news for you."

"Like what?" she asked, lifting her eyebrows.

"I have an excellent plan that will make you very happy. I want you to agree to it," he teased.

"Tell me quickly," she giggled. "What kind of plan could you come up with?"

"I talked with Marcos a long time last evening. He is very sad. He wants to get back together with you."

"I can't do that," Nena snapped. "I have another man."

"Yeah, he knows. But he says he loves you and the children. He is willing to forgive you and make a new start. But not here," Aurelio added mysteriously. "He wants to give it a try somewhere else."

"And where would that be?" Nena asked suspiciously.

"Chachagua."

"You know I can't stand your mother!"

"Well, I sure don't know why. She has actually never been your enemy. And she did save your life, didn't she?"

"And how would we get to Chachagua?" Nena changed the subject abruptly.

"I have a good boss who has a truck. We will come get you. He has an empty house on his farm and will give Marcos work. It's all set up."

"But how would I get away from my man? I don't love him, but if he knew I was planning to leave with Marcos Valverde, he would beat me. Not even Dad and Mom would allow me to go back with Marcos."

"We have it all figured out. A week from Saturday you sneak away as if going to visit Manuela's parents at La Peligrosa. That's as far as the truck can come. Marcos says you should bring as much of your stuff as you can, but if you can't bring anything, not to worry about it. He will buy the things you need in Chachagua. My boss and I will arrive around noon. Marcos will be there, and we'll hightail it for Chachagua."

Nena asked more questions and thought for a while. She did not admit it, but she was missing her husband too. Suddenly she made up her mind. "I will go," she announced. "I will be at La Peligrosa at noon. Just please make sure you're there. We will move to Chachagua and start a new life."

Nelson cheered, and tears filled his eyes. Aurelio could see that he missed his dad. Nena looked over to her son and asked, "So, shall we head for Chachagua?"

Nelson was swallowing a huge lump in his throat, so he could not answer, but he nodded vigorously. All three stood there and pondered the future, happy that things were working out for the family to get back together. They all smiled. And though they didn't realize it, there was rejoicing in Heaven too.

The following Saturday an old Land Rover pickup inched up the steep hills toward Zapotal. The driver clung to the steering wheel for dear life, and his eyes bulged as he stared disbelievingly at the road. "Aurelio, what did you get me into? I have never driven up so steep a mountain. It feels as if we could drop right out of the sky and down into the Puntarenas gulf. Does it get any worse?"

"No, this is the steepest part. We're almost there. I told you the hills were kind of steep!"

" 'Kind of' is not the word!" the driver insisted. "It's farther than I thought too."

When they drove up to La Peligrosa just after noon, Aurelio was trembling. He was so afraid that something would go wrong and their trip would be in vain. He and Marcos had promised to pay for the trip with future work, so he was in trouble if things went wrong. But when they swung up to the house that used to be a saloon, there stood Nena with her whole row of children. Marcos came out of the house. Everyone was smiling. They had pulled it off.

Aurelio stopped trembling. But Nena was in a great hurry. They loaded up the children and several sacks of belongings in a rush, Nena and Marcos glancing repeatedly down the road toward the Quesadas, afraid that any minute someone would come to mess up their plans. In a matter of minutes the Land Rover had turned around and was heading down those steep hills again, the wide-eyed driver once again clinging to the steering wheel for dear life.

They arrived in Chachagua late that night, but safe and sound. Nena's heart pounded as they drove up to Don Lico's house. She would have to swallow so many words and learn to accept the Valverdes now. Her own family seemed very far away. But true to Aurelio's word, the Valverdes accepted her, and she accepted them in return. They might never actually become close friends, but things were not too bad, and they all managed to get along. They lived in the house Aurelio's boss had offered them until Marcos built Nena a nice house on their own piece of land.

35

It was a long way from where Marina and her husband Luis Elizondo lived in Guanacaste to Chachagua, so Marina hardly ever visited her parents. But then something happened that made her want to go.

Marina started to attend a local evangelical church and not long afterward was converted. She was happy when Álvaro and Gloria, second and third of their eleven children, started going to church with her.

Soon after her conversion, Marina decided to go to Chachagua to visit her parents. She took Álvaro and Gloria along to help witness to her family. Maybe they could be convinced to consider this new religion.

The family was delighted to receive them. It had been several years since their last contact. Álvaro was big now and fifteen years old. Gloria was thirteen. Everything went well until Marina told them she was an *evangélica*. Lico got angry and warned her not to try to convince them to join a false church. Teodolinda and Gelo said little. Marina soon realized she had no support for her new ideas. Everybody was solidly against her. She was stumped. She could either be quiet and enjoy their time at Grandpa's place or keep on pushing and make enemies. She decided to be quiet.

Marina was shocked later when she overheard Hugo inviting Álvaro to go out with them for the evening. Then she found out Aurelio had had the nerve to invite Gloria out for the night's sinful activities.

Marina was appalled. "My children will not go with you tonight. We are *evangélicos* now. We don't dance or drink or do all the bad things you Catholics do."

Her biting answer made Aurelio angry, but he hid it. "Aw, we won't do anything bad tonight. We're not wicked like you make it sound. We just want to have a good time. Surely you don't force your children to stay at home like babies, do you?"

"They don't want to go with you!" Marina answered confidently.

"Ha!" Ulises butted in. "You say they don't want to go because they are converted. Why don't you ask them if they want to go tonight?"

Marina did not realize that her children's Christianity was strictly social. When they were in Guanacaste, they went to church. But now that they were with the Valverde youth, they went to parties. Marina was shocked to discover that her children were not helping her convert the Valverde family. Instead, the Valverde family was converting them.

At dusk the young people left for town. Teodolinda and Gelo did not say much. Marina thought they seemed almost sad. But Lico and the rest were obviously pleased, which made Marina suffer all the more.

As the night progressed, Marina went into her room and got down on her knees to weep and pray. At midnight when she heard the young people coming home, she ran to the door to meet them. She could hear them laughing and cutting up in the distance. Some of them were drunk. They pushed past Marina, laughing and trying to avoid her angry look.

"Where is Álvaro?" Marina asked.

"He decided to go home with some folks he met tonight," Aurelio answered lamely.

"What? My son didn't come home?" Marina screamed. "It's your fault!" she shrieked, pointing at Aurelio. "If something happens to him, it's your fault!" Then she turned on her heel and fled to her room.

Later Gloria joined her. As Marina tried to reason with her daughter, she smelled alcohol on her breath. She gave up and crawled into bed and tried to sleep.

The next day Marina left Chachagua alone, brokenhearted and discouraged. Her darlings had decided to stay for a month. Instead of saving her parents, she had lost her children. *Why?* she asked herself. *Is it because there is no church in Chachagua? Am I not strong enough? Why, oh, why did evil win?*

What no one knew was that though Marina's first shot had missed its mark, her second shot would fly straight as an arrow, right into the heart. God would use Marina yet, and in such a strange way that it verged on bizarre.

Álvaro and Gloria had a wild, worldly time during their first week with the Valverdes. But soon the fun wore off and reality hit. They had to work hard like the rest of the Valverdes when they were sober. When Marina came for them a month later, they were more than ready to go home.

* * *

Friends kept telling the Valverdes that the hospital in San Juan could straighten Gelo's legs. So several years after moving to Chachagua, Teodolinda convinced Gelo to try surgery. Gelo, now thirty-three, finally agreed and stayed at the hospital for three months while his legs were operated on three times. Doctors were able to move his twisted, floppy leg that stuck up the back so it hung straight down like a leg should, though it still hung limp.

After straightening his legs, the hospital provided Gelo with a pair of braces that made his legs the same length. It was much easier to hobble around with his crutches with two legs rather than the one he had always depended on. To sit down, Gelo needed to push a little lever so the brace would bend at the knee. Soon Gelo was walking better than he had ever walked.

While he was in the hospital, something else happened that left a lasting impression on him. One afternoon he was lying on his bed feeling sorry for himself. It had been two months since he had left home, and he was homesick. He knew he still faced another month of therapy to learn to use his new braces. Staring at the ceiling, he thought about home.

"Good afternoon." A cheerful voice greeted the patients in Gelo's hospital room. Gelo glanced toward the door and was surprised to see a young lady, dressed neatly with her hair done up in a bun. The most refreshing thing about her was her smile. "I have come to visit you and to tell you about the Lord Jesus Christ. I want to give you all some literature; then I will pray for you."

Going from bed to bed, the young lady did just that. She gave everyone a tract called "Help From Above" and chatted with each patient. But she stayed by Gelo's bed longer than anybody else's because she sensed that Gelo wanted to talk. Gelo admitted that he knew very little about the Bible or Jesus. He told her he had been raised Catholic, but he never tried to defend the Catholic faith. Neither did the lady criticize it.

After the lady left, Gelo read the tract. It was a small booklet full of Scripture verses. Some of the verses made sense, but others he could not understand. He wished the lady would come back and explain them.

The lady returned twice to witness to Gelo before he was released. Though Gelo was not yet ready for the Gospel, the woman's words and prayers helped mellow his sin-hardened heart.

*   *   *

A year after their trip to Chachagua, Marina and several of her children traveled to Naranjo to pick coffee. The local church was having weekend revival meetings, and Marina and her children decided to go.

The evangelist was twenty-one-year-old Johnny Guadalupe Jesús de la Trinidad Rojas Bejarano, better known simply as Johnny Rojas. He had recently been converted on the streets of San José and was going around sharing his testimony wherever he could. Marina loved to listen to him preach. He preached straight from the Bible, which made his message clear and powerful.

The first night of the meetings, Álvaro and Gloria went forward and recommitted their lives to the Lord.

The second night Johnny spoke on outreach. He used the example of Isaiah. "In Isaiah Chapter six we have the story of how Isaiah saw God in all His glory. He felt so wicked and undone before His holiness. He cried out that he was not fit to be in God's presence. So God came close and cleaned the prophet up. Once the work of redemption was done, God called him to His service. Is there anyone here tonight who, like Isaiah, would say, 'Here am I, send me'?"

Then Johnny gave his own testimony. He told the congregation how God had cleaned him up and prepared him. He shared the call he felt to go out to some frontier town to preach. "And tonight," Johnny announced humbly, "I am saying, 'Dear Lord, here am I, send me.'"

He continued earnestly, "I am not sure where God is going to send me. Right now I am considering Puerto Limón out on the east coast. You all know what a wicked city that port is. It would be a difficult place to witness for Christ, but if God sends me, I am willing . . ."

Marina's heart was racing. Her mind kicked into high gear. *Could this be from God? Would this man be willing?* Suddenly there was nothing in the world she wanted more than for Johnny Rojas to witness to her family.

After church Marina was determined to talk to Johnny. But it seemed everybody wanted to talk with him. For an hour she waited patiently. Finally only the usher and Marina's children were left. Marina could see that Johnny was tired, but he turned to her and asked kindly, "What can I do for you, sister?"

"I want to talk to you."

"Here, have a seat." Johnny turned and set a chair for her. Then he sat on the front pew. "Go ahead and tell me what's on your heart."

Marina started slowly, hesitantly. "It's my family. I'm the oldest daughter in a family of sixteen. My family is very wicked. I am the only one who is a Christian."

"Where do they live?" Johnny probed gently.

"They live in Chachagua. It's far away. You have to go through Ciudad Quesada, then down off the mountain. Since you said tonight that you were willing to go wherever God called you . . . I just couldn't help but think about my poor family in Chachagua."

"What makes you think they would listen to me?" Johnny asked.

"Well, I don't know that they will listen to you. They're die-hard Catholics. But the way you explain the Bible is so clear, I just have a feeling that my mother, and maybe one of my brothers, might be ready to listen."

Then Marina told him about her trip home the year before and how she felt she had failed. By then Marina's tongue was loosened, and she launched into the Zapotal story. She went way back to the beginning and told the story briefly, but in enough detail that Johnny would know what he was getting into. She knew her story would scare most preachers right out the back door. But as she talked, the weariness vanished from Johnny's face, and the gleam in his eyes grew brighter and brighter.

"Why didn't you ask the local pastors to go talk to your family?" Johnny asked thoughtfully.

"Local pastors?" Marina asked. "There is no evangelical church in the whole area."

"Really?" Johnny asked, his eyes really lighting up now. "I like that. Like the Apostle Paul, I would love to go to a place where the Gospel has not been preached." Johnny pulled out a tablet and started to jot things down.

"Who could go with me?" Johnny asked.

"I have an uncle who was converted recently. His name is Paco Soto, and he lives here in Naranjo. He was in church tonight. I'm sure he would take you. He has never been to Chachagua, but he knows my family well."

"Well, I will think and pray about it. It does sound exciting. It just might be from the Lord. If I decide to go, how would I find your family?"

"They're the Valverdes. When you get off the bus, ask for Calle Rojas. Walk a mile down that road and ask for the Valverde family. I imagine everybody in Chachagua knows about the Valverdes by now. Chachagua is a small town."

As Johnny got up, Marina felt strong hope. "I will pray that this will work out," she concluded. "I will pray every day."

"It's wonderful to see how you love your family," Johnny said. "I will pray too. This does sound as if it is from the Lord. I won't promise tonight that I will go, but I do promise that if it's the Lord calling me, I will say with Isaiah, 'Here am I, send me.' "

36

The old jalopy bus lurched to a stop for what seemed like the hundredth time. The driver yelled, *"Servidos los de Chachagua."** Two strangers quickly rose from their seats and gathered their bags from the overhead compartments while the others vacated the bus. They were tired from the long ride, and their clothes were crumpled. They had been on the bus from San José for seven long, bumpy hours.

As the two men exited the bus, the younger man asked the bus driver, "Do you know where Calle Rojas is?"

The driver arched his eyebrows and said, "Sure. You just go down this road until you cross the bridge, then take the first lane to the right. You can't miss it." Then, as an afterthought, the driver asked, "And what could you strangers want on Calle Rojas?"

"We're looking for the Valverdes. Do you know who they are?" the young man asked.

"Wow!" the bus driver exclaimed. "Everybody in Chachagua knows who the Valverdes are! But now I'm really curious. What do you want with them?"

---

* The ones for Chachagua are served.

The young missionary recognized an opportunity to witness when he saw one. "We are planning to tell them about salvation through Christ Jesus."

The bus driver rolled his eyes and laughed. "Well, you are after the wickedest people Chachagua has to offer! But let me warn you, those people are crazy. It will snow in Chachagua for a week before they reform."

Johnny Rojas laughed as they walked down the bumpy hill toward the bridge. "Do you know what, Paco? We've just started the juiciest rumor Chachagua has known for a long time. Two strangers coming from who knows where to reform the Valverde clan! That's the best propaganda we could get for this venture."

"Yes," Paco threw in. "Once you start having meetings, everybody will come just out of curiosity."

The two men walked slowly, hunched over, heads bowed against the rain. They had stopped at a store and bought a yard of plastic apiece and now covered themselves the best they could.

After turning down the little lane called Calle Rojas, Johnny suddenly stopped and said, "Paco, let's pray before we go a step farther. I have a feeling Satan is very angry. I feel it in my spirit. I think we're going to face some opposition."

"You're right about that," Paco agreed. On the long bus ride from San José, Paco had told Johnny more Zapotal stories. He had told him about the fights between the Valverdes and his brother Ángel. He had told enough that Johnny understood what he was getting into. He wasn't exactly afraid; he just wanted to be sure they faced their Goliath head-on and in the name of the Lord.

Under a dripping tree they prayed, and God heard their prayer.

When the two men arrived at the Valverdes' house, they were surprised to find everything quiet and hardly anyone around. A skinny dog charged out at them and circled, growling. As they approached the porch, they saw the first Valverde sitting on a stool, bent over a something he was making out of wood. He stopped his work to watch them walk across the yard. Johnny was shocked at the young man's appearance, especially his huge mane. He must not have had a haircut for years. He had tied a red bandanna across his forehead, which made the hair over his ears stick out even farther than the rest. He wore old, ragged clothes that had been patched many times before and needed it again. He was thin and peaked, his face especially. But by far the saddest thing about the young tramp was the sad, hollow look in his eyes.

"*Buenas tardes,*" Johnny called out cheerfully.

"*Buenas,*" Gelo answered, shaking back his hair. "Come on up."

As the two men climbed the steps, Gelo cleared away the little table he was making and motioned to a bench against the wall. "Have a seat."

Both men shook Gelo's hand; then they sat down and started talking. Gelo recognized his uncle Paco. He explained that Teodolinda was away attending to a birth. "She is at Zona Fluca, a housing development several miles away, where Marino got a house donated by the government. Marino's wife is expecting, so Mama and Luis are over there right now. They planted beans on shares and are going to pull the beans while they wait on the baby. But with this rain, I doubt they are harvesting beans."

The bean harvest had everyone worried. It was supposed to be dry season, and most of the beans were ready to be pulled. But if it kept on raining, the beans would sprout right on the vines.

Lily, a young girl Belén had brought home a while back, came to the door. "The coffee is ready," she announced. "It's here at the table."

They went in and sat down. Gelo felt a strange attraction to these two men, especially to the city slicker dressed in black pants and a neat white long-sleeved shirt. Gelo wondered what they wanted.

The coffee was served in three tall glasses with a plate of biscuits in the middle of the table. Before they served themselves, the two men bowed their heads and prayed. Gelo was embarrassed and half bowed his head too. Johnny's prayer was simple and to the point. He thanked God for a safe trip and for the refreshments; then he thanked him for kind friends to take them in.

While the men prayed, Lily and Mireya peeked from the kitchen. They wondered what these men wanted. "The young guy carries a guitar case," Mireya whispered. "Maybe he's a musician. Gelo and Luis would like that!"

While they visited over coffee, Johnny asked Gelo about his family. He especially wanted to know about his mother. This made Gelo more curious than ever. What did these men want?

Just before dark, the men came in from work, soaked to the skin. Johnny soon saw that they were a rough bunch. Only Lico and three of the boys were home, and they barely saw Lico that first evening. He stayed in the background, obviously suspicious of the visitors. Then there was Ángel, who was the oldest at home, but still single. He was as much a hermit as his father. After Belén had brought Lily home, the couple had fought, and Belén had left to work in Guanacaste. Everybody liked Lily, so she had stayed with the family, and she and Mireya cooked and washed for the men. Last of all was Ulises. Hugo had left for Guanacaste to work with his brother Belén.

The boys said hello to their uncle and the newcomer and then proceeded to do their own things and ignore their company.

As it got dark, Johnny grew worried and told Gelo his concern. "We came to talk to Teodolinda, but now she is not here. Should we go to Chachagua to get a hotel? Your dad and brothers sure don't seem to welcome us."

By then Gelo and the two visitors were friends, so Gelo assured them that even if the others distrusted them, he would make sure they could stay for the night. "My dad is just that way," he explained. "But because of his drinking problem, he doesn't have any authority around here anymore. My mother and I kinda run the show. And my brothers will be all right."

They served a simple evening meal; then Gelo suggested they sleep on the living room floor where he slept. The two men slept fairly well, though the floor got very hard after midnight, and the mosquitoes nearly ate them up.

The next morning dawned bright and clear. Everyone was excited at breakfast because they could finally pull beans.

Most everyone had left for the bean field when Johnny finally got up enough nerve to tell Gelo their mission. They were sitting on the porch steps when Johnny began. "Gelo, we came here to Chachagua to share the Gospel with your mother, but she's not here. What do you think we should do? Should we go to Zona Fluca to find her, or should we go back to San José?"

Gelo cleared his throat. "You can see that my family is not too sure about you, though Lily cooks for you gladly enough. It probably wouldn't work for you to try to share your Gospel with any of the others right now," he sighed. "But," he continued, "I am here. I am your friend. Why don't you start with me?"

Johnny's eyes widened, and Paco nodded vigorously. Johnny pulled out his Bible, opening it thoughtfully. He paged through it slowly and started to read: "For God so loved the world that he gave his only begotten Son . . ."

Gelo hung his head and listened. After Johnny had read several verses, he explained them in a way that was easy to understand. When he looked up to see tears in Gelo's eyes, he was surprised.

"*¡Qué lindo!*" Gelo sighed. "How beautiful!"

Just then Lico marched out of the house. He hadn't gone to the bean field with the others, but had been inside listening to every word they said. Lico whacked the wooden wall of the house several times with his machete as he walked past them. "In this house we are Apostolic Roman Catholics!" he barked.

The three men on the porch froze. Johnny and Paco were pale and praying earnestly under their breath. Gelo got up slowly, ready to confront his father. But Johnny reached out and gently pulled him down again.

Lico was expecting some response to his tirade. When he did not get one, he marched farther down the porch to an old barrel where he kept his precious statues for his Christmas nativity scene. Each piece was wrapped in dry banana leaves and then in plastic bags. He began unwrapping the pieces and setting them up on the floor not ten feet from the men. All the while he was muttering under his breath against the *evangélicos* and all they stood for. He threatened and fumed until he had the entire nativity scene set up. Then he shouted, "This is what we believe in this house!" Then Lico suddenly left for the bean field.

"Let's pray," Johnny said.

Gelo bowed his head with them. Suddenly he felt uncomfortable with his long hair and bandanna. He felt a strong desire to pray like these men. They prayed at the same time and just poured their hearts out as if the person they were talking to was there beside them. They did not shout. They did not repeat. They just told their God what was happening. It was in that prayer that Gelo found out why they were there and that they were planning to stay.

"O Lord," Johnny prayed in anguish, "You know why we came here. We want to see a church sprout here like the church in the New Testament. Please, Father, don't let this dream die. Please arrange things so we can stay and preach the Gospel to this town, and especially to Teodolinda . . ."

After the prayer, Gelo noticed that Lily had sneaked up to the door and heard every word. Was she interested, or would she tell Lico later? Time would tell.

Then Gelo turned to Johnny. "I have an idea. We need to change our tactics. Why don't we all go pull beans? That would show my dad that you are not just going to sponge off us and that you are willing to work. He respects men who work. Maybe that would change his attitude."

Everyone agreed, and soon they left for the bean field. Lily wrapped the images carefully and placed them back into the barrel.

The field buzzed with activity. Everyone except Lily was working. Johnny watched Gelo in awe. As soon as he got to the bean field, he dropped to the ground and taught Johnny how to pull beans.

Paco, of course, already knew. He worked shoulder to shoulder with Mireya, and soon they were talking animatedly.

Johnny watched as Gelo deftly grabbed the beanstalks and jerked the plants right out of the ground. When he had a dozen plants in his hand, he shook the dirt off the roots. Then he grabbed the long stringy roots and wrapped them around the base of the stalks, binding them together in a clump. When he was done, he plopped the bunch upside down on the ground. Smiling, he looked up at Johnny and said, "Now the sun will do the rest. Once they are sun dried, we will thresh them."

That's easy, Johnny said to himself. *I can do that, no problem.*

Two hours later he felt as if his back would break, and the hot sun was making his head spin. But he knew he could not give up. He was no longer a city slicker. He had to become a tough *campesino* like the tribe he was trying to reach for Christ. Like Paul, he would be like the Greeks when he was with the Greeks and like the Chachaguans when he was with the Chachaguans. Pulling beans was as much his calling now as preaching the Gospel.

All day long Lico was cold toward the newcomers, but the rest of the family could not help but warm up to their uncle and the friendly stranger. After supper the ice really broke. Luis came back from Zona Fluca and reported that the beans there were all pulled. "But don't expect Mama back soon," he added. "That little baby just does not want to be born."

Luis was a little quiet with Johnny at first, but soon struck up a conversation. It was clear he was not going to help Lico run the two men off. Soon everyone except Lico was enjoying himself, especially when Johnny started telling San José stories.

Most of the Valverdes had never been to Costa Rica's capital. They had always wondered what life was like there, and now here was someone fresh from San José.

Johnny started telling them about his former street life. "You should see the wickedness on Calle Ocho!" He shook his head as if the memory haunted him. "Every other building is a saloon or a brothel. Drugs are sold on the streets like candy. Tourists are robbed when they get close. Three different gangs claim that street as their turf. Even the police are afraid to go into Calle Ocho late at night. The place is awful. I used to go there before I was converted."

Every eye was glued on Johnny. Could this be true? This sounded like life in Zapotal. *This guy has been around!* they concluded.

Lico was not happy with the storytelling. He had limped to town and gotten himself several drinks. Now, as he sat out in the dark listening to Johnny tell stories, his feelings were mixed. He was still angry at his brother-in-law for bringing this crazy man into their home. But he also knew it was way too late to chase him out. His family loved this visitor. He had lost the battle again.

Then Johnny began shamelessly telling how he found the Lord and how his life was changed. Suddenly he was overcome with emotion and tears streamed down his cheeks.

"And that," he confessed, "is the reason I am here. I have come to tell you about the power of Jesus to change lives."

God's Spirit was in that room. In total silence everyone thought his own thoughts and drew his own conclusions. Paco, off to one side in the darkness, saw some tiny but very beautiful things shining in the candlelight. Tears. Gelo was weeping softly. Luis and Lily had tears in their eyes. Everyone else was dumbfounded. This man had been as wicked as they were, but anyone could see that he was changed. He looked so clean and decent. And it was not just his nice San José clothes. It was something that shone from his very soul.

The next day Johnny pulled beans all day long. Several times he thought he would faint, but he kept working. They finished just before dark.

Over the noon hour Johnny had a good talk with Luis. Gelo listened in. Johnny could see that Luis and Gelo both had a thirst for God. He figured it would just be a matter of time before they committed their lives to Him. He marveled at how God had, in some miraculous way, prepared their hearts before he had even breathed their names in prayer. They were almost in the kingdom. Though Lily did not say a word, she was close too. He could see it in her eyes and in her tears.

That evening Johnny and Paco went to the creek to bathe as they did every evening. Lily had washed their dirty clothes from the day before. When they returned, they were surprised to see a neighbor giving Gelo a haircut. Gelo had hoped it would be done by the time they returned, but shearing his mane took longer than he had thought. Gelo sat on a low stool in the yard, his barber standing behind him, snipping away. The pile of hair was huge, and Gelo looked like a different man. People in town would hardly recognize him.

Later, Johnny and Paco spent an hour out under the trees praying. Gelo sat with them. After their prayer, Paco said, "Boys, I need to go back to Naranjo. I would love to stay, but my own beans are ready to harvest. My wife and family will be wondering about me. I must leave tomorrow on the early bus."

"That's fine," Johnny answered. "You need to go home. I will be without a companion, but God will provide."

Gelo spoke up quickly. "I am not a Christian yet, but I am convinced this is the way. I will be your companion. I will go with you to Zona Fluca tomorrow. That will be best, because I can see that Dad is still not happy."

"Praise the Lord!" Paco and Johnny exclaimed in unison. And the smile on Gelo's face was a sight to behold.

37

Teodolinda was sweeping the dirt patio out in front of Marino's little house. She had just finished washing the breakfast dishes and cleaning up the kitchen and was thinking she might go help thresh the beans.

The baby had been born the evening before, and Marino's wife was in the bedroom taking care of their first child. Marino was outside preparing to thresh beans.

The weather was beautiful. The rainy spell had passed, and the sun was drying the beans on hundreds of little plots of land all through the hills. Teodolinda smiled as she swept. Her own little plot of beans was very nice, and she planned to turn them over today so they would dry more quickly. If the weather held, she could expect several hundred pounds of beans to feed her family for the year.

Teodolinda bent over and swept the dry leaves and sticks onto an old piece of tin with her homemade broom. She walked over to the fence, flinging the debris into the field. She brushed her sweaty gray hair from her face and looked out toward the road. Two men were approaching. One rode, and the other walked. She would not have thought a thing of it if the one on horseback had not ridden just like her son. *That man sure rides like Gelo!* she mused.

The two men traveled slowly. As they drew closer, Teodolinda was sure the rider was her crippled son. She ran to Marino and whispered, "It looks as if we are getting company. Isn't that Gelo?"

"It sure is," Marino exclaimed. "Why would he be coming to Zona Fluca? And who does he have with him?"

Teodolinda turned back to the road. "It sure is Gelo," she said, "but he looks different."

"He's had a haircut," Marino hissed. "His first in how many years?"

The two men turned in at the gate in front of Marino's house. "That man with Gelo looks like some rich guy from the city," Marino whispered. "I can't imagine what they would want."

"He looks like a gentleman," Teodolinda agreed. "He must be here for something important."

The two men stopped in front of the house. Gelo spoke first. His face lit up in one of his rare big smiles that warmed the heart. "Good morning, everyone," he greeted them. "This is my good friend Johnny Rojas. We decided to come visit you all."

"Come in, come in!" Teodolinda responded. She pulled two old chairs out to the porch and invited them to sit down.

For ten minutes they made small talk as Teodolinda's curiosity grew by leaps and bounds. This was no ordinary visit. Gelo and this man Johnny brought something new. She could feel it in her bones.

Teodolinda stood in the doorway. Marino sneaked through the living room and whispered into Teodolinda's ear, "I am going to run to the store and buy some meat. You get the vegetables ready. Let's make a big batch of stew."

Teodolinda agreed and continued listening to the men.

"Teodolinda," Johnny said, "we have come to bring you good news— the Good News of the Gospel. I am a born-again Christian and love to share my faith. Gelo and Luis have already accepted the message, though they haven't accepted Jesus Christ as their Saviour yet. We are here today to invite you to accept Christ."

"How did you find out about us?" Teodolinda asked, changing the subject.

"The Lord sent me," Johnny answered honestly. He did not want to tell on Marina, because he was afraid that if they rejected the Gospel, they would be upset with her. After he had talked to Marina, he had fasted and prayed, and God had showed him clearly that he should go to Chachagua.

"Well," Teodolinda continued, "come on in and I will fix you some coffee. We will talk more later. Make yourselves at home."

Instead of coming inside, Gelo took Johnny behind the house to show him around. Teodolinda prepared the coffee. She needed time to think. She needed to be sure. What the man said seemed right and good, but was it? Gelo and Luis had already accepted his message? That was definitely a shock.

Once Teodolinda had served the coffee, she went to the door to invite them in. What she saw made her stop in her tracks. She stepped back into the kitchen, out of sight, and watched in astonishment. Out under the almond tree stood Gelo and Johnny. Some bushes partially hid them, but Teodolinda could easily see what they were doing. Johnny had his hands raised toward Heaven in prayer. Gelo appeared to be praying with him. Teodolinda could hear their voices, but could not understand the words. But the impression struck deep into her heart.

Two things moved Teodolinda to tears. First, her son Gelo was praying! That in itself was a miracle. Second, she distinctly felt that they were praying for her. At that moment Teodolinda knew this was going to be a special day. She did not understand it all yet, but somehow she knew this was the real thing.

The men drank their coffee, and for the next hour Teodolinda scurried to prepare a big meal. When Marino returned with the meat, he was curious. Teodolinda met him in the kitchen. "This man is an *evangélico*," she whispered. "Gelo and Luis are accepting this religion. I'm not sure what to think. The man seems very nice. I believe what he says is true."

"Humph." Marino challenged her. "We are Catholics until death, are we not?" Then he returned to threshing his beans.

Teodolinda put the meat on to boil and began cutting up the vegetables. She could hear Gelo and Johnny chatting over their coffee. If she stopped beside the wall between the kitchen and the living room, she could hear what they were saying. Once she heard Johnny say, "Gelo, that mother of yours never stops running. She seems to always be busy."

"That's the way she's always been," Gelo explained. "Just have patience. She will serve us first; then she will take time to listen."

"I was starting to think we would never even have a chance to witness to the little woman," Johnny replied.

Teodolinda grinned as she returned to her work. *He wants me to stop so I can listen to their Gospel, and I am busy serving them!*

At lunchtime Teodolinda called the two men in, and they again sat at the table in the living room by the special wall. Just like in Zapotal, the special wall was decked out with *estampas*, flowers, and all kinds of religious symbols. Right next to the table hung Marino's special *estampa:* La Virgen de los Ángeles. The painting of a smiling, angelic face on a piece of cardboard hung in a wooden frame in the center of the wall.

Teodolinda sneaked a peek through a crack in the wall, listening as she looked. She caught Johnny pointing at the *estampa* of La Virgen de los Ángeles. "It's sad to see what these people believe in," he said. "It's all just a bunch of paper."

Teodolinda left her post wondering, *Is this man right? Yes, it is true. Why have I never thought of it before? Just a bunch of paper. A year ago I would never have recognized it.* She shook her head and filled the two plates she had laid out.

Teodolinda carefully dipped a big chunk of meat onto each plate with a ladle full of all the vegetables she had included—pumpkin, cabbage, yucca, green plantains, and potatoes. Next she added a heaping spoonful of white rice. Last she scooped a dipper full of broth onto each plate. Then she plopped two tortillas on top and carried the plates out to the men. She delighted in serving her son and this stranger who sat smiling at her.

"Thank you so much!" Johnny's eyes widened as he looked with obvious appreciation at the loaded plate.

Gelo just smiled.

When Teodolinda returned to the living room carrying two brimming glasses of lemonade, she found the two men with their heads bowed, praying again. She paused behind them holding the two glasses, and waited respectfully as the men finished. After the prayer, they both raised their heads. Slightly embarrassed, she placed the glasses in front of them and stepped back. Just then the picture of smiling La Virgen de los Ángeles fell from the wall and crashed onto the table.

"Gelo," Johnny gasped, "it's a sign! We prayed, and the virgin fell! She had to fall!" The men spun in their chairs to face Teodolinda. "We didn't do it!" Johnny said anxiously.

Teodolinda faced them, her hands on her hips. Johnny looked worried. Would she fly into a rage and chase them out?

To his great relief, she looked him squarely in the eyes and said, "No, it was not you. I saw it all. It was . . . like you said. It was a sign. You prayed, and she fell. God did it." With that she returned to the kitchen to sip her own bowl of stew and to think of many things she had never thought of before.

Johnny and Gelo looked at each other with such joy in their hearts that it just could not be contained. "May God be praised!" Johnny exclaimed under his breath. "The victory is won, brother!"

"Glory to God!" Gelo echoed. "I can hardly believe it!"

After lunch Gelo and Johnny approached Marino about staying for the night. "I will work for you," Johnny quickly threw in.

Marino stared at the young man's soft white hands; then he looked down at his own dark, work-toughened ones. "I can't hire you. I can't afford to pay you."

"I am not asking for pay," Johnny said quickly. "I will work for my room and board only. You won't have to pay me a cent."

Marino accepted. "But we start right now," he said. "I need help threshing these beans."

"Sure, no problem," Johnny smiled. "What shall I do?"

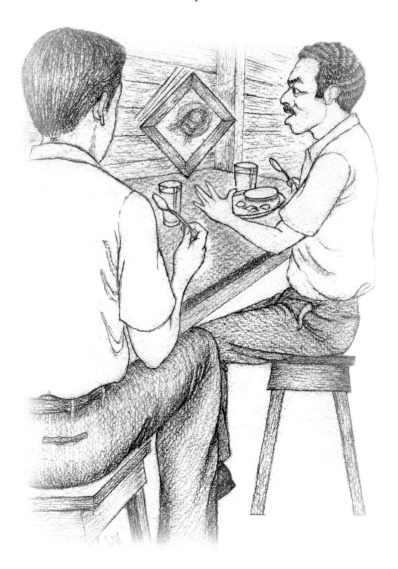

Marino showed him how to thresh. "You stand on this side of the tarp. I will stand on the other side. Then we will take turns whacking that big pile of dry beans in the middle of the tarp. Here's your pole. Let's go."

The long pole was not as heavy as Johnny had expected. He gripped it in his soft hands. Marino brought his stick down on the dry beans with a great *whack*. Then it was Johnny's turn. He raised the pole and brought it down as hard as he could, but it did not make the beans pop like Marino's did. He pulled the pole back, barely missing Marino's next whack.

Whack! Whack! Whack! Whack! The poles were beating constantly. First Marino. Then Johnny. Then Marino again. Then Johnny. At first it was hard for Johnny to keep up with the rhythm and to keep his stick from getting cracked by Marino's. But once he got the hang of it, he stuck to it. *This isn't too bad,* Johnny cheered to himself. But a half hour later his breath was coming in short gasps and his hands felt raw.

Soon, during one of the breaks when they pitched the trash and threw in a new batch of beans, stalks and all, Johnny noticed several nice blisters on each hand. A few had actually burst and were bleeding. He showed Gelo, and Gelo told Marino to let him off for the rest of the day.

Later, when the sun was setting, Teodolinda had finished all her work and was ready to talk. Gelo and Johnny sat in the living room facing Teodolinda. Johnny's Bible was open. He suspected that Teodolinda's heart was open too. He was right.

To Johnny's delight, Teodolinda began. "I have always had questions about our first fathers. Is it true that Adam and Eve raised a whole batch of children just like we mountain people do?"

"How many children have you raised?" Johnny asked Teodolinda kindly.

"We have raised sixteen, though little Sergio died when he was four," Teodolinda explained.

"Yes, I'm sure Adam and Eve raised at least sixteen children. Their life was much like yours toward the end. They had to work hard and suffer just like you do. But it was not always like that. They used to live in a paradise . . ."

With his Bible in hand, Johnny Rojas pounced on Teodolinda's question and launched into a story she had never heard. He told her about Creation, and God's perfect Garden of Eden, and life before sin. Then he told her how Adam and Eve fell, how Satan took advantage of the woman's weakness and deceived her, and how she then convinced her husband to eat of the forbidden fruit. Many times Teodolinda clucked her tongue and nodded as the stories sank deep into her heart.

Johnny soon left the Old Testament and began telling Teodolinda about Jesus—how He lived on the earth and suffered just like she did, but He never sinned. How He suffered and died for her sins and his. When he talked about how awful sin was to God, Teodolinda's eyes welled with tears. "Yes," she nodded. "I have so many sins."

Johnny's eyes were shining as he launched into the love and mercy of God through Jesus. Then he explained repentance. To his joy, by the time he had explained the way, Teodolinda was weeping softly. Gelo sat beside her, sobbing too. Then Johnny coached gently, "I invite you to accept Jesus Christ as your Saviour."

Teodolinda started slowly. "In Zapotal we were so wicked. I drank a lot of *contrabando*. I smoked. And the worst thing was that we sold *guaro* and made the men sick and made their wives, mothers, and children suffer so much. We lived to do evil."

Teodolinda was sobbing. Genuine repentance was evident. Confession came naturally to her heart. "I'd make money. I'd raise vegetables. I'd fatten a pig and sell it. And I'd always use the money for those awful dances and those wicked *rosarios*. Then the *guaro* would make the men fight. Oh, Johnny, our lives were awful! Can Jesus forgive me for all my sins?"

Johnny was crying too. "Absolutely. Let's ask Him to do it now. Kneel, sister."

As she knelt, Gelo grabbed Johnny's shirtsleeve and whispered, "Johnny, I have not accepted Christ either. Now is the time, with my mother." So Gelo knelt beside her.

Johnny put his hand on Teodolinda's head and prayed for her first. He prayed with all his heart and with great joy. Teodolinda wept softly, praying and confessing her sins under her breath. And the Holy Spirit came into her heart. Very distinctly, she felt the presence of God as He washed her sins away.

Next Johnny prayed for Gelo. As Gelo prayed along with Johnny, he knew something was happening. His heart was opened, and now he could understand even better than before the things Johnny had been telling them. And best of all, he felt peace for the first time in his life. After they got to their feet and thanked Johnny, Teodolinda returned to the kitchen to make a fresh pot of coffee. Meanwhile, Marino had just come into the kitchen from his work. She ran over and hugged him. "I am so happy, Marino. I accepted Jesus as my Saviour!"

"Are you sure it's real?" Marino wondered, eyeing her suspiciously.

"Yes, I know it's real. When he prayed for me, I felt the presence of God in my heart. I feel such a wonderful peace, son. Go listen; then you do it too."

Later, when Teodolinda went in to serve the coffee, she found the three men in deep conversation. Johnny was carefully and respectfully explaining to Marino what had happened to the Catholic Church many years before. "The Catholic Church apostatized when it united with the state around three hundred years after Christ. See, the church and state should be separate in the New Testament era. After the church fell away, things went from bad to worse . . ."

They paused for coffee and then continued their conversation. Soon Marino was kneeling on the floor with Johnny praying for him.

Later they all sat in the living room. Johnny began singing as he strummed his guitar. To Teodolinda's surprise, Gelo jumped right in with a clear tenor that harmonized perfectly.

"Jehová es mi Pastor,
Nada, pues, me faltará . . ."
(Jehovah is my Shepherd,
Nothing, then, will I lack.)

As the night lengthened, song after song burst from the hearts of the two men. Praise and worship! There was such joy in the little cabin, and such joy in Heaven. Teodolinda's former master was furious, but her heavenly Father was delighted. His long-lost daughter had finally come home. And her sons were following fast. And the little church He had been planning for Chachagua for a long, long time was on its way.

38

Teodolinda returned to Chachagua a changed woman. She and Gelo brought Johnny and the Gospel into their home. Lico remained unconvinced and seemed angry. Teodolinda tried to explain.

"Look, Valverde, we have to be honest with ourselves. We have not been good people. We have not even been good Catholics. We have been great sinners. What we have always needed is to find something or someone to help us. And Valverde, I have found it."

"But we have always said that changing religion is a mortal sin," Lico snapped. "What are we saying now? Just go change your religion as often as you want?"

"This is not a matter of religion, Valverde. Who told us that becoming an *evangélico* is a mortal sin? The priest, right? This same priest turned around and asked me to come to his house for some romance. So why should we believe the priest? Can't you see, Valverde? We have been deceived!"

"I'm not ready to say that yet, Teodolinda. I won't keep you from listening, but don't depend on me. I am a Catholic unto death!"

"Well, I have accepted Jesus Christ as my Lord and Saviour. There is no backing out for me. Thank you for letting me follow this faith. I will respect you too. And please, I want Johnny to stay here for a while so he can teach us from the Bible. He will work for his room and board. He will work mornings, study in the afternoons, and in the evenings we will have meetings."

Lico did not answer.

"Gelo wants to build a little lean-to room on the back of the house for him to sleep in. No one else in Chachagua will give him room and board."

"Humph," grunted Lico.

The bean threshing was going full swing. Every morning after breakfast Lico would go to the bean field and turn the bean clusters to the sun. By ten o'clock the dew would be dried off the beans. They would set up the tarp in the middle of the field and the threshing would begin. Some of the boys would haul beans to the tarp. Two men would thresh them. Gelo would sit on the ground and help fill sacks with the threshed beans. Johnny would often take the threshing pole. His hands blistered and bled, but he kept right on trying. By the end of the harvest his hands were not blistering as much, and the marks of a working man were emerging—calluses!

A pattern emerged that suited everyone. Forenoons were always spent working. After the bean harvest, it was cleaning yucca, hilling papaya trees, and macheteing fields. Johnny learned it all.

Afternoons were spent studying. Usually Gelo studied when Johnny did. Johnny would study in his new little lean-to, and Gelo would sit at the table in the living room. Often when Johnny found a special truth in the Word, he would come out and share it with his disciple. And when Gelo found a special nugget of truth, he would share it with his mother, who was usually in the kitchen. All three would often end up discussing Scripture for hours on end. Sometimes Lily would listen in. She seldom said much, but Gelo saw that she had a genuine interest. Sometimes others in the family would listen in, though Mireya usually just minded her own business, and Lico avoided all contact with Johnny.

One afternoon Johnny announced, "Today we are going to witness." That was new to Gelo, but he was ready. He hobbled and Johnny walked, stopping at every home on Calle Rojas. As they walked, they talked.

At the first home, the man of the house was out working. Johnny respectfully greeted the woman of the house, but soon said good-bye and walked on. As they approached the next house, Gelo explained, "This is Edin Rojas's place. His father passed away, but he was the one who gave this road its name. They are one of the more well-to-do families in Chachagua. They look down on us because we are poor, and here we, the scum, can tell the big shots about Jesus!" he chuckled.

"I like that attitude," Johnny answered. "When Jesus was here on earth they called Him all kinds of names, and He never got upset. He just told them about salvation."

They arrived at Edin's fancy house, and Gelo called out, *"¡Upe!"*

Soon a short stocky man stepped out dressed in a sport shirt and shorts. When he saw Gelo, he shouted back, "What do you want?"

"Could you spare several minutes of your time?" Gelo asked, showing his winsome smile. "We would like to visit with you."

"Come on in," Edin said, setting out several chairs on the porch.

Johnny did not beat around the bush. Very soon he was asking Edin how he felt about Jesus. Edin was involved in a new Catholic renewal group that called themselves the *carismáticos*. They were very active in Chachagua, and some were actually reading their Bibles. They sang choruses like the *evangélicos* did. They played guitars and clapped in their services. A lot of people were confused, thinking that the *carismáticos* were *evangélicos,* or vice versa. But the *carismáticos* still celebrated Mass, baptized infants, and worshiped Mary. The basic Catholic doctrines had not changed.

Johnny avoided the touchy subjects and discussed Scriptures they agreed on. Johnny's warm personality and tact won Edin's confidence, and they spent a wonderful hour sharing the Word. To Gelo's amazement, the meeting ended with an agreement that they would hold a service the next evening at Edin's place.

That evening after Johnny and Gelo returned home, Luis dropped in. Teodolinda called him aside. "Luis, what are you thinking? Are you ready to accept Christ as your Saviour?"

"I would like to," Luis answered pensively. "I have that New Testament your sister Arcilia gave me. But when I tried to read it, I couldn't understand it. Manuela is not impressed."

Teodolinda told Johnny that Luis could not understand the Scriptures. So Johnny sat down with Luis in the candlelight and read John 3:16 to him. "Can you understand that?" he asked gently.

"Yes," Luis answered. "I can. It tells me that if God so loved the world, He also loves me, right?"

"Perfect!" Johnny exclaimed. "Now go home and think about that; then come to the meeting at Edin Rojas's place tomorrow evening. There you can give your heart to the Lord if you desire."

It was surprising how many people showed up at the meeting. Some neighbors stayed home and raised their eyebrows, but several came, including quite a few Valverdes. Teodolinda, Lily, Mireya, Gelo, and Luis were there. No one knew how Lidier got word of the meeting, but he was there with his wife and their teenaged son Lalo. And, of course, Edin's family.

Edin set up chairs and benches for the service. For a pulpit, he set up a little table in the front of the living room and decorated it with a white doily and a vase of wildflowers. They gathered as the day closed and dusk crept over Chachagua.

Johnny asked Gelo to lead the songs. Gelo had already learned several choruses by heart and led them with zest. Johnny accompanied the songs with his guitar. The little group felt the joy of the Lord and sang with all their hearts.

After the songs, Gelo read a Scripture. It was hard for him to hold his Bible and hold on to the table at the same time, but he managed, and after the reading, he led in prayer. Then Johnny got up and preached a Spirit-filled message on salvation. He explained things right out of the Bible. He spoke out clearly against sin; then he talked about God's love and mercy. He explained repentance and salvation.

Then he warned people about the upcoming Judgment Day. After the message he gave an invitation to accept Christ, and Luis and Lily went forward. Johnny prayed with them, and their joy was full and running over.

The townspeople reacted differently to these new services. Some thought the *carismático* group was holding meetings. Some knew better and kept their distance. Others were interested, but were not ready to commit. Some were angry. Lidier was one of these. He knew the meetings had nothing to do with the Catholic Church. He was sure Johnny had come to Chachagua bringing false doctrine to deceive the people. But his wife and son were touched with a longing only God could satisfy.

The next week Luis was walking to a meeting in another home carrying his guitar. His son Toño was with him. As he passed the house of his friend Chepe, with whom he had once played guitar at the saloons, he called out, "Come to the meeting and sing with us!"

Thinking it was a *carismático* service, Chepe agreed to go along. But soon after they started walking down the road they met one of the *carismáticos* walking toward them. Seeing Chepe with his guitar walking beside Luis, the man asked, "Where are you going?"

"To a service just up the road," Luis answered.

The man turned to Chepe. "Do you know what kind of a service it is?"

"No, not really. He just invited me," Chepe answered.

"Don't let yourself be deceived. These Valverdes have turned *evangélicos*. They are not Catholics at all. They won't have anything to do with the Virgin Mary. They are deceivers."

"What?" Chepe growled. "They don't believe in the Virgin? That's ridiculous! If I would have known where you were taking me, Luis, I would not have come," he barked. "You'd better be glad I'm not going with you. You don't want to know what I would do in a service where they don't respect Mary!"

"Listen," Luis interrupted, "we do respect Mary. We just don't believe it's right to worship her—"

"That book you carry under your arm," Chepe snarled, "it turns my stomach!"

"That's strange," Luis answered. "It's the Bible. Shall I read you some verses?"

That really made Chepe angry. "I would love to beat up all of Mary's enemies and kick them into the air! That's what I would do to you beasts who esteem Mary the same as any mare or swine!"

"Look," Luis tried again, "I'm only trying to change my life. You know what a wicked man I was. I want to change."

"Change your life, yes! That's great! But don't change religions! That's a mortal sin!"

Luis tried to calm his friend down, but Chepe was actually foaming at the mouth as he fumed. Finally Luis left him and walked on to the meeting with his son.

This time the meeting was at another *carismático* home. A bunch of *carismáticos* came with a list of songs they wanted to sing. They approached Johnny just as the service was ready to start.

"Let me see your list," Johnny requested. Just as he had suspected, the group was testing him with a list of songs dedicated to the Virgin Mary.

"No," Johnny announced publicly, "we can't sing these songs. It is not right to worship Mary. First Timothy 2:5 tells us, 'For there is one God, and one mediator between God and men, the man Christ Jesus.'"

The *carismáticos* walked out of the service. And although they were able to go ahead with the meeting that evening, the occasion severed their relationship with the *carismáticos*.

The new little church decided to build a small chapel on Teodolinda's land. Everyone gave what he could to build it. They made it very simple. A tin roof, walls open to the four winds so everyone would feel welcome, simple hand-planed benches, and a unique pulpit Gelo made and trimmed with his sharp machete. They held services Sunday mornings, Sunday evenings, Thursday evenings, and Saturday evenings. Whenever they could, they held services in different homes around town.

Luis and the rest asked for baptism, so Johnny started to offer doctrinal classes. Though Johnny was still learning doctrine himself, the classes were wonderful. They took turns reading a portion from the Bible and then studied it carefully. The classes were held on evenings when there were no services. Even after the first converts were baptized three months later, the Bible studies continued and became the basis of the new church's doctrine and practice.

Luis had trouble getting to church. He could handle Manuela's daily hounding and the many people who tried to convince him that the new religion in Chachagua was dangerous and erroneous. He stood up to that with courage. His problem was a dog.

Every time Luis walked to church, he had to pass Chepe's place. Chepe's house was perched on a little knoll beside the road. Sunday mornings Chepe enjoyed sitting on his porch watching the world go by. Soon after the day he raked Luis over the coals for joining the *evangélicos,* he bought himself a vicious hound. He was proud of his new watchdog and trained her to hunt. But what he taught her to hunt on Sunday mornings was no laughing matter.

It all started one bright Sunday morning when Chepe saw Luis coming up the road on his way to church. Luis had his Bible in one hand and an umbrella in the other in case it rained on the way home. Just as he passed Chepe's gate, Chepe's dog started to bark at him. Instead of calling her off, Chepe hissed, "Get him!" And the hound sure knew what to do. She rushed at Luis like a tiger, snarling at his feet. Luis used his umbrella to push her back, sidestepping to avoid her teeth. When the dog paused in her attack, Luis looked up to see why Chepe did not call her off. The reason, he discovered, was because Chepe was too busy laughing, slapping his leg, and making fun of his former friend.

This hurt Luis more than the dog had, but he did not say a word and hurried on his way. Chepe made sure he was in position every Sunday to enjoy this new sport.

God tried the new converts, and they tested true. Three months after Teodolinda's conversion, Johnny asked an elder from Naranjo to come for a weekend. While he was there, they celebrated Chachagua's first adult baptism.

Everything went smoothly. The day dawned bright and clear. The service was held down by the Chachagua River, and Teodolinda, Luis, Gelo, Lily, and Lalo were baptized in its chilly waters.

The persecution in Chachagua did not let up after the baptism. Many people just could not stand that an evangelical church could take root in their little Catholic town. But try as they might, they could not stop it. Not even the gates of Hell could prevail against the little church God had planted according to His plan. The fires of trial only served to fan the flame of their faith.

39

Belén Valverde built his tiny cabin right at the foot of Rincón de la Vieja in Guanacaste. Lumber abounded in the virgin jungle at the base of this huge active volcano, so he built a unique little cabin totally out of the finest lumber, including mahogany. Even the roof was made out of overlapping boards. Though the area would later be declared a national reserve, at this time people still cut its precious wood.

Belén had taken a contract to saw out railroad ties with his brand-new chain saw. Eighteen-year-old Hugo had moved out months before to be his helper. Since it was a big contract, they decided to build the little cabin and live in the jungle for a year. They cooked for themselves and washed and bathed in the creek.

Belén and Hugo both enjoyed the out-of-doors. This place was not quite as high in altitude as Zapotal, but its beauty was similar, and there was even more wildlife, so hunting was easy. They bought their scant groceries at the little town of Las Lilas on the main road. But Hugo and Belén lived back in the jungle like hermits.

The area was well-known for its snakes. There were bushmasters, fer-de-lance, and rattlers. Hugo was glad he got to sleep on the top bunk in their tiny bedroom. They also were cautious of the *leones* that supposedly infested the area. Hugo had never completely gotten over his fear of the *león*.

Rincón de la Vieja had its own sad *león* story. One night neighbors had heard a woman scream, but nobody had had the nerve to investigate. In the morning she was gone. Several days later some fishermen found what was left of her mangled body under a tree in the jungle.

Hugo was glad their little cabin was built securely.

One night Hugo woke with a start. He could hear an animal on the roof right above him, scratching and growling. He lay on his hard board bed, afraid to breathe. Suddenly the cat screamed and leaped from the roof to a nearby tree and fled into the night.

Hugo and Belén worked at the foot of Rincón de la Vieja for almost a year. Sundays were the only time they sought social life. They would go to Las Lilas to play soccer and drink. Hugo bought enough cigarettes on Sundays to last him a week.

Evenings and Saturdays Hugo loved to fish. The rivers in the area were not overly fished, and it was usually pretty easy to pull in a *guapote.**

Hugo's life was lonely and empty. They worked hard during the week and played hard on the weekends, but nothing satisfied. The last several months had been especially rough for Hugo. He would often find himself thinking of home and wondering how everyone was doing. He would get a tight feeling in his chest as the loneliness grew into a desperate longing. *What is wrong with me?* he asked himself again and again.

One day he was helping a neighbor boy move some cattle. Hugo's mare had been bred for speed, and Hugo was proud to be able to ride a horse that was so quick on her feet. As they chased the cattle along the trail between the towering jungle walls, a calf broke loose and ran ahead of the herd. Hugo recognized his chance to try out the mare. He kicked her in the ribs and hung on for dear life. She ran like the wind.

---

* rainbow bass

Just as Hugo and the mare caught up with the calf, the trail parted into a Y. The calf slammed to a stop right where the Y split. The mare kept right on going. She was moving too fast to stop, and she was not sure which branch to take. Hugo, busy hanging on, was not giving her any direction. At the last second the mare still had not made up her mind, so she plowed into the middle area between the two branching trails. Fortunately, she swerved before hitting the tree that stood right in the center of the Y, but horse and rider flashed past so close that Hugo scraped his foot. The mare finally stopped, and Hugo brought her around, both breathing hard.

That night Hugo could not sleep. The near accident had really affected him. His mind wandered and questions haunted him late into the night. *Why wasn't I killed when that mare almost ran me into that tree? That was way too close for comfort. It's a miracle I'm still alive!*

The thoughts of death sobered him. *What is wrong with my life? Why am I not happy? Why can't I stop drinking and smoking? Why is my life so empty?*

His thoughts, as they often did lately, turned to home. *What's going on at home? I know something unusual must be happening. I need to get home and find out. When I think of it, my chest gets tight and it's hard to breathe.*

Hugo did not know that his family was being converted one by one, or that they were praying for him. Every night before she went to bed, Teodolinda knelt and prayed for every one of her children, and she always remembered her grown baby far away in Guanacaste. Johnny and all of the new Christians were praying for Hugo too.

The next evening Hugo was out fishing. He selected one of his favorite spots—a pool at a bend in the river. First he used a tiny hook to catch some sardines for bait. Then he sat on a log and put a whole sardine onto a larger hook, which was attached to a thick hand line. After baiting the hook, he wrapped the hand line up in a coil like a lariat, swung the bait around his head, and flung the hook out into the center of the pool. The bait sank to the bottom, and Hugo did what all good fishermen do—he waited patiently.

But the fish did not bite. The only things biting were the mosquitoes. Hugo was smoking cigarette after cigarette and blowing smoke at the mosquitoes to make them leave. After an hour of changing positions and even pools, Hugo decided to give up if he didn't catch something soon. As he sat, his thoughts again turned to his family. *Why am I thinking of home again? And why, when I think of home, do I think of God?*

Hugo had never really put any stock in the Catholic Church. Neither did he appreciate it when his sister Marina or his aunt Arcilia witnessed to him as *evangélicas*. He had never found any solace in religion. But now his thoughts were not on religion. His thoughts were slowly waking up to what really mattered: God.

Does God really exist? Where is He? What does He do? Does He listen when people pray? Does He love me? Does He even think about me at all?

Suddenly Hugo had an idea. He would test God. He would pray to God and see if He answered. As Hugo formulated his prayer, he began to feel self-conscious and bashful. He almost felt a presence in the jungle with him. He glanced around to see if anyone was watching, but he was alone. Even so, he could not make himself pray aloud. He doubted seriously that God would hear him if he only thought his prayer, but he decided to do it anyway.

God, do You exist? Hugo felt a strange tingling on his skin and looked around again. Nothing. *If You exist, I ask You to answer my prayer. If You answer my prayer, I will stop smoking and drinking. I will be a better man. My prayer is that You make the fish bite.* As Hugo finished his prayer, he chuckled. Surely God didn't have time to pay attention to a wicked Valverde way back in the jungle. And why would He care about catching fish?

But Hugo's line was already moving. The coiled line lay loosely on his fingers, and he clearly felt the little tug. Soon the line was skimming across the pool. A *guapote* had taken the bait and was heading for the deep. Hugo waited, his hair standing straight up, until the line had picked up just the right speed. Then he pulled in hard. Hugo shook his head in disbelief as he pulled in a sixteen-inch *guapote*. "I can't believe this!" he swore.

Half an hour later Hugo was walking home along the jungle trail. Never had he caught so many fish in such a short time. He had enough for him and Belén and several neighbor boys they hung out with. Though he was glad for the meat, something more important had happened in his heart. He knew that somehow God in Heaven did care for him. He now knew that God watched him wherever he went, and that God had made the mare miss the tree the day before. And He, and only He, had made the fish bite. He looked again in amazement at the string of fish hanging from his shoulder. "These must be God's fish!" he said.

Several weeks later Belén came from town with a letter for Hugo from home. Hugo had never received a letter from his family before. *This must be important,* he thought. Sitting on a stump under the trees, he ripped open the envelope. Gelo's sprawling handwriting jumped out at him.

> *Dear Hugo,*
>
> *We would like it if you would come home. Some wonderful things are happening here, and we would like you to join us. We are finding God!*
>
> > *Your brother,*
> > *Gelo*

Hugo stared at the letter for a long time. Never had he felt love from Gelo like he felt in this short letter. Gelo, concerned about him? That was new. Not only that, but his family was finding God! That was incredible for sure. Suddenly he knew why he was feeling the way he was lately. *If my family is finding God, could it be that God is trying to find me?* In his heart Hugo knew it was true. And though he did not understand it all, he was glad. The tiny thirst in Hugo's heart grew.

Finally their work at Rincón de la Vieja was done. Hugo hunted and killed a great big paca for his mother. He salted the meat well and the next day bused home alone. Everyone was overjoyed to see him, even Lico, who was aging and limping more than ever. Teodolinda was especially happy for the fresh meat. She made a wonderful meal for the family that night.

Johnny was not there that day. He was spending several days at Zona Fluca with Marino. But Hugo could tell the difference in his family right away. He was surprised at the peace he found. A quiet joy and an underlying excitement pervaded their home.

That night after supper, Teodolinda and Gelo told Hugo the whole story. Hugo listened quietly. He not only listened, he watched. His heart was struck to the core to see his mother, the former owner of La Peligrosa, so full of joy. When she smiled and when she wept, Hugo saw the Lord's image clearly on her face. Gelo, neatly dressed with his neat haircut, convinced him too. This was a totally different man. Though Hugo did not show it, the story gripped his heart like nothing had ever done before. He wanted a miracle too.

After talking for an hour, Gelo said quietly, "Let's pray."

The three rose to their feet. Gelo led out. "Dear God, we are so glad Hugo came home. He has also been a great sinner. Put a desire in his heart to seek You. We need You. We love You. Please help us. And, Lord, we pray for Dad too. Soften his heart to Your Gospel. We ask this in Jesus' name. Amen."

When Gelo finished, they were surprised to see that Lico had hobbled up to them during the prayer and now stood right beside Gelo. His face was sad, but his old, wrinkled features showed signs of more than sadness. A longing flickered in his dark eyes. *It's only a matter of time,* Teodolinda thought.

The next day Gelo spent hours explaining the simple Gospel to Hugo. Hugo did not say a word. In the afternoon Johnny came back. He was glad to meet the youngest Valverde. Johnny gave Hugo a Bible, and the pair became friends on the spot.

That evening Hugo took his Bible and went early to the little building they were using for their meetings. It was still half an hour before services. Hugo arrived at the building alone. He walked in and felt a strong urge to kneel. His heart was so ready it could not wait until the service. It did not need to.

Hugo knelt by one of the benches and started to really pray for the first time in his life. He just poured his heart out to God. God was there and heard, just as He had that day by the river. But now Hugo was not testing God. He was repenting of all his sins. As he confessed them, Jesus forgave them and washed him clean in His blood. Why wait until the church service? Now was the time. And this time, God did not send *guapotes;* He sent His Holy Spirit. Hugo felt as if a great shaft of light, truth, and love shone into his heart. He rose just in time for the service. He was a new man, and he knew it.

During that service Hugo felt a part of the little group. The worshipers were his mother, Luis, Gelo, Lily, Lalo and his mother Gregoria, and several other visitors. Gelo led the songs and read the Scripture. Then Johnny preached. Hugo had never heard such a message before.

The next day Johnny and Gelo were perplexed. Hugo seemed so ready to be a Christian. It seemed as if he was one with them already, and yet he had not made a public statement for Jesus. They were both surprised he had not gone forward the evening before.

Johnny finally asked, "What are you thinking, Hugo?"

"I haven't told you and Gelo," Hugo confessed, "but I made my commitment to God last evening before the service. I have already been converted."

"Praise the Lord!" Johnny shouted.

And Hugo, just like all the rest, was changed. The morning of his conversion he had not bought any cigarettes. He did not need them now. Every one of the converts dropped their awful vices. The saloon owners in Chachagua felt their loss. A few Valverdes still drank, but fewer were showing up every day.

A week later Johnny invited Hugo to go for a walk. Carrying their Bibles, they walked down to the river that rushed past Chachagua. They sat on some rocks beside the river and talked.

Johnny started. "I'm not sure how our baptisms should be handled." He threw a pebble into the white churning rapids. "The first baptism we had here, we waited for three months; then we asked an elder to come from Naranjo to conduct the baptisms. But I am not sure it is right. Philip didn't wait for months and then go find Peter to baptize the eunuch. He just took him to the water and did it. The Apostle Paul didn't think he had to baptize everybody. He actually got others to do it. Even Jesus got His disciples to baptize people. I am ready to do it that way today. How do you feel?"

"I am just learning," Hugo said humbly. "I'll do it however you feel is best. If you want to go ahead today, I am willing."

"How is your heart with the Lord today, Hugo?" Johnny asked.

"I have peace in my heart," Hugo confessed.

"Are you willing to renounce Satan and serve God forever? That's what baptism is all about."

"Yes, by the grace of God I will be faithful until the end." Hugo nodded as he spoke.

The two men spent a lovely hour there under Chachagua's trees beside the river. They read Scriptures about baptism and prayed. Finally Johnny said, "I feel God is leading us to go ahead with your baptism today."

"I agree." Hugo smiled. "I am ready to commit my life to the Lord forever."

"As we read," Johnny added, "it's not that the water itself will wash your sins away. They are already gone. That happened last week, and was by the resurrection of Jesus Christ and His blood that was shed. But what we will do today is 'the answer of a good conscience toward God.' "*

Johnny and Hugo walked up the river until they came to a deep pool. Then they both waded into the water and Johnny baptized Hugo in the name of the Father and of the Son and of the Holy Ghost.

Hugo's emphasis rapidly turned to evangelism. The men often traveled together because they appreciated Johnny's way with people and how well he could explain Scripture. But sometimes they divided into

---

* 1 Peter 3:21

groups. Gelo, Hugo, and Luis were learning fast. They all fit into the pattern Johnny had set. They worked hard in the morning; studied, prayed, or evangelized in the afternoon; and held meetings or Bible studies in the evening.

During Johnny's stay in Chachagua, the Word spread. He and the other men visited most of the homes in Chachagua, at least the ones that allowed it. Then they went out and visited all of the towns and communities surrounding Chachagua.

Persecution was rampant, but it did not dampen their fire. Wherever they went, the Catholic community rejected them, but they found some souls ready for the truth of the Gospel. In the first year the church grew to a membership of fifteen. And Gelo, formerly the long-haired fighter and moonshiner, was chosen as Johnny's co-pastor.

One afternoon when Johnny was out visiting with Hugo and Luis, Gelo and Teodolinda were at home discussing the new church. Gelo sat on a stool in the kitchen while Teodolinda finished washing the lunch dishes.

"Just think of it, Mamita," Gelo said, shaking his head slowly. "A year ago we were still up to our ears in sin. I was drinking and fighting, full of the devil. I still can hardly believe it at times."

"Neither can I," Teodolinda agreed. "And even your father is coming around." She glanced around to see if Lico had heard her.

"The other day when we prayed," Gelo threw in, "he came right up and stood with us as we finished the prayer. He is very close. We need to pray for him. We also need to pray about the persecution. It seems like it's getting worse. We have not 'resisted unto blood,' but we may get there. Some of the *carismáticos* are furious. Why don't we pray right now, Mamita?"

"Yes," Teodolinda said. "And let's remember Leyla as well. The other day I sent her a Bible with some folks traveling to Tajo Alto. I would like to ask God to use it to touch her heart."

Teodolinda stood beside her son. Hunched over on his stool, he started to pray. He thanked God for all His marvelous gifts, especially for salvation. Then he prayed his heart out for Leyla and his father. Last of all he prayed for their antagonists by name.

Sometime during the prayer, Gelo and Teodolinda sensed that someone had come up beside them. Teodolinda peeked and saw her husband standing beside Gelo, his head bowed. She quickly closed her eyes and prayed harder under her breath. Gelo finished his prayer without knowing who was beside him. But as he looked up after the "amen," he saw his dad. Something about his stance spoke to Gelo of repentance.

"Dad," he asked softly, "would you like to be saved?"

Old Lico nodded and began to weep. The floodgates let loose. Teodolinda cried harder now than she had for her own sins. Gelo's eyes were fountains of tears too, but he contained them enough to lead his father to the Lord. In the end, Gelo asked his father to kneel in front of him. Lico prayed aloud between his sobs, pouring out his heart to God. Gelo laid his hands on his father's head, just as Johnny had done for him, and prayed him home.

40

A young woman stood in the aisle at the supermarket in San José pretending to look for coffee. She had white skin, but her features were Latin. Her hair was black and she wore a modest skirt and blouse.

In the same aisle two ladies were choosing spices. The older one was short and plump, the younger one slim and petite. The young lady pushed the cart. The older woman stooped to read the labels on the bottom shelf, found what she was looking for, and pitched the tiny jars into the cart, straightening her prayer veil as she stood.

The pair did not notice the young woman, who took down a pack of coffee from the shelf as if to read the label. *Who are these two Americanas?* she wondered. *Where do they live? I wonder why they wear that white kerchief on their heads. That girl is pretty. I would love to ask them some questions, but I'm so bashful that I'm trembling just thinking about it.*

Rosita was a young evangelical Christian who worked in a sewing factory right up the street from the supermarket in the heart of San José. Her coworkers often sent her to the store to buy snacks and drinks for their noon meal. This was the first time she had seen the *Americanas.* But it would not be the last. She saw them and others often after that, though she never gathered enough nerve to talk with them or to ask about the white cloth they wore on their heads.

About six blocks from the supermarket was a little restaurant right beside the bus station. A young man, white-skinned and with plump cheeks, worked for the old man who owned it. The young man's name was Fernando Rojas. He was an evangelical Christian, and he enjoyed serving people delicious coffee and good food.

One day Fernando noticed a strange man walking into the restaurant. He was tall and obviously an *Americano*. He wore a light blue shirt and a pair of dark suspenders. He had a head full of black hair and a full beard. He sat down to one of the tables, pulled a newspaper out of his bag, and began to read.

Fernando approached his table curiously.

"I'd like a meal," the tall man said with a heavy accent and a big smile. "And a bit of coffee too."

After eating his meal and drinking his coffee, the man paid his bill, waved to Fernando, and left. From then on, the man came to the restaurant regularly, about every two weeks. He was so friendly that soon Fernando looked forward to his visits. He often wondered where he lived and about his religion, but he never had the nerve to ask.

A year later Fernando and Rosita were married in their home church in San José. One thing that had attracted them to each other was that they each sincerely wanted to be genuine Christians. They were both repelled by the many who professed to be Christians but acted just like the rest of the world. They were looking for something better.

After they married, they talked many times about serving the Lord with all their hearts. One day Rosita surprised Fernando. "Honey, I have felt for quite some time that Christian women should wear something on their heads to pray. Have you read 1 Corinthians 11?"

"It seems to me that if that was something God wanted, there would be a church somewhere that practiced it," Fernando answered.

"There is!" Rosita answered excitedly. "I've seen ladies at the supermarket several times. They dress plainly and wear white kerchiefs on their heads. I love it, Fernando. It seems so right, and if you read 1 Corinthians 11, it's all there."

"I learned to know a man at the restaurant who must have been from that group," Fernando said. Then he told Rosita about the *Americano* with the suspenders. After pondering the issue some more, Fernando said, "Well, I still don't know. Let's ask our ministers and see what they say."

"We can ask them, but we already asked them why they allow makeup and jewelry in the church, in spite of what the Bible says. The minister said that any old barn looks better with a little paint. I don't think that answer was nice, or Biblical. I hardly trust them anymore."

That evening Fernando and Rosita studied 1 Corinthians 11:1-16 together. They discussed each verse as they read. By the time they got to verse fourteen, they were absolutely convinced that the Bible meant what it said. If a sister wanted to pray or prophesy, she needed to cover her head. The last two verses confused them somewhat, so they decided to pray about it and ask their pastor.

The next Sunday after church they discussed the issue with their pastor. He asked for time to study the passage. A week later he explained to them that in verse fifteen, the Bible said that the woman's hair was given to her instead of a covering. He encouraged them not to worry about it.

"But, Pastor, why would the Apostle Paul come across so clearly in the first fourteen verses and then turn around and say that they didn't have to worry about it after all?" Rosita asked.

"Oh, Rosita," the pastor joked, "you always take things so seriously and so literally. I'm sure Paul wanted them to wear some sort of covering back then, but it has nothing to do with us today."

The answer did not satisfy either Rosita or Fernando.

Some time later, on a Sunday morning, their minister brought a box of magazines to church. "These were given to me by an *Americano* I met at the bank," he announced. "We had a good talk, and when I came out of the bank he was waiting to give me these magazines. He said they are for our families, so help yourselves."

Fernando and Rosita took one home. They became so engrossed in reading that they did not make lunch until much later. *Luz de la Vida.* Rosita savored the title almost reverently. "Fernando, I'm almost sure this is printed by those people I saw at the supermarket."

"Sure enough!" Fernando exclaimed. "Here's a drawing of a lady with a kerchief on her head, and the man looks just like the guy who used to come to our restaurant."

Soon Rosita found an article that answered one of her biggest questions. "Here it is, Fernando! Now we know the name of this church. They are *Menonitas.* I wonder what the name means."

"Yes," Fernando agreed. "We now know their name, and we know that somewhere in Costa Rica there is a church."

"I wish I'd asked those ladies where they were from!" Rosita lamented. "I so want to learn more about them. I would just love to belong to a church like that!"

"Well," said Fernando, ever practical, "we could write to this magazine and ask if they know where the *Menonitas* live in Costa Rica."

"Perfect!" Rosita exclaimed. "I'll write a letter right away."

About a month later they received an answer from Rod and Staff Publishers, who promised to send Fernando and Rosita their magazine and told them there was a church in La Merced.

"Oh, no," Rosita groaned. "That's so far! It must be at least six hours by bus! But someday we will go, right, Fernando?"

"Yes. Right now we can hardly afford the trip, but someday, dear, we will find them, and if we like it, we will join them."

*　　*　　*

One day Fernando and Rosita were both at home when a young man stopped in. Fernando jumped up and hugged the man, exclaiming, "Johnny, it's so good to see you again!"

"Hey, it's good to see you too. How have you been?"

"We have been fine," Fernando assured him. "But we really want to hear how it's going with you. We heard about your call to Chachagua. Tell us, how's it going?"

"Things are going well in Chachagua. I came out to see Mom and Dad and will head back tomorrow, Lord willing."

"Tell us," Rosita insisted, "are there any converts? We heard that you went to evangelize a wild, wicked family that moved down from the mountains of Zapotal."

"Yes, that's true. And the Lord has had mercy on them. One by one they are being converted. Right now we have quite a few members, and the Valverde who used to be the wildest is my co-pastor."

"That's wonderful!" Fernando exclaimed. "I'd like to come visit you down there some time."

That night Johnny Rojas and his brother Fernando talked for hours about what the Lord was doing in Chachagua. When Johnny left, Fernando promised to come visit him soon. Johnny felt that Fernando could be a real encouragement to the new converts. And Rosita was excited because Chachagua was closer to La Merced, where the *Menonitas* lived. Maybe, just maybe, they could meet with them while they were there.

*   *   *

The little group sat in a circle in the simple chapel during one of their weekly Bible studies. They had decided to hold it in the morning this time, since their visitors were planning to leave on the early bus the next morning. The group numbered fifteen. Johnny led the Bible study on 1 Corinthians 10 and 11. The visitors were Fernando and Rosita.

The Bible study lasted two hours. The discussion in Chapter 10 was lively and interesting as they compared the things the Israelites faced and how that applied to them. But the study really got interesting when they discussed 1 Corinthians 11.

The Valverdes were surprised. They had never heard of a woman covering her head to pray. Hugo and Gelo challenged Fernando when he expressed their desire to practice the teaching. But Hugo and Gelo grew quiet as they moved from verse to verse. It was obvious that the apostle expected the sisters to wear a covering of some kind.

"If our sisters wear coverings, people will think they're nuns," Hugo remarked.

"That's right," Fernando answered, getting more excited. "Did you ever stop to think why nuns wear veils and modest dresses? It's because that's the way the early church sisters used to dress. Shouldn't all of our sisters be willing to dress like the early Christians used to? My dad says he remembers when the women of the Methodist church in San José still wore veils."

The others were silent. Fernando and Rosita were convinced. It was no use trying to change their minds.

No one, not even Johnny, could solve the mystery of the last two verses. They seemed to contradict what was taught so clearly in the verses before.

As their discussion stalled, Fernando and Rosita mentioned that there actually were churches that still wore the veil. They mentioned the *Menonitas* in La Merced. The others were surprised. The Chachagua group was willing to take an honest look at the Scriptures. They were used to that under Johnny's leadership. But no one was ready to accept the veil.

Johnny knew he needed to conclude the study. Though no one was upset, it was unsettling to leave a study hanging, so he asked for several minutes of quiet, and pondered as he read the Scripture to himself one more time.

Suddenly he had an inspiration. "Brethren, look what it says here: 'Judge in yourselves: is it comely that a woman pray unto God uncovered?'

"I believe it is saying that each one of us should judge for ourselves. We will leave it up to everybody's own conscience. If Fernando and Rosita think she should wear it, God will bless them. And if the rest of you don't feel you should, God will bless you too. Let's pray."

Although Johnny's conclusion did not really solve the mystery, it did bring rest to the little group that day. It gave the ones who had questions time to dig deeper and learn more. And it allowed Fernando and Rosita to go ahead with their plans.

After the session, Rosita pulled out several white kerchiefs she had sewn for the occasion. "Look, sisters, let's put these on and see how they look and feel."

Some of the sisters were reluctant, but they all cooperated. Rosita helped Teodolinda get hers on, then Gregoria, Marina, and her daughters. None of the ladies had put up their hair to fit under a veil, but Rosita put them on anyway. Lily's veil really fit funny and produced some laughs from the men who were watching. Last of all, Rosita put on her own veil. She had done it dozens of times before at home and often wore it to pray, but this was the first time she had tried it on in public.

Once the ladies' heads were all veiled, Rosita announced, "I want a photo of this occasion. Come, sisters, line up here. Fernando, take a photo of us," she said as she dug a camera out of her purse.

The ladies thought it was fun. They lined up and Fernando took the picture; then the sisters took their veils off. They started to hand them back to Rosita, but she insisted that they keep them. Then she said, "Sisters, I have felt for several years that I should wear a veil at all times. Often during the day I feel a need to pray. Fernando and I have decided that today I will start. I plan to wear a veil until the day I die. And someday," she whispered wistfully, "I want to join a church that practices this doctrine."

Though the rest were not ready to do the same, they admired Rosita's conviction and courage. They wondered if she would keep her vow.

41

At first Aurelio did not accept Johnny and his new teaching. Determined to be faithful to his mother church, he clung to it like a bulldog and would not let go. He was seeing a girl from town who was helping him reform, and he had almost totally stopped drinking. But she hounded him about confessing his sins to a priest.

One day Aurelio's girlfriend was excited when he stopped by to see her. "There is a grand Catholic meeting being planned in Chachagua next week," she informed him. "There will be a special time of taking confessions and giving Mass. Aurelio, here is your chance. You can get your life straightened out."

"I do have something hanging over me," Aurelio admitted. "When I was so sick from the stroke, I promised God that if He would heal me, I would walk all the way to Cartago and give a gift to the Virgin. Every year when her day comes around, I remember it, and it bothers me. I always chicken out. It's a three-day walk to Cartago, and I've never had the money. I could ask the priest what he thinks of my predicament."

The next week Aurelio and his girlfriend went to the big Catholic meeting. The young girl had already told the priest that her friend, a man from the wicked Valverde family, wanted to reform and was coming to confess his sins. When Aurelio entered the big Catholic church, he sat on the back bench. He noticed the priest eyeing him as he mingled with the people. The priest wore a long tan robe that reached down to his feet. All this made Aurelio nervous. He had never talked to a priest before.

After a while the priest came and sat beside him. Seeing how scared Aurelio was, he started by saying, "Don't be afraid." Then he asked, "How many times have you confessed your sins to a priest?"

"Never," Aurelio mumbled.

"Well, today you will. And I also want you to take your first Communion. What are the worst sins you have committed?"

"I have done a lot of drinking. Some stealing. And other bad things . . ."

"That's enough. You are forgiven. Go get in line to receive the Host."

"Father," Aurelio stammered, "I once made a vow to walk to Cartago, and I have not fulfilled it. What shall I do?"

"Don't worry about it. Just pay a *misa*. It only costs ten colones. Then you are free from your promise."

Aurelio went home relieved. That night he got drunk again. When his girlfriend found out, she dropped him in disgust. In a way Aurelio was relieved. He just couldn't be a good Catholic like she was. It just did not feel real to him.

Some time later Aurelio started taking night classes in Chachagua to learn how to read and write. He was embarrassed whenever his ignorance was exposed, especially to girls. At school he met a girl named Carmen who could not read either. He was attracted to her, and they often sat together in class.

Soon Aurelio started visiting Carmen's home. Her father, Miguel Barahona, was a short dark man well-known for three things. He talked almost nonstop, he could drink large quantities of liquor without falling over, and he had a row of nice-looking daughters. It was no small wonder that Aurelio started hanging around his place.

Aurelio and Miguel had something else in common. They were both staunch Catholics and vocal in their opposition to *evangélicos*. That and the drinking drew them together.

A year into Aurelio's courtship, Miguel agreed that Aurelio could marry his daughter. As Miguel's family and the Valverdes' merged, he and Aurelio joined in opposing the Gospel. Soon after that, Miguel moved to La Merced.

Aurelio continued opposing the *evangélicos*. But in fighting against the Gospel his mother and brothers had accepted, he was exposed to it time and again. He argued with his mother and his brothers and even with Johnny. But every time they argued, Aurelio had to listen to the Word. And slowly it won him over.

Things came to a head during a week of meetings. Julio Solís from Ciudad Quesada was the evangelist. Aurelio and Carmen went to all the services. On the third night during the altar call, Carmen grabbed Aurelio by his arm and whispered, "Let's go!" And they did.

After Aurelio's conversion, Johnny was determined to teach him to read. Aurelio had tried so many times that he was sure he could never learn. He had learned his letters as a child, but no more. Johnny took Aurelio into his room and told him to open his Bible. Then they prayed together. Johnny made Aurelio choose a verse from the Bible and slowly pronounce each letter.

Aurelio was soon ready to give up. "I can't," he concluded.

But Johnny did not give up. "No, no! You don't walk out on me. You are going to learn to read the Bible."

After several sessions, and with Carmen's help at home, Aurelio suddenly caught on. It was as if God had opened his mind and loosened his tongue. He could read!

Evelio, the man Aurelio worked for, was a staunch Catholic. He really liked Aurelio's work and considered him a friend. But when Aurelio humbly confessed that he had been saved, his boss was disgusted. As he and Aurelio hashed it out, Evelio suddenly had an inspiration. "Look," he said scornfully, "you can't understand the Scriptures. You can't even read. The priests are the only ones who can interpret the Bible. I will talk to the priest and get him to explain the way to you."

At first Aurelio did not want to meet the priest again, but he felt a sudden inspiration. "May I bring someone along when the priest teaches me so I won't be nervous?"

"Sure!" Evelio agreed. "Let's meet tomorrow at the church. I will come too."

Aurelio ran home to talk to Johnny. "Johnny, I have really gotten myself into a pickle. My boss convinced me to go with him to the Catholic church tomorrow so he can set me straight. I asked to bring someone along. Will you go with me, please?"

Johnny slapped his leg and declared, "Aurelio, you don't know what a good thing you did. You have set up a public debate. This is an important opportunity. Oh, I hope they invite many people! Let's pray about it, and tomorrow we will be ready. Of course I'll go with you."

The next day found four men sitting around a table in the church: the priest in his long robe, but without his Bible; Evelio in his farming clothes, without his Bible; Aurelio, sweating profusely, holding his Bible; and Johnny, wearing a big smile on his face, his Bible in his hands. Aurelio and Johnny let the priest talk first.

"I know you," the priest began, nodding to Aurelio. "You confessed your sins to me not long ago."

"That's right," Aurelio admitted. "But since then I have discovered that I need to confess to God in order to receive forgiveness for my sins. But I am not here to do the talking. I came to listen. Ask this brother your questions," Aurelio added, nodding to Johnny.

The priest turned to Johnny. "Why did you leave the Catholic Church?"

Johnny never stopped smiling. "I found something better," he said humbly.

"Why don't you people respect the Virgin Mary?"

"We do respect her. We just don't worship her or pray to her."

The priest looked hard at Johnny. "And why not?"

Johnny opened his Bible and read several verses about Mary and about worshiping God only. The priest tried again and again to trap Johnny, but Johnny always found an answer in his Bible. It became obvious to Evelio and the priest that they were losing ground. They could say nothing that Johnny could not refute with the Bible.

Finally, enraged, the priest ordered them out of his house. "You are heretics! Get out of here!" he screamed as he rose from his chair. "A person can't talk with you. You don't understand. You are like donkeys that can't understand a thing."

"I'm sorry you feel that way," Johnny said as they rose to their feet. "We appreciate the meeting, and may God bless you." Then they left. Aurelio lost not only his friend Evelio, but his job as well.

Some time later, Aurelio, still a new Christian, came to Johnny with a concern. "My father-in-law Miguel Barahona is coming to visit us. He expects us to baptize our new baby. I know we shouldn't, but he will be very upset."

"Well," Johnny answered thoughtfully, "you can't keep him from coming. You can't change the fact that you are a Christian now and will not baptize your baby. You have to tell him the truth. I will show you some verses proving that, to be baptized, you need to have faith and repent. Your baby can do neither."

Johnny wrote several verses down on a piece of paper. "The best thing you can do is pray," he said. "Then share the Scriptures as kindly as you can. Don't fight with the man. Be humble and stick with the truth. Who knows? Maybe he will be the next man converted to the Lord Jesus Christ. God will help you!"

Aurelio took Johnny seriously. Every day he looked up the Scriptures and practiced reading them. He wanted to be ready.

As Aurelio expected, when Miguel came he wanted to set Aurelio straight. But Aurelio respectfully got out his Bible, and they discussed the Scriptures until midnight. Though Miguel rejected everything Aurelio said and insisted Aurelio was wrong, no one got angry. And Miguel had heard the Word of God, which, being alive, had an effect on his heart.

Though Aurelio did not find out till later, on his way back to La Merced Miguel bought his first Bible.

42

The little church shanty was packed with fifteen members and quite a few visitors singing choruses with all their hearts. Luis and Hugo strummed their guitars in the amen corner. Gelo stood at the makeshift pulpit leading the songs. He could not clap with the rest because he had to hang on to the pulpit, but his radiant, joyful expression more than made up for it.

Gelo felt things were almost too good to be true. His life had changed. Tears streamed down his face as they sang,

"Si no hubiera sido por el Señor,
Mi alma se hubiera perdido,
*Si no hubiera sido por el Señor."**
   —Robert C. C. Savage
(If it hadn't been for my Lord,
My soul would have been lost,
If it hadn't been for my Lord.)

Gelo was thrilled to watch his family find the Lord one by one. He was especially blessed to see his father quit drinking, stop getting angry, and finally start enjoying life. Though Lico was old and growing more crippled each day, he was clearly a changed man. Gelo's mother was going strong, as always. She was a pillar in the church, and everyone knew how she loved her Bible.

Gelo's brothers who had decided for Christ were being used in the church more frequently, especially young Hugo. Johnny often asked Gelo and Hugo to preach.

Adding to Gelo's happiness was one of the new converts, Rafaela Gómez, who was developing a friendship with him in spite of his handicap. Their relationship had started slowly, and Gelo wanted to be sure, but so far the girl seemed sincere. Lately they had been discussing marriage.

After the singing, Luis read the Scripture. Johnny sat on the front bench and supported his brethren with his warm smile. Though no one realized it, Johnny had been preparing the church to go on without him. As he sat there and watched the men he had trained lead out, he knew the time had come.

After the Scripture reading, Johnny got up and stood behind the pulpit. He was silent for a minute, fighting to control his emotions. He started slowly. "Brethren, I think all of you know I have the gift of evangelism. An evangelist is sent out to preach the Gospel. That is my calling. I never expected Chachagua to be my final home. God wants me to move on."

The whole church held its breath. Surely Johnny did not mean that he would leave now, when the church was still so young!

"I have been watching you as a congregation," Johnny continued. "You are growing. If I leave, you will become stronger yet. It will force this young church to become a pillar in God's temple. I have confidence in you, brethren. You can do it. I think the time has come.

"I still need to find a mission to take responsibility for you. I am thinking of the Movimiento Misionero.* I think they would fit the

---

* Missionary Movement, an evangelical denomination

bill. Gelo would continue as your pastor and would work under the elder from the mission. I have been here for ten months. I will stay one more."

Another wave of emotion washed over Johnny. "Brothers and sisters, I feel the Lord wants me to move on. I am still thinking of Puerto Limón. I am not sure that is where the Lord wants me, but I am willing to go. I know this will be hard for you to accept. I am sure it was hard for the churches to accept when the Apostle Paul needed to move on before they felt ready. Pray, and God will confirm it in your hearts. He wants you to be so unselfish that you are willing to let me go so others can be saved, even if you still need me. God will be with you, and all will be well."

Then Johnny preached another one of his powerful messages on outreach. There were tears in many eyes that night. The service felt like a funeral. But how could they refute Johnny's logic? It was Biblical. The time had come to release him. And the church submitted.

The elder the Movimiento Misionero sent a month later to take on the work was a lady. She arrived with several deacons, and Johnny turned the church over to her. They met and agreed that Gelo would be the local pastor, under her leadership. She would come once a month to check on things. She would perform the baptisms and marriages and help whenever there were problems. She also promised to get money together to build a new church house out of cement to replace the simple board structure they were using. Then she left.

After Johnny left, the church members became discouraged. Teodolinda worried for her boys. Would they go back to their life of drinking and fighting? She did not think so, but what would they do without Johnny? Several times Teodolinda cried herself to sleep worrying about what might happen.

Hugo was hit hardest. He and Johnny had become inseparable friends. When Johnny left, Hugo went to Guanacaste for three months to work with Belén again. Though he didn't plunge back into his old sinful vices, he allowed his spiritual life to suffer.

Convicted by the Lord, he returned and put his hand to the plow with his family. They would do all they could to keep the church in Chachagua going.

Luis's trouble with Chepe and the dog continued. Before leaving, even Johnny admitted, "Luis, if I were in your shoes, I don't think I could have held out this long. I would have killed that mutt!"

One time a man from Chepe's church came over the rise just as Chepe sicced his dog on Luis. He heard Chepe laugh. He saw the dog try again and again to bite Luis. And he saw Luis dance as he held the hound at bay with his umbrella without hitting her. Chepe's friend was mortified. He yelled, "Luis, I would kill that dog! Rebuke that mutt in the name of the Lord!" Then the man walked on past.

Chepe stopped laughing. Luis took the man's advice. "Dog," he shouted, "I rebuke you in the name of the Lord! Get thee behind me, Satan!"

To Luis's surprise, the dog immediately stopped barking and slunk away. And that was the last time she attacked Luis.

Gregoria and Lalo attended church faithfully, but Lidier was still opposed. Most of the brethren kept coming to church, but after Johnny left, things just were not the same.

*   *   *

A small dark man swayed loosely in the saddle. He was drunk. Not raving drunk, just drunk enough that his mind and his body were not coordinating well.

It was a bright, sunny Sunday morning when this Tico rode from town toward his house in La Merced. The birds were singing in the bushes beside the road, but the man did not notice.

Miguel Barahona did not realize he was approaching the La Merced church. He did not remember it was Sunday, or that some people went to church and worshiped God. Just as he rode past the church, the preacher raised his voice, and it somehow sank into his inebriated brain. He pulled his horse up short. The preacher sure had a loud voice, and he was really serious about what he was saying. In his stupor, Miguel wondered, *Is that man hollering at me?*

"Remember, my brethren and friends," the preacher almost shouted, "it's not what enters the mouth that defiles a man."

The white clean-cut church house stood just fifty feet from the gravel road. Miguel stopped his horse right where the road dipped down past the church. The folks inside did not see him there, holding his head slightly sideways like a robin listening for an earthworm.

Only God knew why those words would interest a drunk.

"It's not what enters the mouth that defiles him," the preacher repeated, "but it's what comes out of the mouth."

Hmmm, Miguel pondered. *I know that man who's preaching. That's Don Sanford. Why does he think it's not what goes in the mouth but what comes out that defiles a man?*

The preacher explained. "What goes into the mouth is not really what does the damage. It goes into the belly, passes on, and goes out into the latrine. It's what comes out of the mouth that does the damage. That's because it comes from the heart. From the heart come evil thoughts, murders, adultery, fornication, theft, and so many other wicked things. Our problem is not what we are doing as much as it is a heart problem. Brethren, let's be honest. If we sin, we have a serious heart problem."

Ouch, Miguel grumbled. *That man is stepping on my toes.* He kicked his little black mare in the ribs and rode on. He heard no more of the message, but he had heard enough for now.

The next day, Miguel could think of nothing else. *It's not what goes in, it's what comes out,* he thought, over and over. *My problem is not the guaro I drink, or the tobacco I chew, or the cigarettes I smoke. My problem is my heart. And because my heart is rotten, I do all of these stupid things to myself and to others.*

Soon after the experience at the La Merced church house, Miguel accepted Aurelio's invitation to go to church. Soon after that, he was converted. After Miguel's conversion, Hugo often went with Aurelio to visit Miguel's family. He could not help but notice Carmen's younger sister Irene, and soon Hugo started to visit Miguel even when it did not suit Aurelio to go.

One day Aurelio, Carmen, and Hugo bused to La Merced to visit Miguel. When they arrived, Miguel announced that the *Menonitas* were having a service at his house the next evening. He explained that he had become friends with the gringos in the area. He was working part-time for Sanford Yoder, and on the job he had become great friends with Sanford's son Pablo. Miguel had invited Pablo to lead a service in his home. Knowing the boys enjoyed guitar music, Miguel explained that the *Menonitas* did not use instruments.

Aurelio and Hugo were not too sure about it, but decided it couldn't hurt to watch. "After all, we all serve the same God," Hugo concluded.

When Pablo came for the service, Miguel was surprised to see a group of youth with him. The young man was blond, talkative, and friendly. He came right into the house ahead of the others and shook hands with everybody. Hugo was surprised that he acted so much at home. The gringo had obviously been there before.

Hugo and Irene sat in the background. They were engaged, so they stuck together. The young fellow came right over and shook hands with them. "Hello, Irene," he greeted her respectfully. "And who is this friend of yours?"

Irene blushed. She was not used to being put on the spot in public. "This is my friend from Chachagua. His brother Aurelio is married to my sister Carmen."

"I knew Carmen was married, but I've never met her husband," Pablo said. Then he marched over and shook hands with Aurelio and Carmen.

"Let me explain what's happening, Pablo," Miguel interrupted jovially. "These fellows are coming here from Chachagua in hordes and stealing my daughters."

"So that's what's going on!" Pablo laughed. "Well, they look like fine fellows. Are you happy with the thievery?"

"Yes," Miguel answered; then he added more seriously, "They are good Christians, and my daughters are marrying in the Lord. That makes me happy."

"I'm sure!" Pablo said and called the rest of the youth to come in. Carmen, Irene, and Miguel's younger daughters scurried to get chairs as the youth poured in.

It was soon obvious that there would never be enough chairs for the big group. Pablo raised his hand. "Hey, Miguel, when we sing, we like to stand. Why don't we just stand here in this corner, and you people keep your seats."

The youth formed a half circle in the corner of the living room while Pablo gave a short introduction. "We want to thank our dear friend Miguel for inviting us into his home. We love to visit homes to share the Gospel message through song. We want you to join in and sing with us if you know the words."

Hugo glanced at his guitar in the corner and grinned. He would have enjoyed playing with this group. He was sure it would sound so much better.

Then the youth started to sing. Hugo stole a glance over at Aurelio. Aurelio was staring at the youth. Hugo looked at Irene. Her eyes were shining. She whispered into his ear, "I love to hear these folks sing!"

The youth carried no songbooks, but sang all their songs by memory. And the harmony those fifteen youth produced was electrifying. As song after song burst forth, the listeners' hearts were filled to overflowing. Irene nodded toward a little dark fellow who threw his head back and sang with his whole heart. She whispered to Hugo again, "That dark guy is a Salvadorian and used to be a singer in the world. He used to play guitar like you do. But he is converted and is a member of their church now. They call him Chente."

After singing for half an hour, Pablo's brother Mark read a Bible passage. He did not preach loud like his dad; he just talked about the Word. As Hugo listened, Mark reminded him so much of Johnny that he actually got tears in his eyes. *This young man loves the Bible like Johnny does,* he thought. *And he has Johnny's gift of explaining it. I wish so much I could have a pastor like that again someday.*

After the service a woman suddenly appeared. No one had noticed Miguel's wife Milda working in the kitchen. As soon as the service was over, she and her two youngest daughters served hot coffee and corn flour pudding.

The next hour sped by as they enjoyed the fellowship and refreshments. It did not matter that some had to sit on the floor. Pablo's sisters helped Milda and her daughters in the kitchen. Pablo and Miguel both talked a lot and kept the room buzzing. At one point Pablo motioned apologetically to the guitars in the corner. Hugo and Aurelio were a little self-conscious about their instruments being in the room. To put them at ease, Chente admitted that he used to play one himself. But Hugo quickly smoothed everything over by saying, "You all don't need instruments. You sing wonderfully without." And he meant it from the bottom of his heart.

After the youth had left, Irene announced, "Someday I want to be a member of that church." Nobody said a word, but they could understand in part the longing of her heart.

Several months later Hugo and Irene were married. They made their home in Chachagua.

43

When Johnny left Chachagua, the church had fifteen members and many others who were on their way into the kingdom. Lidier was converted soon after he left, but when the church reached its peak of about twenty-five members, the problems began.

For seven long years, the church in Chachagua wallowed in the soup of selfish church administration. Gelo tried his best to keep things under control locally, but it was harder all the time. During the seven years of church strife, the Movimiento Misionero changed the elder in charge of them twelve times, and each new one seemed less effective than the one before.

Membership in the little Chachagua church dropped until only a few were left. Several men stepped out hoping to find something better. At first they did not try to join another church; they just gathered in their homes, prayed, and studied the Scriptures. They did not compete with Gelo and his leftovers, and Gelo did not resent them. He knew they had left the church because of its inconsistencies, and he could not blame them. Gelo just felt he should keep on with the church he was called to lead as long as he could.

The new group was made up of sincere followers of the Master. One was Luis Carvajal, a newly married man who had been converted recently, and the other was Roberto Chinchilla, a single brother. Soon after they started their Bible studies, Hugo and Luis joined them.

Lidier was discouraged with the situation with the elders from San José. The last straw was when he gave a big hog to the mission for a celebration. The service itself was all right, but when the food was served, the meal was so skimpy that Lidier was shocked. He knew how much meat his hogs produced. He stood in the distance and watched the food distribution. From where he stood, he could see around the back of the church house, and what Lidier saw made him so angry he never returned to that church again. One of the big-shot preachers from San José had backed his fancy black car behind the church and was packing a large quantity of the meat into his trunk. As soon as he finished, he pulled out quietly and drove away. As Lidier walked home, he fumed. *I donated the pig. They stole the meat. I didn't even get a taste! Good-bye to those people.*

Lidier developed a permanent allergy toward preachers that day. He would hardly ever go to church, and when they came to evangelize him, he often ran them off. He believed in God and claimed to be a born-again believer, but he put no stock in preachers and did not want to belong to a church.

During this difficult time, Gelo and Rafaela got married. Gelo hoped his new wife would be a spiritual asset in his work as pastor. But it did not work out that way. She was even more discouraged with the church than he was.

One of the main reasons Gelo and the original members clashed with the elders was because of the leaders' liberal tendencies. The local members dragged their feet when the elders suggested changes. The locals did not want to encourage cut hair or makeup for the women. But some of their leaders tried their best to bring those ideas into the church. The original members did not think women should preach since the Bible prohibited it, but even some of their elders were women. When the new leaders started bringing in electric guitars, drums, and wild music, Gelo and the original members stood their ground. This caused conflict with the newer, more liberal converts. And of course Gelo and the others made their mistakes and exposed their weaknesses too.

One of the last straws was when the mission wanted to bring in a special music box for the youth. It was a sort of jukebox that played rock-and-roll music. Gelo, usually calm and quiet, now stammered, "No . . . no. I can't go along with that. The devil is coming right in the front door of the church with that machine. I will not agree!"

Finally the mission threw in the towel and sold the church house, which became a simple home and stood as a silent witness to their failure. They did not even say good-bye to Gelo.

Gelo tried his best to pick up the pieces. Teodolinda was still with him. He invited whoever was willing to come to his house for three days of fasting. Hardly anyone showed up. Gelo was ready to give up too.

Before the Chachagua church died, a little group of believers showed up in a place called La Lucha, about forty-five minutes from Chachagua. It started with some land the government gave to poor farmers. Aurelio received a piece of land. Cuyo Villegas, who had also married one of Miguel Barahona's daughters, received land there too. Lidier Valverde's son Lalo had married a girl from La Lucha and also received some land. These folks and others wanted an evangelical church, so they asked Aurelio to help them establish one. Aurelio became a sort of homemade pastor for that church. Aurelio and Gelo worked as a team, both under the same mission, and often exchanged pulpits or held joint services. So when the Chachagua church died, it greatly affected the La Lucha church. Would the La Lucha church die as well?

When Johnny found out the Chachagua church was dying, he traveled to San José and talked long and earnestly with his brother Fernando and his wife Rosita. "Please go to Chachagua and help that church get on its feet again," Johnny pleaded. "My evangelistic work just won't allow me to go right now."

"How would I make a living?" Fernando wondered. "I am a poor man and hardly know a trade."

"Go by faith," Johnny admonished. "You know I did that when I went for a year. I didn't know a trade either. I learned to work like they do. I never suffered want."

"Yes," Fernando agreed, "but you were single, and I am married and have small children. And you know how Rosita and I feel about the Movimiento Misionero doctrinally. We don't agree with many things."

"That doesn't matter. Just go prayerfully, and God will lead you. Get them back on the narrow way. Encourage them and help them get back on their feet."

Several months later Fernando and Rosita moved to Chachagua. Johnny helped them find finances to buy a shack of a house. Fernando put in a little furniture shop and planned to do what he could for the church.

But Fernando found the church so nearly dead that he did not even try to get it going again. The Movimiento Misionero had just pulled out. So instead of trying to work with Gelo and Teodolinda, he joined the few men who were praying and having Bible studies. He fit right in with them. They were seekers. They were serious. They would pray until they found answers.

As sometimes happens, the very ugly thing called church trouble brought a breath of fresh air called revival. When things get really bad, people call upon their Lord and get serious about their Christian lives. So the death of the first Chachagua church brought about the birth of a second.

44

When Fernando joined the small group of seekers, it was like adding fuel to a fire already lit. The brethren looked to Fernando for leadership since Johnny had sent him. Fernando, a natural leader, not only fanned the revival, but began to put some shoe leather to their ideas.

The little group consisted of Luis Valverde, Hugo and Irene Valverde, Luis Carvajal, Roberto Chinchilla, and now Fernando and Rosita. Their main goal was to establish a brotherhood like the one they read about in the Book of Acts. They went to the source: the birth of the church of Jesus Christ.

Though they did not realize it, the Lord led them to the two most important things in a revival. They fasted and prayed together, and they studied the Bible. They never thought of studying the Bible just to learn what was in it. They knew that if they studied it, they also needed to put into practice what they learned. That was exactly what they did. And the results were what they always are. Revival!

They gathered Sunday mornings in Fernando's living room for their normal worship service. Then they gathered one or two evenings a week to study and to pray. They would start with several choruses, and then, sitting in a circle, they would study the Bible. Everyone took turns choosing the Scripture to be studied. Then they would read the chapter and discuss it together.

These Bible studies became real highlights for the little group. They would start at six o'clock and seldom finished before ten. Several times the prayer sessions lasted until midnight. More than once they found their way home in the wee hours of the morning.

These sessions not only provided for their immediate spiritual needs, but also laid a solid foundation of doctrine and practice. With hardly any influence from anybody outside their group, they learned God's will for their lives.

Luis Carvajal could not read. He had never gone to school. When he tried to understand letters and words, his mind went blank, and he was worried that he would never be able to read the Word of God.

Instead of doing the natural thing and going to school, Luis decided to go to Jesus. Jesus knew how to read, and Jesus could teach him. He did not want to learn to read someday; he wanted to read now. His love for the Lord and his desire to know the truth brought him to a decision. In simple faith he would plead with Jesus to teach him to read. He would plead until Jesus answered his prayer.

So besides taking time to pray and study the Bible with the others, Luis started spending time alone with the Lord, asking Him to teach him how to read. He would lock himself in his bedroom and weep and cry out to God. After several weeks of this, his wife was worried that he was losing his mind.

Finally Luis took a leap of faith. He decided to fast for a whole day. By nightfall, his tall skinny frame knelt over the simple cot where they slept, his long straight hair hanging over his face. His Bible was open before him on the bed. He closed his eyes and, weeping and begging, told the Lord what he had in mind. "Jesus, I want to learn how to read today. I am going to point to a verse in the Bible, and You will help me read it. Will You?"

Trembling like a leaf in the wind, he opened his eyes and jabbed his finger at the page. It landed among the hundreds of letters that had never made any sense to him. His eyes focused. Miraculously, the words of that verse cleared before his eyes. He could read it perfectly. His tongue savored the words of Romans 1:16: "For I am not ashamed of the gospel of Christ: for it is the power of God unto salvation to every one that believeth; to the Jew first, and also to the Greek."

As soon as he had read the verse, Luis leaped to his feet, keeping his finger firmly clamped at the place. In several mighty bounds he rushed into the kitchen. "Miriam! Listen, dear wife of mine! I can read! I can read!"

He finally calmed down enough to prove to his wondering wife that what he was saying was true. "Watch!" he shouted. Then he held his Bible still and read those precious words again. Miriam shook her head in disbelief.

Luis raced out of the house shouting. In his excitement he forgot his shoes and ran into the street barefoot, his finger still clamped firmly on Romans 1:16. On his way, he met several neighbors. He didn't know them well, but they had to listen to him today. He showed them the place his finger marked and read the verse to them.

When Luis returned to his home, he sat on a chair and tried to read more. What if he could? What if he couldn't? Without releasing his finger, he looked past his special verse and tried to make sense out of the hundreds of letters that came afterward. But, as before, it was all just a big jumble of letters, and he could not read a thing. Luis was disappointed. Obviously, God had chosen to bless him with a verse he could read. But for some reason God had not given him the whole Bible. Luis decided not to be discouraged, just enjoy the verse God had given him and continue praying for the ability to read the whole Bible.

For the next several weeks, Romans 1:16 was all Luis could read, and almost all he could talk about. He accepted Fernando's request to lead out in a Bible reading at one of their meetings, something he had never accepted before. And, of course, he read Romans 1:16.

Meanwhile, Luis kept praying for the ability to read the whole Bible. He locked himself in his bedroom and begged like before. But he also tried to see the letters as syllables, and he tried and tried to read

them. It was difficult work for Luis, a hardworking outdoorsman who never had patience for spending time in the house. But now he spent more and more time in his bedroom praying and trying to read.

God answered Luis's prayer again, though not as dramatically as the first time. As Luis knelt over his bed fighting to read syllables, all of a sudden it started to make sense. Words formed. Sentences lined up. Luis was reading the Bible. He was so happy, and he loved his Lord more than ever.

Roberto Chinchilla was the serious, practical type. He got a big kick out of how excitable Luis was. They got along fine. Roberto's strong points complimented Luis's weaknesses, and Luis's enthusiasm helped keep Roberto awake.

Fernando was also an easygoing person. Those three and the Valverdes made an interesting group. Although they would have said they were seekers trying to find a church, Jesus had already proclaimed the truth: *They are already a church, because where two or three are gathered together in My name, there am I in the midst of them.*

45

Miguel Barahona felt just a teensy bit of pride as he led the group down the rough gravel road. They had left his house a mile behind, and now the road dipped down into a little valley. As they walked along the flat, they all noticed a big U-shaped house set on a hill off to one side and tucked in among fruit trees. Behind the house were a big shed and a barn.

"That is Don Sanford's homestead," Miguel announced. "I have worked for him some. He's the pastor of the Mennonite church just up the road."

Rosita exchanged a smile with her husband. The evening before they had come in late and been unable to see the scenery. Now they had passed several of the Mennonite farms, where spotted Holstein cows grazed in green grass on the rolling La Merced hills.

Fernando and Rosita Rojas, Roberto Chinchilla, and Hugo and Irene Valverde had traveled to La Merced to formally ask for help starting a Mennonite church in Chachagua. The delegation was staying at Miguel's place, and they planned to attend the Mennonite church for Sunday morning worship. Aurelio and Carmen were also along for the visit, but neither Aurelio nor Miguel were as interested in the La Merced church as the rest of the group was.

When the delegation had arrived at Miguel's place Friday evening, Miguel had invited them to go with him to an *evangélico* vigil* at La Tabla the following evening. That's where they were headed now as they walked past Sanford's house.

Just as Miguel's tribe climbed the little hill right at Sanford's lane, a young Tico rode out the lane on horseback. Miguel recognized him right away and yelled, *"Buenas tardes,* Jorge."

Jorge Molina, a convert from the streets of San José and now a member at La Merced, reined in his horse and answered, "Good afternoon! And where are you going?"

The whole group watched as Miguel and Jorge talked. "We are going to a vigil in La Tabla," Miguel replied. "And I am very proud to say that most of these folks are my relatives."

Jorge surveyed the big group. "Nice group of people, Miguel. You have reason to be pleased. But I pity you! You have a full five kilometers to La Tabla, and the sun is hot."

"It's early, and we don't mind walking," Miguel grinned. "What will be fun is the walk home at midnight."

"That's right," Jorge sighed. "That will be an awfully long walk in the dark. Maybe I can get a friend of mine to come pick you up tonight."

"You don't have to do that," Miguel answered. "But of course, if you want to . . ."

"I want to." Jorge grinned. "What time?"

"We will probably leave La Tabla about midnight."

Soon the arrangements were made, and Jorge rode off on his errand while the group walked on toward La Tabla.

The vigil at La Tabla was quite lively. Meanwhile, Jorge talked to Chente about going to pick them up with another brother's truck. At the stroke of midnight, Chente and Jorge drove up to La Tabla Pentecostal Church. The service was just ending, and soon Miguel's whole group was climbing into the back of the truck. Chente and Jorge took them home.

---

* a service that lasted until midnight

"You're welcome to come to church tomorrow!" Jorge hollered as they pulled away, unaware that that was precisely why they had come to La Merced.

The next morning dawned bright and clear. La Merced's white church house was perched on a little knoll with its doors wide open. As Fernando, Rosita, Roberto, Hugo, and Irene approached the building, they felt nervous. Many of them had never talked with a Mennonite before this trip. Aurelio and Miguel kept insisting they were the friendliest people you could find, but that did little to ease the group's anxiety.

Americanos and Ticos mingled on the porch. Some looked up in surprise as they saw the group of strangers walking across the yard. But as Hugo and Irene had said, the people were friendly, and they greeted the Chachagua group warmly. They soon found themselves being ushered into the chapel.

Rosita realized right away that these were the people she had seen at the supermarket. Most of the women wore white prayer veils and sat on one side of the chapel. The men, who looked like the man who had frequented the restaurant where Fernando worked, sat on the opposite side. The children sat on the front benches. The bigger ones sat farther back. It was all so new, and Rosita's heart raced as she sat among the sisters. Finally her longing was being fulfilled. She immediately felt at home.

Chente got up to lead the singing. His clear soprano got the congregation going. Fernando and Rosita stared at each other from across the aisle. They had never heard four-part a cappella singing before. Hugo watched Fernando and Roberto. His eyes seemed to say, *See, I told you they could sing!*

As the last song faded, Sanford Yoder's son Mark got up and read a psalm. Hugo remembered him from the meeting in Miguel's home before he and Irene were married.

A tall *Americano* got up then and led the Sunday school discussion. After Sunday school, Sanford Yoder got up and preached the message. Like the rest of the service, the message was something totally new for the visitors. The pastor taught about nonresistance. As they followed along in their Bibles, verse after verse spoke about how Christians should love their enemies and not use violence against them. Though the teaching was new, Johnny had taught his disciples well that the Bible was the final word on any subject, so it was no surprise that the little group left the church house convinced that here again was a doctrine that somehow had been missed in their circles. After just one sermon they were more than ready to go home and put it into practice.

After the service, everyone just stood around and talked. The visitors really enjoyed that. They were used to services where, as soon as the minister said amen, everyone hurried away as if the building were on fire. During the visiting time, Fernando approached Sanford and asked for a meeting. So Sanford met with them in the schoolroom, which was the other half of the building.

Fernando briefly told the story of their church and all its problems. "A group of us have started to get together on our own, seeking truth. We would like to ask your church to come visit us in Chachagua. If we see things alike enough, we would like you to teach us and help us start a church like this one."

"Well," Sanford answered, "I can't make that decision by myself, but I will discuss it with my brethren. I can at least promise you a visit where we can sit down and discuss things."

"Good." Fernando nodded, satisfied. "You choose the date, and we will expect you."

Minutes later they had chosen a date and time for a service in Chachagua.

Sanford invited the group to their home for lunch. There they spent several pleasant hours learning to know Sanford's family and enjoying the fellowship. Later, Sanford's youngest son drove the group out to catch the bus for Chachagua.

After their time at La Merced, the little group was as united as they had ever been. They looked forward to the meeting in Chachagua with all their hearts. Would the rest of the dispersed flock follow them? Time would tell.

46

Hugo and Irene sat together on the rustic bench in Fernando's living room. Irene watched the song leader. Hugo's eyes were closed as he listened to the singing. He had never heard the song before, and its message was reaching all the way to his heart. The young song leader put his heart into his song:

> "*No puedo yo limpiar el alma*
> *Manchada de su mal.*
> *Conozco a un Varón que puede bien.*"
> (I can't take a heart that's broken
> Make it over again;
> But I know a Man who can.)

Hugo glanced at his wife. He could see that she was enjoying herself immensely. He was not enjoying the singing as much as he was being touched by the message. This was so different from what he was used to, where the instrumental music rather than the words tended to draw out people's strong emotions. Today Hugo could keenly sense the Holy Spirit ministering to his heart as he listened to the words of the new song.

"Se llama Cristo Jesús el Salvador.
Tanto te ama que él por ti murió.
Si te sientes agobiado y cansado de vivir,
Jesús, mi Señor, te cambiará."
(Some call him Saviour, the Redeemer of all men.
I call him Jesus, 'cause He's my dearest friend.
If you think no one can help you,
And your life is out of hand,
Well, I know a Man who can!)*

—Jack Campbell and Jimmie Davis

Sitting in the congregation of this first Mennonite service in Chachagua were Luis Valverde, Hugo and Irene, Fernando and Rosita, Roberto Chinchilla, and Luis Carvajal. Quite a few Mennonites had showed up from La Merced, including Sanford Yoder and his wife Martha and three of their children, Phil, Pablo, and Judy.

After Pablo led the singing, Phil read a short Scripture and led in prayer. Then Sanford got up and preached the message. The hearts of the Chachaguan brethren were like the rich, fertile Chachaguan soil, plowed and ready to receive the seed of the Word of God.

After the service, Sanford and Phil met with the group of interested brethren. Sanford opened the meeting by asking, "What makes you come to us for help?"

Hugo answered eagerly, "We have come out of a bad church situation and are looking for something better."

Sanford hesitated. "Well, I can understand that it's tough to be surrounded by problems, but if you are only running away from trouble, I'm not sure how we can help."

Fernando answered quickly, "We have also seen things in your church that seem more Biblical to us. We have been having Bible studies together for a long time, and your doctrine seems to match the Bible more closely than anything we have seen yet. You have something to offer us."

---

* "I Know A Man Who Can" by Jack Campbell and Jimmie Davis © 1969 by Peermusic Ltd. Copyright renewed. Used by permission of Peermusic Ltd.

The whole group nodded in agreement. Then the brethren took turns sharing how God had brought them to the place of asking the Mennonite church for help. Fernando told the story about Rosita's longing to wear a veil and how they had read *Luz de la Vida* and discovered there were some who wore the prayer covering. Then he shared how Rod and Staff had written back to them and suggested they get in contact with La Merced.

Hugo shared how God had spoken to them through the service at Miguel Barahona's house years before. He confessed that ever since that night, Irene had wanted to join the La Merced group. "It's not only that we're running away from problems. We feel there are many doctrines our former churches did not practice that you do. We have had many Bible studies and agree that women should not preach, that women should wear a prayer veil, and that feetwashing should be practiced literally. What we want now is to learn more. We are asking you to come and teach us."

The others were nodding enthusiastically.

Hugo then told the brethren from La Merced about the rest of the group in Chachagua. "My brother Gelo and my mother are still trying to make the old church go. He was the pastor before the Movimiento Misionero left, and he is determined to pull the church back together. Actually, Gelo and my brother Aurelio and the rest of the discouraged brethren have turned against us since we've shown interest in the Mennonites. They even preach against the new doctrines we are embracing and call them doctrines of devils. It will take a miracle to convince them, but we pray for them and try to show them love." Then he told them about Lidier, Gregoria, Lalo, Lico, and Lily. "And many more might follow if we can get a Biblical church going in Chachagua," he concluded.

By the time the meeting was over, it was clear to the La Merced group that they had found revived brethren who were hungry for the Gospel. Sanford finally suggested, "I think Phil would be the man for the job. I suggest that he come here to teach you once a week. You and he come to an agreement on which day and what time. After some time of teaching doctrine we will talk about church membership."

"Would it be possible for a minister to eventually move here to help us?" Fernando asked.

"I can't promise that now," Sanford answered, "but let's pray to that end. I do believe God wants to raise up a Scriptural church in this town, and that you are called to spearhead it. Keep getting together on Sundays for worship. During the week, get together to pray and have your Bible studies. If you are sincere, you won't go wrong. Remain humble and seek God's face daily. The gates of Hell cannot prevail against you. God will raise up the church He is planning for this town."

They all felt God's blessing during the closing prayer, and on the way home a very excited group of missionaries discussed the events of the day. God was obviously working in the hearts of the brethren from Chachagua. A new church was being born, and they had been asked to be a part of it.

Teodolinda, Gelo, and Aurelio stuck with what was left of the church Johnny Rojas had started. One of the Movimiento Misionero ministers had preached a message about how wrong it was to leave the church. And it did not seem right to give up on Johnny's dream, even if it had virtually died already.

A nucleus of evangelical people in Chachagua was very critical of the new Mennonites. Some were sure they were linked with the Catholic Church since the ladies dressed like nuns. Others thought there was a touch of the occult because of the different way of worshiping. But mostly the critics claimed that the Mennonites did not have the Holy Spirit. Since they did not use musical instruments and did not shout and get carried away, the services were supposedly boring and dead. Aurelio was the most vocal in his criticism. Teodolinda and Gelo followed his example.

But the mild persecution only kindled the fires of the revival. Hugo and Luis gave up trying to convince their family members who did not agree and got on with living out the Christian life themselves. Someday the others would need to see the truth and come to a better understanding of the Scriptures. But that time had not yet come.

47

The table was set. The breakfast was simple. Refried beans and rice, fried eggs sunny-side up, and a cup of coffee. Phil Yoder led a sincere prayer asking for grace for the long day ahead. After prayer, two-year-old Diana rapped her high-chair tabletop with her spoon. "Toffee," she hollered. "Toffee! Toffee!"

Elaine, Phil's young wife, chuckled as she quickly fixed a cup of Diana's coffee, which consisted of mostly warm milk with a dash of black coffee and a dab of sugar.

"Phil," she said wistfully, "I so wish I could go with you today."

"I wish you could too," Phil answered, helping himself to the food. "But it's way too rough a trip for you and Diana."

"I just pity you having to go alone, and the trip is so rough," Elaine continued. "Besides, I admit that I get very lonely when you aren't here."

Phil squeezed his Kansas-born wife's hand. "I know, dear. You didn't know what all you were getting into when you married this old missionary, did you?"

"I'm not sorry!" Elaine assured him quickly. "I'd marry you again a hundred times! It's just that missionary life isn't always as glamorous as the pictures."

"You said it!" Phil agreed. "It's just common everyday living with a lot of hard work thrown in. But, honey, it's worth it. When I see Luis Valverde come walking in for instruction class . . . He's so faithful. He's not a great orator, but he's so sincere. Actually, all of them are. They drink in the truth with such thirst. I have a feeling God has something really great in store for Chachagua. I feel privileged to be part of God's great drama."

Elaine's eyes shone as she listened to her husband. Diana kept banging the high-chair table. "I know, honey. I shouldn't complain," Elaine said. "You don't, even if you have to be gone for ten hours, bumping on horrible roads and getting so covered with dust that you look like a cowpoke from Australia. I don't know how you do it without complaining."

"Well, like I said, it's worth it to see the brothers change. The last time I went to Chachagua, Luis was there early, as usual, and he told me Zapotal stories. They used to live up on the continental divide, way up in the Costa Rican highlands. They owned a saloon and sold moonshine. He was a miserable drinker and fighter. Now if you talk with him, you just know you're talking with a saint. That's what makes it all worth it!"

"Oh, Phil! Do you see what time it is? It's five till eight. You have to run. The bus leaves in five minutes."

Giving his wife a quick hug, Phil grabbed his briefcase and dashed out the door, barely catching the bus half a block from his house.

The bus took Phil to Ciudad Quesada, a sizable city nestled at the base of the lovely green mountain range that carried the Central Plateau on its back and in which rested Costa Rica's capital, San José. The problem was that Ciudad Quesada was over an hour in the wrong direction. The bus headed almost straight south when Phil should have been heading straight west. But there were no roads to the west.

After a lengthy layover in Ciudad Quesada, Phil caught an old jalopy school bus headed toward Chachagua. The bus dropped out of the foothills in a series of nasty curves and dangerous hills. After hitting the flatlands, it crossed the blue-green Jabillos River, which originated somewhere high in the mountain range near Zapotal. Then the road got so bad that the bus crept along in first and second gears. The dust swirled into the windows and settled on everything. Phil's black wavy hair and even his black eyelashes were soon a gritty, dirty red.

It was almost noon when Phil finally got off the bus at Chachagua. He slapped at his clothes, raising billowing clouds of dust. During the half-mile walk to Fernando's house, he stopped at a creek and washed his face and arms, making himself presentable. Minutes later he arrived at Fernando's shack. Luis Valverde was already there.

Later, sitting around the circle for their weekly instruction class, Phil announced, "Today we will study the Christian woman's covering as taught in 1 Corinthians 11."

Fernando and Rosita exchanged a look and smiled. Maybe Phil would explain how to interpret those two verses at the end of the passage.

As they opened their Bibles, Phil continued, "Let's read it first. Let's take the Bible for what it says. That's the best way to understand the Scriptures. After the reading, I will explain some things."

Verse by verse, much as they had done years before with Johnny Rojas, Phil led them through the chapter. Every verse confirmed what the verse before had said. And again, by the time they got through verse fourteen, the message was clear. Every Christian woman should cover her head to pray or to prophesy. If she did not want to, then it would be better if she just shaved her head, something no normal woman would do.

Next Phil taught the principle behind the teaching. "Both men and women were created in God's image. They are the crown of God's creation and were called to rule over all the things God made. But man was not to cover his head when he prayed or prophesied since he was called to be the leader in this project, directly responsible before God. The woman was chosen to be a suitable helper for the man, in a subordinate position. Subject to her husband, she would minister to his needs and submit to his leadership. For that reason," Phil explained, "she is to cover her head to show that she voluntarily accepts her position. Even the angels respect that sign and grant the veiled woman their special protection.

"Now," Phil explained, "we have a subject change. The first fourteen verses talk about the headship order. Now verses fifteen and sixteen talk about the hair. Unfortunately, the Bible does not show a break here, which makes it appear as if it were a continuation of the headship order when it isn't. First it mentions that long hair naturally doesn't look good on a man. Then it explains that long hair does look good on a woman. God made it that way. So men should cut their hair and women shouldn't. A woman should not cut her hair because God gave her hair for a covering."

Phil could not have asked for a more attentive audience.

"This is talking about a natural covering and uses a completely different word in the Greek language. That's where the translators confuse us. What verse fifteen is saying in essence is that a woman should not cut her hair because God gave her that blessing as a natural covering for her scalp. It is unrelated to the covering the Christian woman wears to pray or prophesy."

"How should it be translated?" Fernando asked.

Phil opened a small Bible he carried in his bag. "Let me read it in the *Dios Llega al Hombre* version," Phil answered. "It's the best Spanish translation of the original Greek I have found. 'For long hair is given to her as a covering. If anyone wants to be contentious about this, we have no other practice—nor do the churches of God.' "

"That sounds reasonable and clear," Hugo said. "In other words, a woman should have two coverings—a natural one and an artificial one."

"Exactly! The Greek word for 'to be covered,' which refers to the artificial covering in the first verses, is *katakalupto*. But in verse fifteen where it says the woman's hair was given to her as a covering, the Greek uses the word *peribolaion*."

Rosita sighed deeply. "Finally, someone has explained to me what I knew had to be true! I just knew God would not inspire Paul to write something as clear as verses one to fourteen and then turn around and annul it with two verses at the end. It just never made any sense to me. But now I understand it clearly."

After the class, Rosita fed Phil a quick lunch, and Phil hurried to catch his two o'clock bus back to Ciudad Quesada. It rained as they bumped along the worst part of the road. The passengers scurried to close the windows. The lack of fresh air converted the bus into an oven. Soon everyone in the packed bus was dripping with sweat, until the smell of body odor and the lack of air became almost unbearable. Finally the rain stopped and the windows were opened. The bus chugged its way up the mountainside to the much cooler Ciudad Quesada.

At Ciudad Quesada, Phil caught a bus for home. It was dark when he finally burst into their little mission house, gave his wife a dusty hug, and rushed for the shower.

The next time Phil went to Chachagua for a class, not only Rosita wore a veil. Irene did too. From then on the Chachagua church sisters all wore the veil voluntarily.

For over a year Phil traveled to Chachagua, giving the new church instruction and direction. He was busy, preaching four to six times a week, but the work was rewarding as he watched God's Word bearing fruit in the lives around him.

*   *   *

The morning the first Chachagua brethren were received as members was special. They all came to La Merced for the ceremony. Roberto Chinchilla, Luis Valverde, Hugo and Irene, and Fernando and Rosita were received as members that memorable day. There was great rejoicing in the La Merced church that Sunday morning.

Soon after receiving membership, the little Chachagua church faced some discouragement. Persecution from their families was strong. Teodolinda, Gelo, and Aurelio still stuck with the little group that the Movimiento Misionero had abandoned. Aurelio was being asked to preach more and more. Since some people were claiming the new church was a cult, Aurelio began preaching against them. Teodolinda and Gelo were not as vocal, or as sure, but they kept their distance from the Mennonites.

During this time most of the brethren stood firm. But Fernando, the leader and the one who should have been the strongest, turned out to be the weakest. Some unworthy conduct in his life disqualified him to continue to lead. And, having once held a position of leadership, it was too hard on him to come back and repent. The church finally had to excommunicate him. Rosita kept on serving the Lord faithfully.

Luis Carvajal was not ready to be received as a member when the rest were. After Fernando gave up, Luis became discouraged and dropped out, much to the disappointment of the church. They missed the enthusiastic Luis and his wife as much as they missed Fernando.

One request continued to pour from the hearts of the Chachagua brethren. They petitioned Sanford and Phil, "We want a leader in Chachagua. Please send us a minister." Their cry was especially urgent since Fernando was no longer their leader. The others felt they were too young in the faith to minister to the new Chachagua church.

But the Lord had a man. And a plan. It was only a matter of time.

48

It was a clear, cold December morning. The black, rugged maple branches hung over the eves of the white farmhouse under their blanket of sparkling new snow. Inside, Ruthanna Schrader knelt by her bed. Her open Bible lay in front of her, but she was not thinking about the passage she had just read. She was thinking of her future. Several days before, Mark Yoder from faraway Costa Rica had suggested that they pray about becoming engaged. Now Ruthanna had chosen this lovely winter morning to prepare her heart for such an overwhelming decision. If Mark asked to marry her, and she consented, she knew that she was not only committing to be his for the rest of her life, but she was also committing to move to Latin America, where he clearly felt called to serve.

Ruthanna was serious about her commitment to her Lord. Her family lived in Freeport, Illinois, and worshiped with a small, newly formed church that lived by faith. Her father, Ron, was not afraid to be different. They sang together as a family and visited many churches. Growing up under Dad Schrader's keen interest in missions, Ruthie, as her Mark called her, was more prepared than most girls to face missionary life.

Ruthie sighed and again faced the doubts that had nagged her throughout their courtship. *I so love and appreciate Mark, and I know the Lord brought us together,* she thought, *but can I cope with living so far from my family? How could I stand the loneliness?*

As Ruthie pondered these things, a question crystallized in her heart. She knew it was from her heavenly Father. *Ruthanna, are you willing to go and serve Me in Costa Rica?*

As the question sank into her heart, Ruthie pulled out her diary and began to write.

> *Lord, sometimes I still have questions. Costa Rica seems so far away. I see I must put myself completely into Your hands. I see my own unwillingness. If You have led me here, then this must be my call, not just Mark's. So if I say, "No, it's too far from my family," I am saying, "No, I don't want Your will." How awful, Lord! I do want Your will!*
>
> *So now I just want to give all to You—myself, my health, my place of service. Have Your way. If You call me to move that far away, I will follow, knowing Your plan is worked in love. I am precious in Your eyes, and You will take care of all the details. How can I but rest in Your love and provision? Thank You for being trustworthy. Thank You for peace.*

Once Ruthie realized who was calling, she bowed her head and said, "Yes, Lord."

Her spiritual experience that day not only prepared her for engagement and the move to Costa Rica, but later, when all the things she feared became reality, she never doubted her calling once. And God was faithful beyond her expectations!

*　　*　　*

Mark stood waiting, leaning on the wooden gate. Any minute the sale would start. He needed to be ready to chase the first group of calves into the ring. Ron was sitting up high on the platform of the old sale barn. The clerk was getting the last-minute papers on the table for Ron while Ron's dad helped with the preparations. The seats around the ring were filling up fast.

Mark grinned. He had never dreamed he would be chasing cows and pigs in a sale barn in the States. It was certainly a change from teaching school in Costa Rica.

The manure and animal odors not only filled his nose, they also penetrated his clothes and hair. He had spent all morning with other helpers receiving the animals, penning them, and getting them ready for the sale. Now he was all sweaty and smelled like the sheep, hogs, and bulls he had been handling. He grinned again. He enjoyed this. He had always liked animals, and chasing these critters was almost as fun as teaching children.

A shout from Ron's dad woke Mark from his reverie, and he opened the gate and chased the first calf into the ring. Ron started to do what he loved—auctioneering. The bids started, and excitement gripped Mark as it always did. This was American life. Though Mark had lived most of his life in Costa Rica, he still loved the land of his roots. Though he missed the Tico lifestyle, he enjoyed the *Americano* way almost as much. While he was in the States, he fit in.

Later, after the sale, Ron was finishing up the last paperwork before closing the barn and heading for home. Mark flung himself down on an old couch in the office to catch a nap, but sleep eluded him as his thoughts raced faster than Ron could auctioneer.

Mark remembered vividly the day he had first met Ruthie. A group of youth from the States had visited the church at La Merced. Friday evening they had attended the youth chorus practice and sung with them. Ruthie had stood in front of Mark, and they had visited between songs. By the time the evening was over, Mark was struck. Ruthie was pretty, sensible, and mature. Something about the way she took life seriously, yet wore that sweet smile, grabbed at his heartstrings.

Mark had a long talk with his parents. Something had happened. Was it really love at first sight? Mark said nothing to Ruthie about his interest.

Time went on, and Mark kept track of Ruthie's whereabouts. Later he found out she was serving in El Salvador as a missionary. After much prayer and seeking advice, he wrote her a letter asking for her friendship. Before he got her answer, it worked out for him to travel to El Salvador for a visit. While he was there, the friendship deepened, and they courted for over a year by correspondence.

Now, a year later, Mark had decided to work in the States for a year to learn to know Ruthie and her family and to give Ruthie's parents a chance to know him. Ron had given him work at the sale barn. Since living in Freeport, Mark and Ruthie's relationship had deepened, so he had just asked her to marry him, and she had consented.

Mark had called Costa Rica to shout the news, never dreaming that the churches in Costa Rica would grab the fact that he was engaged and come up with a plan that would change his life forever. Just the evening before, Mark had received a telephone call from his dad in Costa Rica. Now, slouching on the old dusty couch, Mark replayed his father's message in his mind. *Would you consider moving to Chachagua after you marry to help the small church that is starting there? We will give you two weeks to pray and decide. If you can't, we need to find someone else.*

Ever since his conversion, Mark had accepted service as part of his call. Just before he had turned twenty-one, the church had asked Mark to teach school. When Mark started to teach, he felt like a catfish dropped into a pool of cool, murky water—right at home in his element. So Mark had continued teaching school for six years. He never became involved in making money like a lot of boys did. He spent all the money he ever made buying books and traveling.

Now he had asked for a year off to pursue and marry Ruthie, but he had always figured he would go right back to teaching. School ran so much better with experienced teachers teaching year after year. *And yet,* he thought, *Chachagua would be an interesting challenge too. God, what is Your will? I am willing to do whatever You ask of me.*

During his next date with Ruthie, Mark asked how she felt about it. Neither Mark nor Ruthie felt a clear leading. They called Costa Rica and told Sanford they were willing to serve wherever the church asked them to, whether that meant teaching or moving to Chachagua. The answer from the church was clear: "We ask you to move to Chachagua to help with the little church there. We would like you to move soon after your marriage."

So Mark and Ruthie went to the marriage altar knowing God had chosen them to be missionaries in remote Chachagua.

Years before, in Miguel's living room, Hugo had heard Mark teach and had prayed that a man like that would be his pastor someday. God had heard Hugo's prayer, and answered it.

49

The date was January 21, 1985. The evening was lovely, and the first stars were doing their best to share their twinkling light. Mark stood out on the front porch of the old wooden house leaning against the railing and listening to the evening sounds. The crickets were singing with their whole hearts, as if welcoming Mark and Ruthie to Chachagua. A nighthawk sang his mournful song, echoing a lonely "amen" to the crickets' choir.

The old wooden house Mark and his wife had moved into was perched on a spacious lot on the outskirts of town right beside Chachagua's graveyard. Crowded with stone and wooden crosses, cement vaults, and tropical plants, the graveyard was not exactly the warmest company on a dark, lonely evening. *We just have to get used to whatever there is to face at this place,* Mark thought. *And we may as well start now.*

Ruthie came out and joined her husband on the porch. Leaning against him tenderly, she said, "A penny for your thoughts, dear."

"I was thinking about the brethren. They all live out of town. We are alone in Chachagua tonight. I don't know anybody in town yet. Don't you almost feel lonely?"

"I know what you mean. But remember, the God who called us is right here with us." She slipped her arm through his. "Come on in; supper is ready."

As they turned and entered the house, Mark said as an afterthought, "Honey, it's not just loneliness I feel tonight, but a certain excitement too. Isn't it wonderful to be part of God's great work here on earth? I feel good about our move to Chachagua. It's just so new and overwhelming."

As the couple bowed their heads in prayer before their simple meal of rice and beans, they told the Father all about their mixed feelings. He swiftly answered their prayer by giving them peace in their hearts and a keen sense of His presence.

Mark and Ruthie enjoyed setting up house in Chachagua. They had electricity, but no inside bathroom. There was no ceiling, and the rafters were bare under the tin roof. One night in bed Ruthie was startled to see a rat running across the rafters. Chachagua had more than its share of creepy creatures. Many of these exotic bugs and beetles zoomed around the lights and even found their way into the soup. Besides the zooming critters, there were cockroaches, scorpions, spiders, and tarantulas. She commented to Mark, "It sure is different to be uneasy and insecure in my own house." She despised the roaches and spiders, but she had no choice but to get used to them. They were an abundant part of Chachagua life.

The family that had lived in the house before Mark and Ruthie had owned several dogs that always slept under the house. After the dogs left, the flea population they had left behind exploded. Finding no dogs, they swarmed up through the cracks in the floor and attacked anything warm-blooded—including Ruthie. Mark soon borrowed a sprayer and eliminated the plague.

The neighbor's chickens were used to laying eggs under the porch floor, so Mark closed it off. Then the persistent critters came into the house to lay their eggs. The first week Ruthie was constantly chasing chickens out of the house. Mark and Ruthie wanted to leave their door open as a sign that anyone was welcome, but finally Ruthie had to decide: a sign of friendliness, or a house without chickens. The door was closed until the chickens gave up.

Mark and Ruthie fit in well and learned to love Chachagua. In spite of the inconveniences, Ruthie was a good supporter and a wonderful help in Mark's ministry.

One of the biggest adventures was getting to know the neighbors and townspeople. Mark also enjoyed visiting the brethren and getting to know their families. He soon knew the many Valverdes, both those in and out of the church. He found he could identify them by their heavy eyebrows and distinct features.

One day Mark sat at Teodolinda's table after a cup of black coffee. He often stopped in to visit and listen to her stories, though he never pressured her to join the new church. Teodolinda was sorting a pile of beans, picking out the dirt and trash. As they talked, Mark found himself helping her with the beans. Teodolinda's eyebrows rose in surprise, but she did not stop sorting. Tico men did not generally help women, especially sorting beans. But she was glad for the help.

"What about your husband?" Mark asked. "I have never met him. Is he a Christian?"

"Yes, he accepted Christ," Teodolinda answered. "He has changed. He used to drink and curse and swear. He had a terrible temper. But anymore he is very humble, and he follows the Lord. It's just . . . well, he is so timid. He limps and is ashamed of it. He's always been shy. Many people call him a hermit. He would rather do anything than meet new people. Like today," she chuckled. "He was here when you arrived, but he went out through the back door when you came in the front. By now he is out in the fields somewhere and won't be back until he's sure you are gone. That's Valverde for you."

"Well, someday I want to meet him. I will ask God for an opportunity."

Mark first saw Don Lico in the distance behind the Valverde house sitting among the yucca plants. He was thin and bony, dressed very poorly, and his hair was unkempt. Thick black eyebrows and high cheekbones made his sunken eyes appear almost hollow. At first Mark was not sure what the man was doing. But as he watched, he saw that he was macheteing. Because of his crippled feet, he sat on the ground, just like Gelo, and slashed away at the weeds. When Lico saw he was being watched, he crawled out of sight.

Some time later Mark got his opportunity. He arrived at the Valverdes' house and found Teodolinda reading her Bible. "Teodolinda, I came to talk with Hugo. Is he around? I stopped at his place, and Irene thought he had come down here."

"Last I knew he was out in the yucca field with Valverde. Go talk with him, and I'll have the coffee ready by the time you come back."

Mark walked back through a grove of fruit trees and made his way through an edging of brush. As he stepped out into the yucca patch, he stopped in surprise when he saw Lico cleaning the yucca.

"*Buenos días,*" Mark shouted.

Lico started. At first he did not answer Mark's greeting, but as Mark walked closer, he mumbled a quiet, "*Buenas.*"

Mark shook his hand and hunched down to his level. The conversation started slowly, until Mark discovered another reason Lico avoided people—he was half deaf. At first Lico only answered Mark's questions, but Mark's friendly manner won his confidence, and soon Lico was throwing bits of information into the conversation on his own accord. Hugo had already left, so Mark sat in the grass and visited with Lico for a long while. By the time he left, Mark had a new friend. And Lico never ran from the gringo preacher again.

By far the most rewarding thing for Mark and Ruthie in Chachagua was gathering with the brethren for services. They met in a lean-to porch off Mark's house. It was a small group, and they accepted Mark's leadership with joy. For the first time since Johnny had left, they had a man living among them who had a real shepherd's heart. Mark put them to work leading songs, having devotions, and even preaching, but they were so glad to have Mark teach them the Bible. That and the rich fellowship made church life a joy for them all.

Not only Valverdes were converted. Soon many others joined the ranks. Gerardo Araya, who got so excited that he gave his testimony at almost every service, and Jaime Araya, his son; Aurora Rojas; Denia Saborío; Isabel Molina; and many others. And the Valverdes kept on being converted too. Two of Marcos's sons, Nelson and Ronald, and their sister Nuria soon joined the growing church. Two of Luis's boys, Edwin and Toño, also joined. During the first years someone was in instruction class almost constantly.

To make his living, Mark worked for Lamp and Light, a publishing house in the States that provided Spanish materials. But his church responsibilities kept him so busy that it was difficult getting in hours for the publishing house. Ruthie had a savings account from before they married that they used to buy some of the appliances they needed, but the cost of Ruthie's residency papers abruptly cleaned up her savings.

Again God ministered to Ruthie's insecurity. He spoke to her need through a fitting Sunday school lesson and Bible verses on trusting God's provision. Ruthie soaked in these verses, along with God's promise in Hebrews 13:5, "I will never leave thee, nor forsake thee," and found peace. Time after time, in miracles great and small, God proved that He could take good care of His own. No, Ruthie did not have as many conveniences as even a lot of the other missionaries did, but God always met their needs.

When money was short, Mark did not think he should cut back on church work to earn more. They refused to go into debt, so he and Ruthie prayed about their financial situations and trusted the Lord to provide. Often Mark had to decide if he should work for a wage to buy groceries or do his pastoral duties. Ruthie would remind him, "What is your first calling? Do that first, and trust God to provide." God was always faithful.

Mark had originally been commissioned to preach in Chachagua. After four years he was ordained to be pastor of the Chachagua church. The ceremony was held in La Merced. In the same service, his brother Pablo was ordained as pastor for a little church that was just starting up in Pital.

*   *   *

The old bus's brakes squealed as it made yet another stop on its way through Ciudad Quesada. It was raining, and the windows were misted over. Gelo rested his head against the glass and closed his eyes. Try as he might, he could not shake the gloom of discouragement. Not even a trip to the city had lifted his spirits. All he could think of was the death of his dream—his and Johnny Rojas's dream. They had both dreamed about the church God wanted to raise up in Chachagua, and now there was no one left except his mother and him. He sighed and opened his eyes.

An *Americano* got on at the bus stop and staggered back toward him, hanging onto the pipe above him as the bus belched out another spurt of black smoke and jerked on its bumpy way. The *Americano* was young, not more than twenty-five years old, slim, and blond. To Gelo's surprise, the young man plopped down beside him on the empty seat, with a big smile and a friendly, *"Buenas tardes."* Gelo returned the greeting and rested his head against the window again, not expecting the stranger to pay attention to a cripple like him. But he was wrong.

"Where are you headed?" the stranger asked.

"I'm on my way to Chachagua," Gelo replied. "That's where I live."

"I see," the *Americano* answered. "I live in Pital, but my wife and I have a set of twin girls in the hospital right now. We didn't know they were going to be twins and weren't prepared. They were born very prematurely and are both in an incubator. We knew they'd have to be there a while, so we moved here to the city, and I travel to the hospital twice a day to see my wife and little daughters."

"Does the doctor expect the twins to live?" Gelo asked.

"They sure didn't give us any hope at first, but now they say the bigger one might make it. She weighed 3.4 pounds. The little one weighed 2.1 pounds. God knows what is best."

Gelo nodded.

"Have I ever met you before?" the *Americano* asked.

"I don't think so, why?"

"You look so much like someone I know. Are you a Valverde?"

"Yes, I am," Gelo answered, surprised. "My name is Domingo Evangelista Valverde Soto. What do you know about us?"

"I know your brothers Luis and Hugo. I'm Pablo. I have been to Chachagua several times to worship with their little group. You Valverdes sure look alike!"

Now Gelo knew who he was talking to. This was one of the *Menonitas* who were starting the new outreach in his hometown. He answered, "Everybody says we look like our father, Don Lico. Is Mark your brother? You look alike too!"

"Yes, people often get us mixed up."

Changing the subject again, the missionary kindly asked Gelo, "Do you know the Lord?"

Gelo did not answer immediately. He looked the friendly missionary in the eye and finally said, "Yes, I know the Lord. I accepted Him as my personal Saviour seven years ago. But I'll be honest; I am very discouraged right now."

"That's too bad," the young stranger sighed. "Tell me about it."

Something about the *Americano* made Gelo want to share his story. He told Pablo about his dramatic conversion and how he had been asked to take the church on after Johnny left. Then he shared about all their troubles with the Movimiento Misionero and everything that had happened since. "Just this morning," he said, hanging his head, "I decided to stop going to church altogether. It's just no use if no one wants to follow me except my own mother."

"That is a sad story," the missionary agreed. "But I don't think you want to be discouraged. That would be a double tragedy. First a church dies, and then a soldier dies too. You can't let Satan discourage you. I have a suggestion."

Gelo looked eagerly into the missionary's face.

"I don't want to sound as if we are the only church, but why don't you give the new group a try? You have nothing to lose. If I understand right, you have no more commitment to the Movimiento Misionero since they pulled out."

"That's right." Gelo nodded bitterly.

"Talk with Luis and Hugo. If they seem to have found something, maybe you want it too."

"I will consider your suggestion. I have thought of it. And you are right, Luis and Hugo are very happy. Like you said, I don't have anything to lose."

"But most of all," Pablo said as he rose to get off the bus at the next stop, "don't let Satan discourage you. It would hurt Jesus so much after all He did for you."

"Thanks so much, Brother!" Gelo clasped Pablo's extended hand firmly.

"I will pray for you every day, Brother Gelo. It has been such a blessing to share with you today."

With that, the man got off the bus. Gelo watched him as he walked over to the sidewalk and gave a quick hug to a young lady wearing a long blue dress and a white veil. Then they walked across the yard toward the hospital hand in hand, and the bus lurched forward again.

Gelo laid his head on the window again with tears in his eyes. *I know God sent that man just for me. I feel as if I could go on again with more courage. Yes, I will try the new church. I don't know why I've resisted it so long. I feel courage to fight again. I will go to church. I will keep on preaching. I will keep on living this life I love. And I will never think of denying my Christ again!*

A few days later Gelo hobbled about two kilometers to attend his first Mennonite service. The brethren were happy to welcome him. He seemed open and attentive to the preaching. Soon he asked for instruction for membership.

Gelo was a dedicated disciple. It was not long before Mark and the brethren felt confident about taking him in as a member. He was such a blessing to the little congregation. And he always walked the two kilometers to church and home again with a big smile.

Gelo was very poor. Soon after he joined the Mennonites, his mother gave him a *manzana* of land. His new church helped him build his own house. Gelo raised crops on his land, sitting in his fields to plant, machete, and harvest, and he saved his money. He had a gift for managing money. He knew he had to save up because of his inability to work. After a few years he actually had money to loan, and the interest was helping to cover his living costs.

Teodolinda was still concerned about the young church. As she watched Luis, Hugo, and Gelo change, she could not help but marvel. But she just was not sure this new group was sound. She had found a deep walk with the Lord in the other group, and she did not feel comfortable changing churches. In her sincere concern she even shed some tears.

* * *

Time ticked on and God's work continued. The young Chachagua church was tried by fire. They had definitely met the Lord Jesus Christ and loved Him with all their hearts. They also really liked the order and discipline in the Mennonite churches. But they had never dreamed what taking the cross really meant in daily living. Living out a total commitment to the lordship of Jesus Christ was not an easy road. They found themselves continually surprised by the demands of discipleship, such as making restitution, building healthy family relationships, and managing their finances Biblically. They found it especially hard to learn to obey the law.

The Valverdes had a long history of evading the law in Zapotal. The *resguardo* were, in their eyes, just an annoyance. The more you avoided them, the better off you were. Later, when they converted, no one thought to teach them that they needed a change of attitude about the Costa Rican laws and those who enforced them.

Hugo loved to work with lumber and made his living by it. His chain saw was his right-hand man. The Costa Rican government required a permit to cut down trees, but getting a permit was an extra bother. Hugo was used to outwitting the law and actually enjoyed the challenge of seeing how much he could do without getting caught. He never realized it was wrong—it was what he had done all his life.

One day when Hugo was delivering some lumber in a neighbor's truck, the police stopped him. They confiscated the lumber and made him unload the logs on the spot. They would allow him to load it again, but only after the proper legal steps were taken.

Hugo went home that evening and shared his troubles with his wife. "Irene, what can I do?" he asked. "I can't afford to lose the load, but the paperwork takes so much time and money."

Irene left Hugo sitting on the porch thinking. She soon returned with a cup of coffee, which she handed him.

"Irene," he groaned, "those law enforcers are just a bunch of ungodly men who make life hard for us. We have to make a living somehow, and I am working honestly with my hands. What would happen if I just ran over this evening and loaded the logs after dark? No one would see us . . ."

So Hugo and his buddies sneaked out into the night, loaded the lumber, and delivered it to its destination. No one saw them, so there was no proof he had taken it.

Several days later Mark and Hugo sat on Hugo's porch talking. Hugo tried to explain everything so Mark would understand why he'd had to evade the police.

"But Hugo," Mark said, "you disobeyed the law. You should have gotten a permit to start with. I think you should go confess your wrong."

Hugo hung his head.

Mark continued, "One day when we were young, my brothers and I went fishing in a mountain stream the county had stocked with rainbow trout. My oldest brother Tim snagged eleven beauties. The legal limit was eight. When Tim got home, Dad was shocked. He gave Tim a licking he'd never forget and took him to find the game warden so Tim could apologize and pay the fine. That is how I feel about your error."

Hugo's heart was in turmoil. He could understand better than ever why Mark believed as he did. But he had not been raised like that.

Mark tried again. "Hugo, you need to respect and obey the law. You shouldn't disobey. The leaders are ordained by God."

Hugo was shocked. He shook his head slowly. "How can they be ordained by God if they aren't Christians? Why should I respect them if they are ungodly men? They are wicked men, and if I hadn't sneaked my own lumber, they might have taken it and sold it for themselves. Plus, I need the money to make a living for my family."

Mark gently took Hugo to Romans 13 and helped him see his mistake. Then he suggested, "Hugo, I think you should go and make this right."

The next day Hugo walked into the police station alone and told them the truth. They let him off without a fine, admiring his honesty and humility. And Hugo, though he did not fully understand, took his humiliating experience as a stepping-stone in learning to obey his authorities.

*   *   *

Luis Valverde had been genuinely born again a few years before, but he was not tactful in the way he went about cleaning up his life and his household. One of the first things he did was rip all the *estampas* off the wall and burn them. When Manuela opposed him, he raised his voice and reprimanded her in the name of Jesus. This sudden change did not go down well with Manuela or her mother, who lived with them. Similar incidents, added to the things the neighbors were saying, sincerely convinced her that her already distant husband was falling for a cult. His manner did little to convince her that this was the true Gospel of Jesus Christ.

All his life Luis had struggled with feeling he was not accepted. So how could he now be a gentle, loving husband, father, and son-in-law? After he was converted, no one taught him how to love and lead, so he approached his new faith and its conflicts harshly. Manuela already had some old, deep-seated Zapotal resentments, and this only added more hurts to the list, especially since he was now harsh toward her beloved mother and the faith they shared.

After Luis joined the Mennonites, Mark discovered this home problem. He soon learned that young Edwin had not talked with his father for a few years, though they lived in the same house. Edwin and his sister María had not spoken to each other in years either. So Mark called the whole family together.

"The reason I am here is because we want to find healing for you," Mark said as he opened the meeting. "You are a hurting family."

Mark continued, patiently explaining how a Christian home should be.

For the first time ever, Luis humbly confessed his anger problem to his wife and children. Young Toño supported Mark's suggestion and forgave his dad. Then Lillian expressed herself, and so did Manuela. Edwin and María just sat there and cried for at least half an hour. Mark sat with them and directed the discussion. By the time they were done sharing, healing was well on the way.

Toward the end of the meeting, Mark and the children encouraged Luis and Manuela to kiss each other. Luis had never learned to express his love to his wife, but now the children all clapped and cheered as he took his wife's hands and kissed her tenderly—for the first time ever.

Several evenings later Mark took some games over and taught them how to play. Mark watched in delight as they played together, something they had never done before. They played dominoes by candlelight, laughing riotously to see Dad's excitement in the game.

*　　*　　*

Several years after Mark moved to Chachagua, the Chachagua church gave a program at the Pital church with the theme "How to Overcome Trials." Pablo, the minister in Pital, had heard his brother speak of some of the difficult things the Chachagua brethren were facing and was looking forward to the service. As he took his seat, he noticed directly in front of him the man he had met on the bus in Ciudad Quesada—Gelo.

Mark motioned his church to the front to sing. Pablo watched as Gelo reached down to his knee and pushed a lever through his pant leg. Then, gripping the bench-back in front of him with small, tough hands, he heaved himself to his feet. He hobbled up to the front, leaning on crutches attached to his forearms, and quietly took his place with the rest. Then he smiled.

Gelo was a small man, scarcely five feet tall. He was dressed poorly, but he stood out in his little group. The church softly sang "What a

Friend We Have in Jesus" and then returned to their seats. Gelo limped back. Just before easing himself into his seat, he again groped for the lever at his knee, releasing it to bend his leg mechanically.

Pablo, sitting right behind Gelo, watched him closely. As the program progressed, Pablo thought about the little man's life. He knew his lot had not been an easy one. He was too crippled to hold a job, and his wife had turned bitter and left him for other men. Now Gelo lived with one of his three daughters. Pablo eyed the curly head in front of him with pity.

The Chachagua brethren all talked about different aspects of their own trials and what they had learned through them. Soon Mark announced, "Now Gelo is going to tell us how to face trials and how to conquer them."

Gelo flipped his lever, pulled himself to his feet, and slowly limped to the pulpit. He gripped the pulpit edge with both hands and smiled again. Such a smile! Tears welled up in Pablo's eyes and the pity he had formerly felt fled, replaced with awe.

"Trials," Gelo began, "will always come. The best way I've found to conquer them is to face them with joy." The smile never left his face.

Tears streamed down Pablo's cheeks as he realized that he was seeing James 1:2-4 fulfilled before his eyes: "My brethren, count it all joy when ye fall into divers temptations; knowing this, that the trying of your faith worketh patience. But let patience have her perfect work, that ye may be perfect and entire, wanting nothing."

As Gelo continued to explain how he faced trials and how he found victory, Pablo felt ashamed. He began looking at his own life. Sure, things got rough at times, but he knew nothing of what Gelo faced. Mark had mentioned that half the time Gelo did not have a cent to spend, and that Gelo still loved his wife, even though she had left him and had taken two of their daughters. And yet Gelo smiled that radiant smile as he spoke about his Saviour from a heart filled to overflowing.

50

"Hey, Pablo, are you in a terrible hurry?" Mark asked one Sunday morning after the Pital church had given a program in Chachagua.

"No, not really. What do you have in mind?"

"I would like to go visit Don Lico Valverde. He is Luis, Gelo, and Hugo's father. He's too weak to go to church, so we like to go to his house and have a little service for him. He considers himself an evangelical. It's obvious that he is genuinely born again."

"Hey, let's go. The Pital church would enjoy that."

Later, as they bumped down Calle Rojas in Pablo's old white Suburban, Mark suggested, "Let's sing for them. Pablo, why don't you and Eunice sing that duet you sang in church this morning?"

"Sure. We'd enjoy that."

Mark and Ruthie led the way into Don Lico's small house. Pablo led his small son, Jacinto, by the hand and carried a tiny twin girl. His wife Eunice held the other tiny twin in her arms. The small Pital church followed. Among the members was Miguel Barahona, who had recently moved to Pital and decided to join the Mennonites. Teodolinda received them with open arms and asked them to find seats.

"We don't have a lot of time," Mark explained. "We'll just stand and sing several songs."

Pablo was amazed at how crudely the house was built. As they entered, Mark pointed out the two lean-to bedrooms on either side of the house. "One of those bedrooms belongs to Ulises," Mark explained. "The other is Ángel's. They live in the same house but are arch enemies. They don't talk to each other even if they eat at the same table. They both drink, and often you can find Ulises in the ditch or on the bar porch in the early morning. Not all the Valverdes have found the Lord."

There was hardly any furniture in the house. Smoke from their lean-to kitchen had blackened the tin roof and wooden walls. In a small side room was a bed. On the bed lay a man who was little more than skin and bones. Mark and Pablo walked over and tried to talk to him, but he only rolled his eyes and grunted. Clearly, Lico was dying.

As the group sang several songs, a young, rough-looking Valverde stood in the backyard, listening. Then Mark motioned to his brother, asking him for the duet. Pablo and Eunice had just learned the new song. They sang it joyfully.

"Venid amados míos, Jesús les dijo,
A aquellos pescadores, Simón y Andrés.
Si habéis pescado peces, sabed de fijo;
Que pescadores de hombres también seréis.
Sus redes abandonan los pescadores . . ."*
—Alfredo Colom M.

(Come, my dear ones, Jesus said to them,
To the fishermen of old, Simon and Andrew.
If you have learned to fish, mark it down,
You will also become fishers of men.
The fishermen drop their nets and follow . . .)

After the song, Mark and Pablo returned to the bedside, and Mark read a Scripture and led a stirring prayer for Lico. Then his prayer went beyond Lico as he prayed for Teodolinda and all of her children—even the young man in the backyard.

Nineteen days later, on November 21, 1986, Don Lico made a journey to a place much higher than Zapotal. He left the lowlands of this world behind and traveled first class, carried by angels, to the feet of Jesus.

*   *   *

Gelo's joy and the way the Mennonite brethren supported and helped over the time of her husband's death were working on Teodolinda. It was becoming obvious to her that this new group was Biblical and loved Jesus. Gelo had joined them. Lico was gone. Teodolinda was lonely. Her two sons still at home were not Christians. More and more Teodolinda found herself going to Hugo's house for fellowship. Without realizing it, her heart was preparing for a change.

Soon after Lico's death, Sanford Yoder was having evangelistic meetings in Chachagua. Community people were coming, and folks were being converted. Teodolinda attended the meetings and could not help but like the preaching. One night especially, as she listened to Sanford preaching, she thought, *He preaches straight from the Bible like Johnny used to.* Suddenly she got a startling thought. *If Johnny came to live in Chachagua again, he would come to this church. He would love it, and the brethren would be of one mind with him.*

A severe pain had been attacking Teodolinda's leg for several weeks. It ached so badly to walk that she had decided she would not walk any distance again. But during the meetings her desire to hear the Word was greater than her fear of the pain, so she hobbled to church in spite of it.

Toward the end of the meetings, Teodolinda and Gelo stood outside the church house after the service until everyone else had left. Sanford and Mark came out of the building, chatting with their wives and the last few folks around. Just as Sanford was ready to crawl into his vehicle to leave, Teodolinda stepped out of the shadows and asked quietly, "Could you pray for me? I have a bad pain in my leg that just won't let me go. I can hardly walk to church."

"Sure," Sanford answered. "Let's just pray right here and now. Martha, come join us."

Sanford's wife stepped over and joined the foursome. Sanford laid his hand on Teodolinda's head, bowed his head, and prayed for her leg. After the prayer, Gelo and his mother thanked Sanford, and everyone left for home.

Gelo and Teodolinda walked through Chachagua slowly. As they walked they discussed the evening message. Mother and son agreed. This was real Gospel preaching.

"What I love about the preaching," Teodolinda said, "is that it's so much like Johnny's. These people just take the Bible for what it says and teach it."

"That's right," Gelo agreed. "I got so tired of all the yelling and repeating when those elders came. It seems as if the less the preacher has to say, the louder he has to holler to be heard. That message tonight was Biblical and very, very good."

Looking back over their years of disillusionment, they were sad and glad. Sad because of all the time they had wasted spinning their wheels. Glad because now they could get on with building a true, God-honoring church in Chachagua.

The two were walking up the hill just before the Calle Rojas turnoff. The moon had just come up, and they did not need a flashlight. All of a sudden Teodolinda stopped in her tracks and exclaimed, "Gelo, the pain in my leg is gone!"

"Really? That's great!"

"I am healed! Gelo, this confirms what we were saying earlier. Remember what the people from our old church used to say about these people? They claimed they didn't have the Holy Spirit and were dead spiritually. Our elders were always praying and hollering over people, but they seldom were healed. Now this man simply put his hand on my head and prayed for me, and I got better!"

"Yes, Mamita, this is a confirmation. God is with these people. You will join them as soon as you can."

Sanford went to bed that night without realizing what had happened. He did not find out until Teodolinda gave her testimony many years later that God had chosen to bring about the miraculous healing to convince this precious soul that, though this church did not emphasize healing, they did have God in their hearts, and God could use them in divine healing when He chose.

*   *   *

One evening Hugo was late coming home from work. As Irene served him his hot coffee, he told her a happy story.

"This evening I stopped at Mark's house. Mark was sitting out on the porch talking with Luis Carvajal. After greeting me, Mark smiled and said, 'Hugo, guess what. Luis is back and reconciled with God.' I was surprised. I could see that Luis had been crying, but his eyes were really shining. Irene, I hope this time he'll be strong. He told me that his wife is interested in returning too. I will never forget how the Lord taught him to read. He was always such an inspiration to me. I'm sure he will be a blessing in our small church. I never could figure out how he got discouraged and left the Lord after all God had done for him. Well, praise the Lord, he's back!"

*   *   *

"Did you hear the latest news, Mamita?" Gelo asked as he stopped in one day.

"No. What's up?"

"Old Durando Quesada passed away, and Adelia has come to live in Chachagua with Marcos and Nena."

Teodolinda's eyebrows shot up. "Amazing!" she exclaimed. "I wonder if the woman has changed at all. Do you remember all the heartaches that woman caused us in Zapotal?"

"Do I ever!" Gelo chuckled. "But I pity her more than anything else. Marcos was telling me that she is a bitter, ruined lady. She is very sick, and they don't expect her to live. I want to go visit her. Will you go with me?"

Teodolinda sighed. Her flesh cringed at the thought of facing the woman who had hated her so. And yet her spirit knew she should be willing. "Gelo, I will go. As a Christian I don't have any enemies. I am even willing to apologize for hating her back. Let's go this afternoon."

That afternoon found Teodolinda and Gelo leaning over a bed where a small, frail woman lay wrapped in a blanket. Though Adelia's body was wasting away, her mind was clear, and she could talk.

Teodolinda spoke first. "Doña Adelia, how are you doing? I haven't seen you in a long time."

Adelia held still on her bed and answered, "Yes, it's been a while."

Teodolinda took the plunge. "Adelia, we came to see you as soon as we found out you had moved to Chachagua. I feel bad because we used to be enemies. I am a Christian now, and I love everybody. I want to say I am sorry for having hated you so."

Adelia's eyes were closed, but Teodolinda could see moisture creeping through the closed eyelids. Adelia did not move or say a word, so Teodolinda continued. "Adelia, let's forgive and forget the past, okay? We were all sinners, living lives dedicated to evil and hate. But things are changing. I love you now and have forgiven you. The same with Nena. We get along fine now. Let's forget the past and be friends. What do you say?"

Adelia's tears were running down her cheeks now. Her thin, frail arms reached up out of the blanket. Leaning over, Teodolinda accepted the embrace and kissed her on the cheek.

Gelo spoke. "Adelia, I am here to tell you that Jesus loves you and wants to wash your sins away."

Minutes later Teodolinda and Gelo left. Teodolinda never saw Adelia alive again. Adelia died several months later. During her last months, Gelo hobbled over to Marcos's house every few days to witness to Adelia. On one of his last visits, he asked her if she wanted to accept Christ as her Saviour. She nodded slightly. She could not talk anymore, but everybody in the house felt a difference in her attitude during her last days on earth. Though only God knew for certain, Gelo was sure that when he got to Heaven, the woman who had hated and mocked him on earth would meet him at Heaven's gate with a big smile.

*   *   *

One afternoon Mark was playing with his three children in their backyard. Since they lived at the edge of town, Mark had fenced off a yard for his family's privacy. He had planted hibiscus bushes all around the yard, allowing access only through the house.

While Mark played with the children, Ruthie came to the door and called, "Mark, someone is here to talk to you."

Mark left the children to their playing and walked through the house and out to the front porch. To his surprise, in the yard stood Aurelio Valverde from La Lucha. Mark offered him a seat on the porch. They visited briefly; then Aurelio, the leader of their small La Lucha church group, got to the point.

"We would like for you to come to La Lucha to discuss the points where you differ with our church. Do you think you could?"

Mark was wary. He knew how critical Aurelio had been of their church at one time. But he also had heard through the Valverdes that he was softening, especially since his mother had joined the Mennonite church. Mark answered carefully. "Sure. I'd rather not get into an argument about doctrine, but I'd be glad to discuss Scripture."

"Our little congregation in La Lucha is facing some tough decisions," Aurelio began. "We are considering joining your church, but we want to be sure. If we see that what you teach is Biblical, then you will be our pastor."

Mark smiled broadly, surprised at Aurelio's honest and frank way of expressing himself. "Well, let's pray about it. I want you to compare everything I teach with the Bible. If what I teach is according to the Bible, then follow it. But if I don't teach what the Bible says, don't believe it."

"When can you come?"

"Would Thursday suit you?" Mark asked after checking his agenda.

"Yes, I think it would. What time?"

"How about four o'clock?"

So Mark and Hugo traveled to La Lucha for the next three Thursdays to teach doctrine. The little La Lucha group was convinced that the doctrine was Biblical, so they asked for instruction class. Soon La Lucha joined Chachagua, and the two fledgling churches worked together as sister congregations.

Now Mark had brethren in instruction class in both churches. He taught instruction class in La Lucha every Thursday afternoon and then led their Bible study in the evening. He also preached and taught in Chachagua and traveled to La Lucha to preach for them every Sunday afternoon. That, plus all the personal work, visiting, and evangelizing, made him a very busy pastor. But the work was rewarding, and he was continually amazed at the changes taking place in the hearts of the people in his care.

*   *   *

The lake sparkled blue-green in the bright morning sun. On the far side towered a mountain dressed in all shades of green. Beside the lake was a flat park sprinkled with tropical trees and plants. Far beyond, the majestic Arenal Volcano jutted up into the azure blue sky and towered over the little green lake and the Los Lagos park. It was the perfect spot—not quite as high in altitude as Zapotal, but higher than Chachagua, and close enough for an afternoon outing. Perhaps it was not quite as pretty as the Garden of Eden, but it might have been close.

The park was crowded on this special day. Several paddleboats bobbed on the lake's surface, and the children took turns paddling. The place echoed with the squeals of excited children as they played on the shore and swam.

Standing alone, Mark watched the little church mingle. The adults were scattered all over the park area, watching the children and visiting among themselves. The Chachagua church was enjoying a rare picnic at Los Lagos. Mark enjoyed the chance to get out into nature, but better yet, it was such a blessing for him to see how much the church members enjoyed each other and the warm fellowship. It was almost too good to be true.

He could not help but think of the Valverdes, who made up the majority of the membership. *Where would the Chachagua church be without the Valverdes?* he thought. *And where would they be without Jesus?* Especially Teodolinda. Mark was amazed at what God had done in that little woman's life. He could hardly imagine that at one time she had owned a saloon, drank, danced, and lived a wild, sinful life. Now she was a solid pillar in the church.

Mark looked around. He could not see her. Everyone else was getting together for some photographs, but Teodolinda was missing.

"Marcos, come!" Hugo shouted. "Bring your camera! We want to take some pictures!"

Mark strode toward the dock. The mothers were cleaning up their children while everyone gathered around.

"Where's Mamita?" Gelo asked, hobbling up to the photo site.

Sister Teodolinda makes up for lost time at Los Lagos the day of the church picnic.

Toño left to look for her, and Mark started to set up the group for the photo. Suddenly Toño ran toward them, his finger on his mouth, hissing, "Shhhhhhh!"

As he drew closer, he beckoned to Mark. "Come look at Grandma," Toño called softly, motioning with his hand.

Mark followed Toño. Most of the church followed too, curious to see what Teodolinda was doing off all by herself. Toño led Mark to a gazebo. Mark peeped around the corner and grinned. He should have known what Teodolinda was doing. It was what she did every chance she got.

Teodolinda sat alone at a white ceramic table, her glasses perched on her nose. She was having her daily devotions. Since they had left early

The Chachagua church the day of the picnic at Los Lagos. Notice Teodolinda at the far left carrying her Bible. Behind her stands her grandson, Nelson. Beside her in the front row stands Gelo, then Manuela and Luis. On the far right of the group, Hugo and Irene are surrounded by their family.

in the morning for the picnic, she had not had time to read her precious Bible. She was making up for it now.

Mark sneaked out his camera and got a photo before she discovered what was happening.

Toño convinced Teodolinda to follow them back to the lake for the group photo. As they walked, Mark wondered anew at the change in the little woman. Her love for the Bible had done the miracle. She wanted so much to be like her Master. And the more she drew close to Him through prayer and Bible reading, the more she became like Him every day.

Mark had to start all over lining up people for the photo. Finally all was ready. Teodolinda stood with the rest, her Bible in her hands.

After the photo, Teodolinda withdrew from the crowd again. She sat under a tree off to the side and watched the people having a good time. Her mind traveled back to twenty years before when they'd had a similar gathering in Zapotal—the special *rosario* before they had moved to Chachagua. There had been lots of people in that crowd, much like today. Men, women, and children talking and laughing, just like now. But there were so many differences between the two gatherings.

In Zapotal they had supposedly gathered for a religious ceremony, but it was really just an excuse to drink. Today they had gathered to fellowship with other believers and truly worship the Lord. The leader that evening in Zapotal had been Old Nacho, who was nothing like her pastor, Mark. This evening Teodolinda knew they would end up sharing a simple meal and then, in the moonlight, they would sing and worship the Lord from their hearts. But in Zapotal it had always ended up being a wild, sinful party of drinking, dancing, and fighting. She could still see Juan Gonzales's wound spurting blood, and the old fear gnawed at her innards. She could almost feel the cold wind whipping through the itabo tree by the front porch of her saloon. She could feel the desperate, vile guilt and stark fear. Teodolinda shivered. Then she breathed a prayer and looked at the crowd again. Immediately a stronger emotion filled her heart. Peace. And with it, joy.

On that awful night La Peligrosa Saloon had died. The death of her saloon had been the last straw in her pathetic life. Something had snapped within her, and today, as she surveyed the multitude before her, she was glad. God had used the saloon to hasten her departure from the highlands of Zapotal to the lowlands of Chachagua. And through that providential move, He had hastened her journey from the lowlands of sin to the highlands of His love. Truly the death of her saloon had brought about the birth of a church. And now as she watched the children play and the adults fellowship, she knew that her small worldly loss then could not begin to compare with her great spiritual gain today.

The sun was setting now. Teodolinda bowed her head slightly. She did not notice the crimson color of the sunset on the lake. The pleasant sounds of the picnic faded. She no longer even heard the black howler monkeys in the distance. Her thoughts were far away.

Toño called her softly. "Come, Grandma, supper is ready."

Teodolinda lifted her head. Slowly she got up and walked toward the crowd of people and the table loaded with food. When she sat at the place reserved for her at the head of the table, everyone wondered why she was smiling through her tears. She did not tell them. They could just wonder. But God in Heaven knew why, and He carefully recorded each tear, knowing one day He Himself would wipe them all away.

EPILOGUE

A wind-whipped hilltop perched on what seems like the top of the world. A small plateau covered with drying grasses, wildflowers, and tombstones.

The Zapotal graveyard lies in a forlorn corner of a cow pasture. No fences surround it, so the cows are just as much at home grazing among the crooked crosses as the common bush tanagers that chirp their little songs from the bushes sprinkled among the graves.

I sat on a simple concrete gravestone, leaned back against the tall cement cross, inhaled the nippy morning air, and shook my head. Was it true? Or was it a dream?

It was both. It was a dream come true.

My brother Mark and I had driven out to the graveyard just after dawn for our morning meditation. We both needed to get out of our warm tourist cabin to savor the Zapotal wilds, so we left our cozy beds, braved the morning's chill, and drove to this high spot on Costa Rica's continental divide. We hiked out to the edge of the mountainside and gazed down upon the gulf 4,800 feet below.

Once you top Cerro Pelón, you feel like you are on the top of the world.

Now, sitting on the tombstone, I read about the resurrection of the dead in 1 Corinthians 15 and 1 Thessalonians 4 and 5, and I imagined what Mark and I would witness if the resurrection would just happen to have been planned for that special morning. A sudden joy filled my heart when I realized that the four Valverdes whose bodies rested under the golden bed of orchids would all be raised unto eternal life. All four were children. Three of Teodolinda's grandchildren: Luis's little Gerardo, who died at birth; Lidier's little William, who died when he was just three weeks old; and Leyla's little Xinia, who died just before her first birthday. The fourth was little Sergio, Teodolinda's twelfth child who died when he was four. Moments before he had died, he had snuggled up to his mama in bed and whispered, "Mamita, me voy donde Tatica Dios." (Mama, I'm going to my Daddy God.) When they buried the frail little chap the next day, his mother felt a strange peace in knowing that this one son of hers would never live under the terrible grip of *guaro*.

My heart rejoiced with Sergio, Gerardo, William, and Xinia. *Yes*, I thought, *I would love to be here on that great day of His return to accompany them to their distant home.*

But most of the dead on this hilltop would experience a very different resurrection from that of the little Valverdes. I wondered what kind of life the person under me had lived. Though Zapotal was picturesque enough now, years ago it had been a dark, wicked place where the devil reigned and the light of the Gospel had not yet reached.

After leaving the graveyard, we spent hours interviewing and learning to know the Zapotal people, reliving Teodolinda's story in the process. On our way to Zapotal, we had stopped in Tajo Alto to ask directions. Invariably I would ask, "Do you remember the Valverdes?" Yes, everyone remembered. And the closer we got to Zapotal, the more the locals remembered. During our three days there, we heard many stories about the poor family that made moonshine, held *rosarios*, danced, drank, and fought. Everything we had heard from the Valverdes' own mouths was confirmed as we heard tale after Valverde tale. We could not begin to record it all.

When we met Luis Quesada, he actually sang the *Panadera* for us, accompanied by his guitar, much as Vicente Jiménez would have played it years ago, giving us a little taste of what those wild dances were like. We saw some of the scars from wounds the Valverdes had inflicted on their enemies, often with their teeth. We saw a trail winding up a long, steep slope called Valverde Hill, since it used to be part of their farm. Someone mentioned Valverde Creek.

Several of the Valverdes joined our investigation for a day—Luis and Manuela, Leyla from Tajo Alto, Aurelio and Hugo with several of their daughters, and Marcos and Nena's Nelson. We toured the places where they had lived. We hiked up the mountain and found El Roblón, where Hugo had spent those cold hours of terror with his mother and his drunken father. We drove over Cerro Pelón and hiked down to La Cuesta del Tubo. We saw the incredibly beautiful quetzals.

But by far the most touching moments were at the site of La Peligrosa. When we walked into the cove where La Peligrosa used to stand, emotion gnawed at my innards. *So this was the place,* I thought. Hugo, Aurelio, and Luis pointed out the small wooden pillars the saloon had once rested on. In the middle of the clearing stood an old itabo tree a drunken customer had once chopped off in a rage. It had grown back. Some of the trees in the background were also original sentinels that had guarded the area in its wilder days.

Modern day La Cuesta del Tubo has been bulldozed to accommodate four-wheel-drive jeeps. The road is hidden by the jungle.

This is the first of the eight awful switchbacks winding down the face of the mountain.

We saw this resplendent quetzal close to Tilo Barrantes' sugarcane mill.

Manuela was struck with emotion as she remembered her life as a bartender there forty-three years before. Memories spilled out.

"I learned to hate the saloon and what it represented," she said tearfully. "But I didn't want to move to Chachagua. I wanted to stay in my beloved Zapotal. But I knew we had to move, or Luis would get killed." Then she started crying. Luis listened silently.

Luis pointed to a weed patch. "I fought with a guy out here after dark for half an hour, rolling around in the grass," he almost whispered. "We were both too drunk to hurt each other."

Standing at the site where La Peligrosa once stood are (from left)
Luis, Hugo, Pablo, Aurelio, and Manuela. The little stump beside
Pablo's left foot is one of La Peligrosa's corner posts.

Aurelio pointed out where the main room of La Peligrosa had been. "There," he pointed, "is where Mamita sat, so drunk she couldn't get up." Then he was silent. His daughters stood quietly with the other girls, watching and listening.

Hugo's memories were vivid, but since he was only fifteen when they moved to Chachagua, his hurts were not as deep or binding. His daughters smiled as they listened to their daddy animatedly telling stories about the awful saloon.

Four of Aurelio's and Hugo's daughters, Nelson and his son, Manuela and Luis, Hugo, and Aurelio at La Peligrosa's site.

Suddenly I had an inspiration. "Hey, let's all gather here in the shade. I think it would be appropriate to have a word of prayer before we leave." Emotions surged over me like a tidal wave. "We should thank the Lord for the way He changed you and how He got you out of this situation," I said, weeping openly now. "And we should also pray for the Valverdes who still aren't Christians."

I looked around the circle and asked, "Is there anyone here who could possibly lead in prayer?" My voice cracked. "I sure can't."

My brother Mark was weeping hopelessly. Luis and Aurelio were also overcome by their emotions. I looked at Hugo. The youngest Valverde. The minister of the Gospel we all appreciated so much. Tears filled his eyes, but he said, "Pablo, I will try. Let us kneel."

We knelt in a circle just a few yards from the place where Luis had fought in a drunken stupor. Who knew what all else had happened on that spot!

Hugo began praying quietly: "Yes, Holy Lord, I want to thank You so much. We want to worship You here in this place—this place where so many things happened. You know all about it, Lord. You remember it all better than we do. It's enough for us to know that You know. You don't forget anything, and we are so weak and our limitations are many. We forget so many details, but we remember enough to want to worship You this morning. Enough to move our hearts because of Your mercy and Your love for us . . ."

I heard other noises. Sniffles. Sighs. Luis and Manuela were kneeling in the grass side by side, both crying so hard that they shook.

Hugo's beautiful prayer continued: "O Holy Lord, I want to thank You so much for what You did for us—that You have called us from this remote place to serve You in Your kingdom. And today, as we remember all those experiences and the awful life we led, it's only to give You thanks and glory and honor. You are the only one who is worthy. Please continue to bless us, Father . . ."

We were on holy ground. God was very close to our hearts. He was pleased that we worshiped and praised Him for bringing His salvation to the Valverdes.

Controlling his sobs, Hugo continued, "And, Lord, I want to pray from the bottom of my heart for all my brothers and sisters who have not come to the full knowledge of Your truth. I pray that You would touch their hearts and that this testimony we are seeking after would call them to You."

We were far from modern civilization, but oh, were we close to God!

Hugo finished his prayer, "Blessed be Your name! We give You all the glory and the honor, O Lord. Thank You, Lord. In Jesus' name, Amen."*

---

* Though this prayer is condensed, it is virtually word for word, since it was recorded.

AFTERWARD

December 2010

When I interviewed Teodolinda for this book, she lived in a nice, homey little cabin with her granddaughter Flor. Flor's husband had left her years before, and her children were all grown, so she and her grandmother lived together. Teodolinda had a room to herself and could get around a little in her wheelchair. Flor took good care of her, and Teodolinda was quite happy with the setup.

Flor's little house was built right beside her mother Marina's house. When Flor was away, someone from Marina's house would come over and take care of Teodolinda.

After the interview, Flor's health declined, so the family suggested that Teodolinda move to La Lucha with Hugo and Irene. They have four big girls to help with the work, and Hugo has a vehicle to take her to the doctor if she needs it, so it worked out well.

Teodolinda walked around some, using her wheelchair as a walker. At times she even walked by just holding on to furniture or the wall. She was happy because she could go to church again. The La Lucha church house was built right in Hugo's yard, so it was easy for them to push her over for services, or even for part of the service. She wanted her wheelchair parked up in the amen corner, close to the pulpit, so she could hear the preacher. Even when it rained, she insisted on going to church. "Hugo can wheel me over fast," she would say. So they would wrap her up and go.

Nelson and his wife Naomi have a house very close to Hugo's. Little Yahaira, Nelson's daughter, can watch her great-grandmother rocking on Hugo's porch.

Over the last several years Teodolinda has had mild heart spells. Recently she had another one. For a while they thought she was dying, but she pulled through. The next Sunday she was too weak to go to church, so Irene stayed home with her. At the time for the message Teodolinda insisted that Irene go to church. "I will stay in bed. I promise. Go and tell the brethren to pray for me," she insisted.

At this time Teodolinda is still reading her Bible, *hoja por hoja* (page by page), as she herself says. When I interviewed her in March of 2008, she was working her way through Genesis. By July 26, 2008, she was halfway through the Bible. She read far more than I in those five months!

For her ninety-sixth birthday the family threw a grand party for Teodolinda.

The family rented a tent for the 96th birthday party.

Teodolinda with some of her children.

Left to Right: Luis, daughter-in-law Gregoria (Lidier's wife), Marina, Gelo, Rolando (a grandson she raised), Leyla, Marino, Belén, Aurelio, Victoria, Hugo.

Teodolinda with many of her grandchildren.

One of the highlights of the party was reminiscing about the past. Hugo talked first about how the Lord has led and blessed their lives. Then Mark got up and gave a brief overview of the Valverdes' history. A lot of the youth didn't know much about the Valverdes' past. It was a touching time, and again they ended with a prayer, thanking the Lord for what He has done for their family.

It was interesting to set up the five generations for a photo. Teodolinda, Teodolinda's daughter Marina, Marina's son Álvaro, Álvaro's son Daniel, and Daniel's baby Jayleen. There are other great-great-grandchildren, but this is the first set where all are in the church.

Portraits of Teodolinda's Children

Luis

Luis's story is both happy and sad. Sad, because his home is still divided. Though Manuela is friendly to the church people, she remains Catholic. But she enjoys it when her son Toño comes home and reads the Scriptures to them and to her relatives.

Two of Luis's boys, Edwin and Toño, accepted the faith as teenagers and followed in their dad's footsteps for years. But in recent years Edwin has fallen back. Toño remains faithful, and his story shows up a little later.

The other happy thing about Luis's story is how he has hung in there for all these years, a faithful member of the church. Even when his family has at times turned against him, he has never stopped thanking the Lord for delivering him from sin's trap. If you come to a service in Chachagua on a Sunday morning, he'll always be there. Quiet. Aging. But faithful.

When we made the trip to Zapotal for this book, we had a special prayer right where La Peligrosa used to be, thanking the Lord for His deliverance. Luis and Manuela wept side by side on their knees.

Ángel

Ángel never married. When they moved from Zapotal, he had enough money to buy half of the farm the Valverdes bought. In his later life he withdrew from his friends and most of his family. He became a hermit.

Even when his father was on his deathbed and begged for him to come to his bedside, Ángel refused to visit his dying father. No one was able to get close to him to understand the bitterness from his sin-scarred life. He made his living by farming and taking produce to a farmers' market on Saturdays in San José. He became known for stealing produce to take to the market. He'd spend Sundays in San José wasting his money on booze and prostitutes.

At first Mark had a hard time making friends with him. The first few times Mark went to his little shack, all he was able to see was Ángel's back retreating into the yuca field. But with patience they became friends.

One of the last times Mark saw Ángel, he walked by the little bus stop where he was waiting to go to the farmers' market. Mark thought, *This would be a good time to witness to him,* but decided he was in too much of a hurry. But a still, small voice kept talking to him. *What if this is your last chance?*

Mark was some thirty yards past Ángel. *He'd think it funny if I went back now,* Mark thought, but by now he knew the voice of the Spirit. So, foolish as it might appear, he turned, walked back, and sat beside Ángel.

"I know you live a lonely life," Mark began. "If you ever need help or would like to talk to someone, I'd be glad to help." Mark then witnessed to him about how the Lord can heal a sin-sick person. Ángel seemed grateful and thanked Mark.

It was the last time Mark talked with Ángel.

Soon after that, Ángel sold his farm and moved to San José. None of his brothers and sisters knew where he lived. Mark was on a visit to the States when he received the news that Ángel was dying and was asking for his family. They went to San José and found him living in the slums in a dirty little room, so sick he couldn't even get up. They took him to the San Carlos hospital (the closest one to Chachagua), where the doctors discovered that he had leukemia and was near death.

When Mark heard this, he wanted so badly to return to Costa Rica and visit Ángel and hold his hand and lead him to the Lord. But Ruthie reminded him that there were other brothers who could help him. Mark wrote an e-mail suggesting how to help Ángel, but as he sent that e-mail, he received another one saying that Ángel had died. But along with this news came the good news that both Gelo and

Aurelio had witnessed to him and prayed with him. They are both confident that Ángel received the Lord. Before he died, a large group of Valverdes stood around his hospital bed and sang, read the Bible, and prayed for him. Ángel was so happy. With a big smile he whispered weakly, "Now I have such a nice big family." What a joy that the loneliest of the Valverdes met the Lord just hours before his death!

Lidier

Lidier and his wife Gregoria live close to Mark in Chachagua. Gregoria is a member of the Chachagua Mennonite Church. She is appreciated for her quiet, meek faithfulness and servant's heart. (And also for her delicious tamales with great black Costa Rican coffee.) Lidier was converted and was freed from his past of alcohol and fighting. But after being hurt by some pastors with poor testimonies in the Pentecostal church where he was baptized, he left the church, soured against all ministers. Sometimes he attends the Mennonite church, which he appreciates, but he still has not overcome his distrust to the point of joining the fellowship.

Marina

Marina, by a series of miraculous events, eventually moved with her eleven children from Guanacaste to Chachagua. She still lives with her husband, Luis Elizondo, but he does not agree with her church. This causes a lot of heartache and difficulty, but Marina hangs in there faithfully and does what she can for her family.

Marina's son Álvaro is also in the church. His story comes later.

Marcos

Nelson, Marcos's son, found Marcos's body floating in a small pond. The cause of his death is still a mystery. No one knows for sure if it was murder, accident, or suicide. Nena lives a lonely life with her daughter and is withdrawn and bitter. After Marcos's death Mark visited her. When the youth sang for her she cried freely, but did not choose to seek the Lord for healing from a long life of sin.

Amable

Amable, as well as Mireya, escaped a lot of the sufferings of an alcoholic family by going to work in San José before the Valverdes were converted. In San José she had two sons out of wedlock by different men. She then married and had another son with her husband. She was converted in her old age, then got cancer. They say that in the hospital she would sing and rejoice in the Lord in her illness and in her death.

Gelo

After a story about Gelo's testimony called "The Little Man With the Big Smile" was published in CLP's *Companions* and in *Calvary Messenger,* Mary Jane Beachy, a widow who had been married to a crippled man for years, was moved. She sent Mark some money and told him to buy transportation for Gelo to get to church. There was enough money for a horse, a saddle, a raincoat, and a table and chair for the new house the church helped Gelo build. Later Mary Jane visited Chachagua and met Gelo personally.

Eventually Lidiet, the daughter he raised, left home. But Liliana, one of the girls his wife raised, married a man named Alexander and moved home to live with her father. Alexander and Liliana have four children who also live with Gelo. In 2003 they joined the church too. Alexander works in a grocery store and helps Gelo with his living expenses.

If you join the brethren in Chachagua for a service, Gelo will still hobble in and sit down, and his big smile is still a joy to behold.

Gelo with his married daughter and family.

Leyla

Leyla is the only Valverde who still lives in the Zapotal area. She and her husband Beto live in Tajo Alto. She found freedom from her sins when she accepted the Lord after her mother sent her a Bible. She still treasures it. Well-worn, tattered, and coverless, it gives evidence of the longing of Leyla's heart after God. She attends an evangelical church in Tajo Alto. Beto is not a believer.

Mireya

For years Mireya worked in San José and even spent some time working for her boss in Belgium. The last years she moved out to Chachagua and bought a house, where she lives by herself, bitter and withdrawn from her family. Mark has made different attempts to help her find personal healing as well as healing of old resentments with the family. He still prays for her and waits for that day.

Marino

Marino lives in Chachagua and is a Pentecostal. He was among the first Valverdes to receive the Gospel. Yet his search for identity has not been easy due to his past hurts, and he has not found it easy to work with a church or his family.

Belén

Belén lives off by himself. In the beginning when the family was turning to the Lord he attended the Pentecostal services, but he never was converted. He later joined a Seventh Day Adventist church and married a girl from there, but he was soon back in the world. He has struggled all his life with a serious alcohol problem.

Aurelio

When I met with the Valverdes to prepare them for the interviews and this book, it was Aurelio who started telling stories first. I hadn't planned on hearing stories that first evening; I just wanted to talk about the purpose of the book and discuss preliminaries. But the Zapotal story was bursting at the seams of Aurelio's heart. It had to spill out. And not long into the stories, something else had to spill out. Tears! When Aurelio tried to tell us about the grubs in his head, he sobbed so hard he couldn't talk.

Aurelio was the Valverde who suffered most in his childhood, and Zapotal scarred him much more than the others, emotionally and physically. He still is not totally over his stroke. You can hear it in his speech, though it is very slight.

Aurelio and Carmen are both in the church and have tried their best to raise their family for the Lord. Even so, some of the oldest children left home and sought after the world that Aurelio had left behind. Four of their nine children have married outside the church.

Several years ago Aurelio's family moved from La Lucha to Pital where Duane Nisly is pastor. The move helped pull the rest of the family together. Two of the wayward boys, David and Alberto, came back from lives of deep sin and repented and are rejoicing in the Lord. Today four of Aurelio's children are in the church.

On July 26, 2008, Alberto Valverde married Raquel Villalobos. He was Aurelio and Carmen's first child to marry a fellow believer in the plain church.

Alberto, Raquel, and son, with Alberto's two sisters.

Victoria

Victoria is still Catholic. She and her husband Rigo live about half an hour from Chachagua.

Ulises

Ulises lives in Chachagua and has a family of five children. He still has a serious alcohol problem, which causes family problems. He is not living with his family anymore because of his alcohol. He highly respects the church and the brethren. He openly talks about his problems and wishes he could change and bring his family to healing, but he hasn't made the step of giving his life to the Lord and becoming a clean Christian leader and head of his home.

Hugo

Hugo, the youngest Valverde, was converted to Christ at a younger age than any of the other Valverdes. He wasn't in the plain churches long before the Chachagua brethren saw in him a future leader. In 1993 Hugo was ordained in Chachagua as a co-minister for Mark. He was chosen to minister to his own people, many of them Valverdes. Some years later he was sent to La Lucha and has been lead minister there ever since.

One of the outstanding things about most of the Valverde family is how they respect the Word. During the interviews, it was Hugo who remembered his dad talking about La Sagradas Escrituras (The Sacred Scriptures) when he was a child in Zapotal. Even today, when the church or the ministry faces a tough situation, Hugo will be the first to say, "And what does the Bible say?" Or he will quote a Bible verse that speaks to the situation. Hugo has come to be known as the Man of the Book.

Hugo has a lovely family of five children. His son, next to the oldest, left home and followed the world. He married and has two children. Of Hugo's four daughters, three are members of the church.

Besides his work as a minister, Hugo has a small lumber business. He has a small portable sawmill and goes into the woods and saws out lumber for his customers.

Hugo Valverde and family.

Portraits of Some of
Teodolinda's Grandchildren

Toño Valverde
and family.

Lidier's wife Gregoria (on right) with son Lalo and his family.

Toño

Antonio, Luis's son, was received as a member of the Chachagua brotherhood in 1991. He married Clara Friesen from La Estrella congregation in 1998 and was ordained minister for Chachagua in 1999. They have four children. Besides serving as co-pastor with Mark in Chachagua, he also helps out with ministerial duties in Nueva Armenia, Nicaragua. Toño also loves to farm. He raises crops and cattle.

Lalo

Lalo, Lidier's son, married Maritza in 1985. They were received as members of the La Lucha brotherhood in 1989. Lalo and Maritza have five children. The oldest three are members of the church in La Lucha. Lalo owns a hardware store which his children help him run.

Álvaro

Álvaro, Marina's son, married Isabel in 1980. They were received as members of the Chachagua brotherhood in 1998. They have five children, two of which are members of the church in Chachagua. Daniel, the oldest of Álvaro's children, taught school for five years, then married Orpha Villalobos on December 30, 2006. They taught school together in La Merced the year after they were married. They have two children, Jayleen and Dannél.

Marina with her son Álvaro and his wife, two grandsons, and grandson Daniel's wife and family.

Nelson Valverde and family.

Nelson

Nelson was received as a member of the Chachagua brotherhood in 1989. He married Naomi Schrock from the La Mizpa congregation in 1993. They have adopted two precious children: Yahaira and Jordan. They lived in Chachagua until 2005, when they moved to La Lucha. Nelson has farmed for most of his life. He also worked for Lalo in the hardware store and with Hugo on the lumber project.

The Chachagua Church Today

The Chachagua church is a special church. When my family gave a program there several years ago, we chose to sing songs about suffering. We wept as we sang, and the Chachagua church wept with us. After that program we as a family concluded that the Chachagua church is a special church because it is a suffering church. Suffering makes a church strong. At present Chachagua has thirty-one members, and La Lucha has twenty.

Thirty-six of Teodolinda's descendants are baptized members of the plain churches in Costa Rica, including Teodolinda, her five children, grandchildren, great-grandchildren, and the in-laws.

On September 8, 1994, Mark was ordained bishop over Chachagua and La Lucha. Since then he has been asked to help as bishop in a congregation in Quebradón, Costa Rica, and a church in Nueva Armenia, Nicaragua.

Brethren visiting after a service in the spring of 2011.

Johnny Rojas

Many years after leaving Chachagua, Johnny left his faith and his Lord. For years he worked for the Costa Rican legal system, eventually serving as a judge. But since he retired, he has returned to serving the Lord. After being contacted about this book, he visited Grandma Linda again. It was a touching time with Gelo, Marina, and Teodolinda. Memories were refreshed and tears shed as they all praised the Lord for what He had done for the Valverdes through Johnny years ago.

The brethren are praying for Johnny. Johnny expressed his concern about how the churches in his circles have modernized in the years he was out in the world and have left their faithfulness to the Bible. And in his last days, Johnny is determined to return and stay on the Way he walked on back in those days when he came to Chachagua in search of the Valverdes.

Johnny and Gelo again walking along the Chachagua streets as friends and brethren.

PRONUNCIATION GUIDE

agua dulce	AH gooah DOOL seh
Alcides	ahl SEE dehs
alfeñique	ahl feh NYEE keh
alforja	ahl FOHR hah
Álvaro	AHL vah roh
Americano	ah meh ree KAH noh
Andrés Rodríguez	ahn DREHS Roh DREE gehs
Ángel	AHN hehl
Angelina	ahn heh LEE nah
areno	ah REH noh
Audilio	ah oo DEE leeoh
Aurelio	a hoo REH leeoh
Aurora Rojas	a hoo ROH rah ROH hahs
Avelino	ah veh LEE noh
baile	BAH ee leh
Barranquilla	bah rahn KEE yah
Beto	BEH toh
buenas	BOOEH nahs
cabezón	kah beh SOHN
Calderón	kahl deh ROHN
Calle Ocho	KAH yeh OH choh
Calle Rojas	KAH yeh ROH hahs
campesino	kahm peh SEE noh
canfinera	kahn fee NEH rah
carismático	kah rees MAH tee koh

Cartago	kahr TAH goh
Cerro Pelón	SEH roh peh LOHN
Chachagua	chah CHAH gooah
chayote	chah YOH teh
chayotera	chah yoh TEH rah
Chepe	CHEH peh
chicha	CHEE chah
churuca	choo ROO kah
Ciudad Quesada	seeoo DAHD keh SAH dah
colones	koh LOH nehs
Conchita	kohn CHEE tah
contrabando	kohn trah BAHN doh
cutacha	koo TAH chah
Cuyo Villegas	KOO yoh vee YEH gahs
Denia Saborío	DEH nyah sah boh REE oh
Domingo Evangelista	doh MEEN goh eh vahn heh LEES tah
Doña Chepa	DOH nyah CHEH pah
dulce	DOOL seh
Durando	doo RAHN doh
Edin Rojas	EH deen ROH hahs
El Negro	ehl NEH groh
El Niñito	ehl nee NYEE toh
El Roblón	ehl roh BLOHN
escapulario	ehs kah poo LAH reeoh
estampa	ehs TAHM pah
evangélico	eh vahn HEH lee koh
fábrica	FAH bree kah
fermento	fehr MEHN toh
Fernando Rojas	Fehr NAHN doh ROH hahs
gallo pinto	GAH yoh PEEN toh
garabato	gah rah BAH toh
Gelo	HEH loh

Gerardo Araya	heh RAHR doh ah RAH yah
gongolona	gohn goh LOH nah
gracias	GRAH seeahs
Gregoria	greh GOH reeah
Guanacaste	gooah nah KAHS teh
guapote	gooah POH teh
guaro	GOOAH roh
guarumo	gooah ROO moh
guayaba	gooah YAH bah
higuerón	ee geh ROHN
Ignacio Monje	eeg NAH seeoh MOHN heh
itabo	ee TAH boh
Jabillos	hah BEE yohs
Jabón	hah BOHN
Jabonal	hah boh NAHL
Jaime Araya	HAH ee meh Ah RAH yah
jilguero	heel GEH roh
Jiménez	hee MEH nehs
Johnny Rojas	JOH nee ROH hahs
Juan Gonzales	hooahn gohn SAH lehs
Julio Solís	HOO leeoh soh LEES
Julito	hoo LEE toh
La Cuesta del Tubo	lah KOOEHS tah dehl TOO boh
La Lucha	lah LOO chah
La Merced	lah mehr SEHD
La Palmera	lah pahl MEH rah
La Peligrosa	lah peh lee GROH sah
La Tabla	lah TAH blah
La Virgen de los Ángeles	lah VEER hehn deh lohs AHN heh lehs
La Virgen del Carmen	ah VEER hehn dehl KAHR mehn
Lalo	LAH loh

Las Lilas	lahs LEE lahs
Las Marimbas	lahs mah REEM bahs
Leandro	leh AHN droh
león	leh OHN
Lidier	LEE dyehr
Los Lagos	lohs LAH gohs
Luis Carvajal	loo EES kahr vah HAHL
Luis Elizondo	loo EES eh lee SOHN doh
madrina	mah DREE nah
Mamilla	mah MEE yah
Mamita	mah MEE tah
Manuel Rodríguez	mah NOOEHL roh DREE gehs
Manuel Valverde	mah NOOEHL vahl VEHR deh
Manuela	mah NOOEH lah
manzana	mahn SAH nah
Mariachis	mah ree AH chees
Menonita	meh noh NEE tah
miel	mee EHL
Miguel Badilla	mee GEHL bah DEE yah
Miguel Barahona	mee GEHL bah rah OH nah
Milda	MEEL dah
Miramar	mee rah MAHR
misa	MEE sah
molendero	moh lehn DEH roh
Movimiento Misionero	moh vee mee EHN toh
	mee seeoh NEH roh
muchas gracias	MOO chahs GRAH seeahs
naranjilla	nah rahn HEE yah
Naranjo	nah RAHN hoh
Nena	NEH nah
Ofelia Monje	oh FEH leeah MOHN heh
oficial de paz	oh fee SEEAHL deh pahs

Orotina	oh roh TEE nah
Otilio Chávez	oh TEE leeoh CHAH vehs
Otilio Ulate	oh TEE leeoh oo LAH teh
Paco Soto	PAH coh SOH toh
Padre Nuestro	PAH dreh NOOEHS troh
padrino	pah DREE noh
Palmital	pahl mee TAHL
palmito	pahl MEE toh
Panadera	pah nah DEH rah
Papito	pah PEE toh
Pepe	PEH peh
pesetas	peh SEH tahs
Pital	pee TAHL
ponche	POHN che
Ponchet	pohn CHEHT
Puerto Limón	POOEHR toh lee MOHN
Puntarenas	poon tah REH nahs
quelites	keh LEE tehs
Quesada	keh SAH dah
Rafael Herrera	rah fah EHL eh REH rah
Rafaela Gómez	rah fah EH lah GOH mehs
Ramón	rah MOHN
ranchera	rahn CHEH rah
resguardo	rehs GOOAHR doh
rezador	reh sah DOHR
Rincón de la Vieja	reen KOHN deh lah VEEAY hah
Roberto Chinchilla	roh BEHR toh cheen CHEE yah
roble	ROH bleh
Rosita	roh SEE tah
Sagradas Escrituras	sah GRAH dahs ehs kree TOO rahs
San Buenas	sahn BOOEH nahs
San José	sahn hoh SEH

San Lucas	sahn LOO kahs
San Ramón	sahn rah MOHN
Santo Salvador del Mundo	SAHN toh sahl vah DOHR dehl MOON doh
Sector Ángeles	sehk TOHR AHN heh lehs
señora	seh NYOH rah
Simón	see MOHN
sinvergüenzas chicheros	seen vehr GOOEHN sahs chee CHEH rohs
socolón	soh koh LOHN
Solanos	soh LAH nohs
Tachito	tah CHEE toh
Tajo Alto	TAH hoh AHL toh
tamuga	tah MOO gah
tardes	TAHR dehs
temporal	tehm poh RAHL
Tico	TEE koh
Tilo Barrantes	TEE loh Bah RAHN tehs
Tino	TEE noh
Toño	TOH nyoh
tope	TOH peh
upe	OO peh
Uriel	oo ree EHL
Valverde	vahl VEHR deh
vela	VEH lah
Vicente	vee SEHN teh
Virgencita	veer hehn SEE tah
Xinia	SEE neeah
yigüirro	yee GOOEE roh
yo quiero ir	yoh kee EH roh eer
Zapotal	sah poh TAHL
Zona Fluca	SOH nah FLOO kah

ABOUT
the AUTHOR

Pablo Yoder first got to know the Valverde family twenty-five years ago when the Chachagua mission started. Because of their occasional interaction, he knew many things about them. He knew they received visitors with warm hospitality and plenty of extra-black coffee. He knew he could count on them to drop what they were doing whenever he stopped by, pull up a chair, and spend the rest of the afternoon visiting. He knew how the Valverde men stuck to the Bible. He knew that, though not eloquent in their preaching, they were solid in their commitment to God and His Word.

After hours of interviewing, the bond between Pablo and Teodolinda strengthened.

And he knew Grandma Linda.

But with all Pablo knew about the Valverdes, he knew nothing of their past.

In 2007 Pablo received an e-mail suggesting that a story be written about Teodolinda, a very old sister in Costa Rica who had quite a story. At first, Pablo did not even know she was the Grandma Linda he knew so well. But he soon learned her formal name and made the connection. He found out she was still alert and could answer questions, so he dropped all other projects and ran to Costa Rica to interview her and her sons.

Teodolinda did not want to talk about her wicked past. After briefly sketching a story, she would always revert to telling how God had changed her. It was her sons who told most of the details of their former life. As Pablo watched the family relive their history, he shook his head in disbelief. He had never heard even a peep about their life in Zapotal—about the moonshining, the fighting, or La Peligrosa saloon. These people couldn't be the Valverdes he knew. Could they?

One trip to Zapotal erased all uncertainty. Many folks there testified to the Valverdes' bygone notoriety and to the change wrought in this once wicked family.

This book is the result of what Pablo found when he went in search of that story. And what a story! He now counts it a humbling privilege to be part of it, as terrible and wonderful as it is.

*   *   *

Pablo lives with his wife Euni in Waslala, Nicaragua. They have six children—Jacinto, Jéssica, Janie, Luana, Cynthia, and Kenny—and a growing number of grandchildren. Pablo enjoys hearing from readers and can be contacted through Christian Light Publications.

PABLO YODER
c/o Christian Light
P.O. Box 1212
Harrisonburg, VA 22803
Email: office@christianlight.org

MORE BOOKS BY PABLO YODER

Home on the Rock Pile and *Home on the Blue Ridge* describe the childhood adventures of Pablo and his siblings in the hollows near Faith Mission Home in Virginia. *The Long Road Home* tells of Pablo's growing-up years in Costa Rica. *Angels in the Night* describes the experiences of Pablo, Euni, and their children after they moved to Nicaragua.

Pablo has written two books of nature stories and photography, *The Work of Thy Fingers* and *The Work of His Hands*, as well as the following true stories:

Death of a Saloon: God's work in the lives of a soul-sick Costa Rican family.

From Contra to Christ: a Nicaraguan fighter's journey to the foot of the cross.

Chosen From Among the Worst: Hiding from the law, haunted by his crimes, and desperate for help, Omar finally found God's marvelous grace.

These books are available from Christian Light.

Christian Light is a nonprofit, conservative Mennonite publishing company providing Christ-centered, Biblical literature including books, Gospel tracts, Sunday school materials, summer Bible school materials, and a full curriculum for Christian day schools and homeschools. Though produced primarily in English, some books, tracts, and school materials are also available in Spanish.

For more information about the ministry of Christian Light or its publications, or for spiritual help, please contact us at:

ADDRESS :: P. O. Box 1212
Harrisonburg, VA 22803
TELEPHONE :: 540-434-0768
FAX :: 540-433-8896
EMAIL :: info@christianlight.org
WEBSITE :: www.christianlight.org

CHRISTIAN LIGHT
PUBLICATIONS